On Floating Ice

On Floating Ice

Two Years on an Antarctic Ice-shelf South of 75°S

Joseph MacDowall

The Pentland Press
Edinburgh – Cambridge – Durham – USA

First published in 1999 by
The Pentland Press Ltd
1 Hutton Close,
South Church
Bishop Auckland
Durham

ISBN 1 85821-720 2

On Floating Ice

Typeset in AdobeGaramond 10/12
by Carnegie Publishing, Carnegie House, Lancaster, LA1 4SL
and bound by Bookcraft (Bath) Ltd.

*Man wants to know, and when he ceases to do so,
he is no longer man.*

Fridtjof Nansen 1861–1930.

*The memory of these events he deemed would be a great
thing and most helpful to men of the present time, and to
future generations as well, in case time should ever again
place men under a similar stress.*

Procopius of Caesarea, 5th Century.

Contents

Illustrations

Acknowledgements

A ny account of the Royal Society IGY Antarctic Expedition 1955–1959 would be incomplete without acknowledging the tremendous role of the late Sir James Wordie in its success. As Chairman of the British National Committee for the IGY, Sir James steered the programme so as to maximize our chances of success with skills tempered by first-hand experience of serving with Shackleton. He also provided the information needed for our ship to find the best way through the treacherous ice of the Weddell Sea. Several years earlier, at St John's College, Cambridge, James Wordie and Colin Bertram had nourished my youthful interests in Antarctica.

The late Dr David C. Martin, CBE, Executive Secretary of the Royal Society, made a notable contribution to the success, achievements, and morale of the expedition. Despite his heavy load of duties in London, for over two years he personally kept in the closest possible touch with us, sometimes on a day-to-day basis. He managed a perceptive conduit between the expedition scientists and the scientific community at home. At times of need he was always there and was indefatigable in securing for us the best possible advice and resources. At the same time, he maintained a compassionate interest in our individual needs, never forgetting a birthday, and helping us, with his personal contributions, to relax and enjoy traditional holiday feasts now and again throughout the two years.

I would like to thank my wife, Oonagh, for keeping every letter and telegram I sent back home during the 29 months I was away. These, together with the diary I kept, provided the basis for these memoirs plus the series of weekly signals I sent back to London through 1958. My first attempt to put together a story of the expedition was started in November 1957, to provide an account for my wife and my parents, and has never been published. In 1992 I started again to put my material in order but it was not until early 1997 that I was in a position to give it all the time required. Without the encouragement of Oonagh, that too would not have been possible.

The stimulus of having to give lectures has been helpful and I owe a debt of gratitude to all who organized these lectures and particularly to the audiences who asked so many probing questions. The lecture material I developed in the 1960's and, perhaps even more important, the responses to questions arising, have been included from time to time in the following pages. There were too many lectures to list them all but some were seminal in helping me to organize my thoughts. One of the first I gave formed part of a series repeated up and down the British Isles, starting off with a Christmas lecture to about four hundred high school students in Westminster County Hall, London. This was followed by lectures to undergraduates at the Universities of Glasgow and Edinburgh, which were particularly stimulating in helping me to develop my responses to lively youthful curiosity. As also was the address I gave to the British Association for the Advancement of Science at the meeting held in Cardiff in August 1960, the lecture given on 18 March 1960 at Wallasey Grammar School, for the benefit of the Red Cross, those given to army officers at The Royal Military College of Science in Shrivenham and again in Aldershot, a lecture to the Scott Polar Research Institute, and one to mariners on board the *Discovery* at its moorings in London.

I owe a debt of gratitude to Dr John A Heap, CMG, the Executive Director of the Scott Polar Research Institute, for providing, in May 1997, just that final bit of encouragement I needed to finish off the work I had started so long ago. That was all I needed to keep up the impetus to tell my story of the wonderful work done by all my colleagues at Halley Bay. From that day forward, hardly a day has passed by without some of it being dedicated to the development of this story.

Foreword

by HRH Prince Philip, Duke of Edinburgh

BUCKINGHAM PALACE.

'On Floating Ice' is the fascinating story of the Royal Society's Base at Halley Bay on the ice-shelf above the Weddell Sea in Antarctica. Halley Bay was so named because 1956 happened to be the tercentenary of the birth of Edmund Halley, who was Secretary of the Royal Society from 1713 to 1721 and made investigations into the earth's magnetic field, aurorae and the Trade Winds.

The Base was established in 1956 by an advance party under the leadership of Surgeon Lieutenant Commander David Dalgliesh, RN, who, it so happens, later joined the Royal Yacht 'Britannia' as Principal Medical Officer. The Base was the principal British contribution to the 1957/1958 International Geophysical Year, when some fifty thousand scientists from sixty-three nations took part in a mass investigation into the physical properties of the earth, its inside, its surface and the atmosphere surrounding it. There was also a particular study of the sun as the controlling influence on practically everything that happens on earth.

This vast concerted effort to observe and record the detailed facts about our world, had its origin at a meeting some five years previously at Silver Springs, Maryland, between five American scientists and a British colleague, Professor Sydney Chapman. Professor Chapman was later to be elected President with headquarters in Brussels.

I became aware of this project for two reasons. I had met Dr. Vivian Fuchs, the leader of the Commonwealth Trans-Antarctic Expedition, which was also intending to set off from the Weddell Sea that year. As I was due to open the 1956 Olympic Games in Melbourne and was proposing to go out to Australia in the Royal Yacht, I had discussed with him the vague possibility of taking the Yacht into the Weddell Sea on the way home, but it was obviously impractical. However, it proved to be quite feasible to return home by crossing the South Pacific and visiting some of the Falkland Islands Dependencies Survey Bases on the Antarctic, before going on to the Falkland Islands themselves, South Georgia and other islands in the Atlantic.

Soon after returning home from that journey, I was invited by the BBC to take part in a program about the IGY under the title of 'The Restless Sphere'. The program went out in June 1957 and one of the people I introduced was David Dalgliesh, who spoke about the Royal Society's Base at Halley Bay.

The scientific team under Colonel Robin Smart, RAMC, arrived at the Base in January 1957 and consisted of a meteorological and geomagnetic group - of which the author was Group Leader -, an ionospheric group, a radio-astronomy group and an auroral observer. They were supported by a further group of technicians. The story of life and work at this remote base in the Antarctic during the two years of its occupation is told in graphic detail by the author of this book, who took over as Expedition Leader in January 1958 on Colonel Smart's departure.

  The IGY is largely forgotten today, as is the work of the Royal Society's Base, but it produced a huge amount of information and the fruits of its work remain for future scientists to study and use.

Preface

Recollections of a 'Forgotten'
Expedition to Antarctica

On 6 May 1997 Dr John Heap, the Director of the Scott Polar Research Institute, visited Ottawa. We met at a luncheon of the Ottawa Branch of the Cambridge (University) Society. I first met John on the M.V. *Magga Dan* when he sailed with us to Antarctica in pursuit of his interest in sea-ice. He commented that he had heard people say arguably that the Royal Society IGY Antarctic Expedition (RSIAE) has become known as the 'Forgotten Expedition'. This was no surprise to me but I was very interested to hear that it had become more widely recognized. The lack of national recognition for the expedition was plain to me when, in 1994, I visited the British Antarctic Survey headquarters in Cambridge. In reading their summary of British Expeditions to Antarctica, I noticed that they made scant reference to the work of the RSIAE. This was in spite of the major contributions to geophysics made by the observations there, such as the role of Halley Bay observations in providing a basis for the discovery of the 'ozone hole' problem, assessments of global warming and proving Antarctica was a continent, to mention a tiny sample. The omission I noted in 1994 was actually no great surprise and I made no comment on it to the survey. Perhaps I should have said something along the following lines, written by Sir Ronald Ross, the Nobel Laureate for Medicine in 1902:

> Now twenty years ago
> This day we found the thing;
> With science and with skill
> We found; then came the sting –
> What we with endless labour won
> The thick world scorned:
> Not worth a word today –
> Not worth remembering.

From *The Harvest of the Quiet Eye*, 128:6.

But I did not feel that way. We had our satisfaction in the doing of it.

> The struggle for knowledge hath
> a pleasure in it like that of
> wrestling with a fine woman.

Lord Halifax 1633–1695.

Genesis of the Expedition

'Science' means simply the aggregate of the recipes that are always successful. All the rest is literature.

Paul Valéry 1871–1945.

The Royal Society IGY Antarctic Expedition grew from seeds planted in 1950. They originated in the minds of the world's most accomplished scientists. They pointed out that the time was ripe to undertake the first-ever cooperative, world-wide and coordinated set of geophysical observations required to solve some of the many remaining problems which stood in the way of understanding our planet. How could we hope to improve our lot without knowing how our planet's systems worked? The IGY was designed to provide some answers and time has proven this to be so. They all agreed that systematic scientific observations were required from many parts of the world in the broad range of geophysical disciplines such as aurora and airglow, geomagnetism, glaciology, ionospheric physics, meteorology, radio astronomy and seismology.

The methods they proposed had already been proven sound in two previous coordinated programmes called the International Polar Years, which were held in 1882–83 and 1932–33. But this time the whole world was to be involved and the scheme was therefore called the International Geophysical Year. The scientists set up a Special Committee for the IGY which they dubbed 'CSAGI', from the initials in its French title, and they met regularly. At meetings held in Brussels in 1953 and again in Rome in 1954, the networks of required stations and the appropriate programmes were carefully considered.

When the scientists sat down in Rome, they noticed various serious gaps in the network of Antarctic stations already planned. Amongst their recommendations was one which raised keen interest in Britain because it was for a base to be set up in a region which lay within Britain's Falkland Island Dependencies. With such impeccable, international intellectual forces behind it, plus the direct involvement of the Royal Society, it was hardly surprising that H. M. Treasury agreed fully to fund the project to set up a major geophysical, observatory 'South of 75°S' on the east coast of the Weddell Sea, as the largest individual British contribution to the IGY, to which was devoted about half of all British IGY expenditures. The total cost of the expedition was about £300,000. (Ref. *The UK Contribution to the IGY 1957–58*, 1957 The Royal Society, London.)

It was only the second time in its long history that the Royal Society had given its name to an expedition in Antarctica. The previous expedition was held one and three-quarter centuries ago and was led by James Cook, to observe the transit of Venus.

Our expedition was more fully motivated by scientific objectives than had been the case with regard to any other British Antarctic expedition in the previous 40 years or so. In some ways it might be said that the Royal Society expedition heralded the change in British Antarctic policy from the protection of territorial claims to the pursuit of scientific excellence.

Chapter I

The Adventure Begins

The Opportunity

My life-long interest in Antarctica was first stimulated by a Fifth Form teacher of Rivington and Blackrod Grammar School in Lancashire. Antarctica, and my sojourn there, was directly related to the interest this lady sparked 14 years earlier. By another strange twist of fate, the spark was fanned into an enduring flame by the school's link with St John's College, Cambridge. When I arrived there as an undergraduate in 1948, I found some Fellows of the college had conducted research in Antarctica. Notably the Senior Tutor, James Wordie, who was Shackleton's geologist on his *Endurance* expedition.

After graduation, whilst working as a scientist for the Meteorological Office, I saw an advertisement soliciting applicants to staff an Antarctic Expedition to be run by The Royal Society as the main UK contribution to the International Geophysical Year 1957/58. Because of my well-known and long-standing interest in Antarctica, my friends wanted to know if I was going to apply.

My first thought was to rule out the idea, since I was married, our first son, Simon, was on the way, and we had bought our first house in Pinner. My wife, Oonagh, knew how much I wanted to go. It was a difficult decision I could no longer make by myself. After agonizing together, we finally decided that I should apply.

Interview

The Master said: 'I would not have him to act with me, who will unarmed attack a tiger, or cross a river without a boat, dying without any regret. My associate must be the man who proceeds to action full of solicitude, who is fond of adjusting his plans, and then carries them into execution.

Confucius 551–479 BC.

In due course I was called for an interview in London at the headquarters of the Royal Society, the premier British scientific society and organizer of innumerable expeditions over hundreds of years. It was the first of numerous visits to these palatial and historic offices, opening up glimpses of the workings of the highest strata of the British scientific hierarchy.

A large number of persons applied for the job, as perhaps might have been expected. We were interviewed by a board of about half a dozen members plus several *ex-officio*. The Chairman was James Wordie. Amongst those present were the Director of the Scott Polar Research Institute, the Executive Secretary of the Royal Society, Dr David C. Martin, and the Deputy Director of the Meteorological Office, Dr J. M. Stagg. The latter had led the International Polar Year Expedition to Fort Rae, Canada in 1932, the last time Britain had mounted a similar enterprise. To my delight I was appointed the Leader of the Meteorological & Geomagnetic Group in the expedition on the understanding that I would serve for the full two years in Antarctica. My group was responsible for the scientific programme in geomagnetism, glaciology, meteorology, ozone, radiation, and seismology.

This condition of staying two winters in Antarctica was considered essential by British authorities, because the International Geophysical 'Year' ran from 1 July 1957 to 31 December 1958. We would arrive in Antarctica in January 1957. This provided time to build a scientific observatory and get the equipment running, before starting full scale observations in June. To have a change in staff less than half way through the IGY was not considered wise. Due to the way in which the venture was organized and run by Britain, this was true. I was later to discover that many other nations, however, organized themselves to be able to relieve their bases after one year of service. In our case, however, a complete change over of staff in January 1958 would have been a disaster.

The next step was to interview and select the members of my group. For this phase, I was invited to join the selection board in an *ex-officio* capacity when the candidates were interviewed. All the questioning was done by the members, after which I was asked for my views before the selection was made. I was pleased they picked the same persons I would have done. All those scientists selected for my group also worked for the Meteorological Office. They were: Andrew Blackie, Jim Burton, David Tribble and Derek Ward. They all had extensive practical experience of the various experimental arts of meteorology, including the use of balloon-borne radio-sondes which we planned to send up twice a day. In addition, Peter Jeffries, who had been a member of the Advance Party for the Trans-Antarctic Expedition, joined the group for our first year. Ben Ellis and John Smith arrived for our second year when Jeffries returned home. As I was appointed Expedition Leader in the second year, an additional person had to come in order to keep the number of scientists in the meteorological group up to six persons.

Preparations

In the field of observation, chance only favours those minds which have been prepared.

Louis Pasteur 1822–1895.

The preparations phase of the expedition included staff training, laboratory design, ordering stores and supervising their packing. Your mind and energies are intensely concentrated by the fact that, on an already firmly-set date, you are going off to a part of the world where, at the best, you could only be relieved once each year.

As soon as I was appointed, there were a large number of matters which needed attention in the very brief period of six months available before we sailed away. Firstly, I had to prepare the lists of stores which would be needed fully to equip several observatories, one for meteorology, another for geomagnetism, for ozone measurements, seismology, and glaciology. Fortunately a senior scientist in the Meteorological Office, H. W. L. Absalom OBE, had been holding the fort pending my appointment and he had already placed overseas orders for the geomagnetic equipment which had to be specially made in Europe and had a long delivery time. The expedition stores officer had been busy preparing detailed lists of the stores we needed, based on the experience of the Falkland Island Dependencies Survey (FIDS) in clothing and feeding their staff, and equipping Antarctic bases. Every item of stores had to be gone over with care and I had to ensure we had sufficient spares to last for at least two years. In providing for the meteorological group, I went to see some of my old friends in the Meteorological Office in Harrow, who provided me with invaluable lists of all those items needed to keep a full-scale surface and upper-air observing station running for two years.

I also had to learn a number of new skills. How to make measurements of upper-air conditions using hydrogen-filled balloons, without blowing yourself up. How to make ozone measurements, run seismological equipment, and make useful observations in glaciology. For each of these scientific disciplines, a particular expert, usually a Fellow of the Royal Society, was appointed and he acted as my tutor, going over the observational routines, and showing me how to reduce the observations. There was an immense amount to do in Cambridge, Oxford, Eskdalemuir in Scotland, Liverpool, Manchester, Greenwich Observatory, and in London.

Clarendon Laboratory Oxford

A learned society of late,
The glory of a foreign state,
Agreed, upon a summer's night,
To search the moon by her own light.

Samuel Butler 1612–1680.

One of the more delicate, skilled observations I had to be able to make
were those of ozone in the upper atmosphere. To learn how to do
this I went to work at the Clarendon Laboratory, Oxford under Dr
G. M. B. Dobson, FRS. Actually, the laboratory was on a hill behind
his home, Watch Hill. Here Professor Dobson and Sir Charles Nor-
mand gave me a crash course on the care and use of the Dobson
Spectrophotometer for measuring ozone in the upper atmosphere using
sun- and moon-light.

They were very excited about the prospect of me making midwinter
measurements with moonlight. The moonlight observations made at
Halley Bay were the first to be done in Antarctica and, since the light
is weak, it needed skill and practice. Dobson had already received a
few observations from the Advance Party at Halley Bay and these were
so different from what was expected that they were beside themselves
with anticipation as to what I would find when I got there. It turned
out that the observations we started at Halley Bay were amongst the
very first steps taken which would lead the world to appreciate the
ozone hole problem. If unchecked, this depletion of the ozone layer
due to industrial gases could strip the world of its ozone shield,
presently protecting us from the deadly effect of solar ultra-violet
radiation.

Conversazione at the Royal Society

The business and design of the Royal Society is – to improve
the knowledge of natural things, and all useful Arts, Manu-
factures, Mechanick practices, Engynes and Inventions by
Experiments – (not meddling with Divinity, Metaphysics,
Moralls, Politicks, Grammar, Rhetorick or Logick) ... All to
advance the glory of God, the honour of the King ... the
benefit of his Kingdom, and the general good of mankind.

Robert Hooke 1635–1703.

On 10 May 1956 a Scientific Conversazione was held by the Royal
Society in their rooms in Burlington Place. This is an occasion rather
like a trade exhibition for scientists or the poster sessions at scientific

conferences, where scientists, mostly Fellows of The Royal Society in this case, displayed their most interesting recent findings and talked informally about them. The display was repeated on 21 June 1956.

We prepared a montage of photographs taken by the Advance Party at Halley Bay and presented a coloured slide display. We also prepared material to show the observations we would make during the Main Expedition. Several of us from the Main Party were always on hand to answer questions.

The whole range of recent scientific endeavour in Britain was covered by the various exhibits. It was quite a fascinating event and gave us the opportunity to see some of the most recent advances in science over a very wide field.

Later on in the year, on 31 October 1956, the President and Council of the Royal Society gave a reception for the Expedition. This was the first time all of us had been gathered together.

International Coordination and Standards Meeting in Paris

There shall be standard measures of wine, beer, and corn –
the London quarter – throughout the whole of our kingdom,
and a standard width of dyed, russet and halberject cloth –
two ells within the selvedges; and there shall be standard
weights also.

Magna Charta 1215.

The International Geophysical Year was originally planned under the auspices of the ICSU, the International Council of Scientific Unions, an organisation of most scientific societies, covering every branch of knowledge and with a worldwide membership. The ICSU Special Committee for the IGY (CSAGI) held one of their meetings in Paris. The show was organized and orchestrated by Colonel George Laclavère, Secretary of CSAGI. It was three days after the birth of our first son, Simon.

The British delegation was led by Sir David Brunt, Physical Secretary of the Royal Society, and included James Wordie (Later Sir James), Chairman of the British IGY Committee, and Dr David Martin, Executive Secretary of the Royal Society.

This was the last CSAGI meeting before the Antarctic expeditions left for the field. It therefore provided for us the last possible opportunity to reach international agreement on the details of observing schedules, to iron out some of the problems of standards or intercomparisons of instruments, and to harmonise units and the recording of data.

Accompanying the delegation was Donald Milner, a representative from the BBC, who sailed with us to Antarctica, and a journalist called Angela Croome who wrote for the science magazine *Discovery*, in which she had a special column on the IGY. I sat next to Donald on the plane in its flight to France. He seemed to think that with the current state of technology, there should be little need actually to man an Antarctic base for the whole period of the IGY. Why didn't we just pop down there for a few weeks and leave behind a set of automatic equipment? I'm afraid that I did not find it easy to respond to that level of background knowledge. In fact I thought that I had done a very bad job of responding, so I was quite surprised when, many months later, Donald left with me in Antarctica the big BBC tape recorder to use compiling reports. Several times during the expedition Donald contacted me by radio specifying the quite detailed reports he needed and the interviews he wanted. Many of the reports I sent back to him were broadcast by the BBC.

The meeting started out by each nation giving an up-to-date report on progress and plans with their IGY efforts. Sir David gave an account of what had been achieved by the Advance Party at Halley Bay and what was planned for the Main Expedition which would leave Britain that November. For the first time I heard detailed accounts of the massive USA and Soviet contributions to the IGY, including their epoch-making, earth-orbiting satellite programmes.

Associated with the meeting was an active social programme. One big party was organised by Colonel Laclavière in his commodious apartment in the heart of Paris. There was also a party held at the superb headquarters of Expeditions Polaire Française. This gave me my first opportunity to meet scientists from many nations and some of the people who would also be in Antarctica. Being in France, Expedition Polaire Française was prominent as was their dynamic leader, Paul Emile Victor.

It was my first visit to Paris and my first exposure to the nationalistic approach prevalent in France. I had been used to working with people whose motivation to Antarctic research stemmed from either their interest in a particular branch of science, a fascination with polar regions, or a sense of adventure. It was an intensely personal thing of individuals and not a national promotion exercise. Their work was frequently pursued despite precarious government support. It was as if the French Government and industry saw the challenges of Antarctica as an opportunity to build and burnish their national image. To feed these fires of national enthusiasm, they gave more generously. It was very impressive.

Eskdalemuir Observatory

I learnt the tricky art of making geomagnetic observations at Eskdale-muir Observatory in Scotland. The Superintendent of the Observatory was Mickey Blackwell, whom I had worked with at Kew Observatory several years previously. He had married Helen Godfrey, another old friend of ours. So Oonagh and I drove up to Scotland with Simon in a carry-cot perched on top of a pile of luggage. We had a very pleasant trip, staying in the Lake District on the way.

I had to learn how to set up the La Cour magnetic recorders and to make all the necessary observations. Since the equipment at Esk-dalemuir had been installed many years ago, no one there knew how it was done. All they knew was that it was a black art and they lived in daily fear of their own equipment getting out of adjustment or needing replacement. Successive superintendents prayed hard that they could serve out their term at Eskdalemuir without ever having to repeat the set-up. To make matters more tricky, the La Cours used photo-graphic recording in a dark, underground cavern barely lit by one dim red light. The individual who long ago set them up had by then become almost a legend, whose name was whispered with awe, as a genius with uncanny ability. Stories were told of the various herculean tasks this guy had performed, such as how he transferred the direction of true north down into the cavern. That was not a lot of help to me. But at least I was alerted to the fact that this was a problem – my problem. I would have to figure out how to set up the dreaded La Cour variometers and to use observations of the sun and stars to find out the direction of true north.

The La Cour geomagnetic recorders employed an ingenious, multi-channel optical system, which was created by a number of reflecting prisms fixed on a bar with wax. As far as setting them up, the best I could do at Eskdalemuir was to study the final configuration and figure out for myself how to get there. Andrew Blackie was with me during the visit to Eskdalemuir. He was a scientist highly skilled in the experimental art of making and reducing the geomagnetic control observations, maintaining the recorders and the reducing observations. Like the other scientists at Eskdalemuir, he did not know how to set up the La Cour recorders and was very happy to leave that part to me.

I also paid a visit to staff at Greenwich Observatory, who had arranged a loan from the US Geodetic Survey of an extremely neat set of portable geomagnetic instruments.

Cambridge University

Within this wide great Universe
Nothing does firme and permanent appeare,
But all things tost and turned by transverse.

Edmund Spenser 1522–1599.

Dr Robert Stonley, FRS was my tutor for the seismological observations. He was a Fellow of Pembroke College, Cambridge and had a geophysical laboratory up the Girton Road. I also went to see the seismologists at Kew Observatory in Richmond, set in the middle of the Royal Mid-Surrey Golf Club. I had once worked at the Observatory and was looking forward to seeing several old friends.

We had decided to buy a fairly modern, small set of three-component Willmore seismographs which were not too difficult to set up. It was already known that the base at Halley Bay might be located on a large floating iceberg, which was not exactly an ideal site for a major seismological installation. Indeed no one was quite sure what we would be able to observe. In fact they operated quite well and the results we obtained were specially requested by ten organizations round the world. We sent them off by radio as soon as possible each month.

Twenty years later, when I was working as a diplomat in Washington, the U. S. President's Science Advisor, the geophysicist Frank Press, told me that the observations made at Halley Bay were amongst those used to prove that Antarctica was indeed a continent and not an ocean basin like the North Polar region. The observations were also used to provide a much more accurate estimate of the depth of ice on the continent. Amongst other things, they used my observations to discover how, in some places, the tremendous weight of ice had pressed the earth's crust to below sea level. (F. Press & G. Dewart 1959, *Science* v129, #3347.)

I very much enjoyed visiting Dr Stonley. During the working day at the Geophysical Laboratory it was stimulating to talk with all the other researchers. In the evening after dinner on High Table, we retired to the cosy Senior Combination Room of Pembroke College. There we sat down together in small groups and discussed many interesting subjects.

I also spent time at the Scott Polar Research Institute. One of the main reasons I went there was to consider their advice on how to construct a geomagnetic observatory on an ice-shelf, but their staff were, of course, a fount of information on all aspects of polar activities.

Antarctic Laboratory Design

*An expert is someone who knows some of the worst mistakes
that can be made in his subject, and how to avoid them.*

Werner Heisenberg 1901–1976.

Soon after I was appointed, I had to make a number of detailed decisions regarding the design of our laboratories. This task and my training went on simultaneously. The designers of our buildings and laboratories were from the Crown Agents, an outgrowth of the British Colonial Office, who had learnt much about Antarctic conditions from their association with Falkland Islands Dependencies Survey (FIDS).

The Crown Agents staff included architects and engineers who, for many years, had become particularly adroit at designing anything for the special needs of the remotest corners of the British Empire, which, in its long history, had met just about every engineering challenge the world has to offer. I soon came to learn that if you wanted a geomagnetic observatory for Antarctica, a palace in a tropical jungle fit for a governor-general, or an extension built to your harem in the desert, it's all the same to the Crown Agents. They will do the job, taking due account of the Antarctic cold and wind, jungle termites and mould, or the security and comfort of your wives. The knowledge and ingenuity of those guys knew no bounds. Each week I would sit down with them, working for hours alongside their drawing boards and together we evolved the designs.

Geomagnetic Observatory

*One must learn by doing the thing; though you think you
know it, you have no certainty until you try.*

Sophocles 495–406 BC.

The most challenging building of all was the non-magnetic hut needed for the geomagnetic observatory. It had to be totally free from any magnetic material in its construction. Copper nails and a special non-magnetic brass had to be employed in the screws. The bricks and mortar had to be inspected as free from iron contamination, and so on. We had to exercise great care not to leave even a tiny piece of iron or steel in the building. Its design was hotly debated and just about every expert had a different view.

The challenge and controversy arose because geomagnetic instruments were very delicate and sensitive to any vibration. Moreover, they had never before been set up in the conditions prevailing at Halley Bay. The La Cour recorders needed a firm, solid and dependable base.

They comprised a tiny magnet suspended on a delicate quartz fibre. Both the size and strength of the magnet and the thickness of the suspension fibre were specially designed for the location. The basic design of the recorders was over 100 years old but it was the first time they had ever been installed on a floating ice-shelf.

The hut was to be built on the ice-shelf at Halley Bay on what we later discovered was nothing more than a huge iceberg about 100 by 35 miles (161 by 56 km) in extent, pinned to the shore by rocks deep beneath the surface. It was moving forward three or four hundred yards (274 or 366 m) a year and turning slowly. The ice-shelf was made of compacted snow and I found that it was 470 ft. (143 m) thick floating over 270 ft. (82 m) of water.

The advice received from the Scott Polar Research Institute was to build the hut on a large platform to even out the subsidence and provide a stable base. The Crown Agents engineers, on the other hand, recommended wooden piles driven down through the upper, unstable snow layers to form a solid foundation. After considerable discussion, we decided to adopt this latter solution, which worked out very well. The former idea would have been a disaster because the instruments were very sensitive to the least movement and the 24 hours a day of summer sunshine would have caused any feasibly-sized platform to tilt north. To build this foundation, we first had to master the technique of pile-driving, something none of us had ever done before. Then, on top of 20 ft. (6 m) long piles, we built up brick pillars and topped these with solid marble slabs for the instruments.

The geomagnetic instruments also needed to be kept at an even temperature. The design of hut we evolved was shaped like a cylinder cut in half down its axis; in other words it was shaped like a Nissen Hut. The curved roof was formed of prefabricated plywood and insulation – light, strong and highly insulated. Electrical heating was fitted to the inside of the roof, to give an even heat without stimulating disturbing convective air movements. The temperature was kept between 5°C and 10°C year round. The two doors were over a foot thick with a stepped, felt-lined edge to provide an almost perfect seal round the edge of the doors. There was one tiny window which was normally sealed by an insulating plug with stepped felt edges like the doors. This window could be opened to facilitate the establishment of true north inside the hut. The La Cour photographic recorders were kept in part of the hut which was normally darkened.

Balloon-filling Shed

The design of a balloon-filling shed was another challenge. This was built with a huge garage-type door plus a roof hatch, which were both big enough for the passage of large balloons. The roof hatch did not prove practicable because of its weight and the frequent strong winds. A rotating hut might have been ideal, so one could always launch down-wind. On the other hand, such a hut would have been a problem to dig out from snow drifts in its second year of use.

Radar Mounting and Mobile Ozone Laboratory

We had to design a mounting for our radar and here we had a great idea. What we did was to mount it on three sledge runners so we could haul it up to keep it from getting buried by accumulating snow. This idea was outstandingly successful. Accordingly, in 1958, I suggested that it be applied in 1959 for a new ozone-observing hut. In a telegram to the Royal Society in London, I outlined very detailed specifications for such a hut and the Crown Agents had it made for use the following year. The hut was built on sledge runners so you could keep moving it up to a new higher level as the snow rose. Every now and again you just hitched it up to the tractor and pulled it up to the level of the new surface.

Balloon Sounding of the Upper Atmosphere

We must not wait for favours from Nature; our task is to wrest them from her.

Ivan Vladimirovich Michurin 1855–1935.

Although I knew all about the principles, I had never spent any time actually doing the job of making measurements of the temperature, humidity and winds in the upper atmosphere. To learn this art, I was posted for a few weeks to the Royal Air Force Station at Ormskirk near Liverpool, where the Meteorological Office had located one of its Upper Air Stations.

The atmospheric sounding process starts by filling a balloon with hydrogen, which at Ormskirk was delivered regularly from a nearby plant in steel cylinders in which the gas was kept under pressure. One of the first things I had to do after appointment was to decide how we would make our own hydrogen in Antarctica. It boiled down to a choice between two methods. The first method had been developed in France and had been shown to be quite practical in polar regions. The gas was made in a steel pressure vessel which looked like a very large bottle about 5 ft. (1.52 m) tall. You started by putting some hot water into the bottom of the vessel, taking care that it did not freeze. Then you put a carefully measured amount of aluminium chips and caustic soda crystals into a container which held it above the water. You sealed up the vessel with a steel plug and valve which screwed into the neck of the bottle, sealing it. The bottle was then turned upside down so as to mix together the aluminium chips, caustic soda and water. Then you stood well away from the device. The chemicals reacted energetically, producing hydrogen which was kept under pressure. You turned the bottle over again so the valve was at the top, and you let out the gas needed to fill the balloon through this valve. The reaction inside the bottle was violent and you needed to do it all with great care. Once the cylinder was empty of gas, you cleaned out the residue before it all froze solid.

I read several expedition reports on this remarkable method and it just did not appeal to me – so many things could go wrong and it seemed very dangerous indeed. I was also put off because no one I met seemed to know just exactly what went on during the reaction under high pressure. However, I had spoken to some individuals who had used it with satisfaction on polar expeditions. It had the important advantage of being the most compact piece of equipment for the job. We took two sets of this equipment with us as a back-up to the Gill generator we finally selected.

Because the gas production capability of the pressurized method was insufficient to fill the large balloons we proposed to launch at Halley Bay, the method we finally chose had been developed in Canada for routine operational use in the Canadian Arctic. The machine was called the Gill Generator and at 1200 lb (544 kg) (1600 lb or 726 kg in its packing case) was one of the heaviest single items of equipment we took with us. We used it twice a day for over 18 months and we found it remarkably dependable when used with care. That is not to say it was trouble free. In fact in its second year of operation, we had to overcome some nasty problems when minor chemical explosions shot out at us a stew of hot caustic chemicals.

The operation of the Gill was not done under pressure. It comprised a reaction vessel on the top of which was a massive condenser tank containing anti-freeze solution to cool off the hydrogen gas produced and to condense out the water vapour which was made at the same time. The whole thing was about eight feet tall (2.44 m) and three feet (91 cm) in diameter. First you took a lot of hot water from the Main Hut to the unheated balloon shelter and placed it in a tank on the side of the Gill Generator. Then you put a carefully measured mixture of aluminium chips and caustic soda crystals into the bottom of the reaction chamber. There was a tap which allowed you to add the water to the aluminium and caustic soda mixture at a controlled rate, thereby controlling the rate at which hydrogen was produced.

Immediately beneath the balloon you placed a radar reflector made of metal foil which looked rather like a kite. Then on a long piece of string you attached a 'radio-sonde', a device which measured temperature, pressure and humidity and transmitted the results back to earth on radio signals transmitted through the aerial which trailed out below the sonde. A calibration check was made of the sonde before it was taken out to the balloon.

Having launched the balloon, another team of three individuals listened to and processed the radio transmissions. As the sonde was carried upwards, a windmill device on its side rotated, sequentially switching to measure temperature, humidity then pressure. These values were converted to a sound, the pitch of which was proportional to the temperature, pressure or humidity. All this is done automatically now but in those days someone had to measure the frequency of each pitch before the windmill moved the switch on to the next measurement, call out the frequency to someone else, who in turn converted this frequency to the appropriate value of temperature, pressure or humidity. This whole process comprised hard, concentrated effort for the whole of the balloon flight, from which you constructed graphs of the observations against time.

Yet another team was busy in a radar, tracking the position of the radar reflector as it was carried away by the winds and up by the balloon. From these observations we could measure the height of the balloon and the strength of the winds at various levels in the atmosphere, up to a height of about 30 km (97,500 ft). Two persons were required to do the job in the radar. One person was responsible for keeping the dish of the radar pointing at the balloon. This was controlled by two hand wheels which moved the whole radar round or controlled the elevation of the radar dish. Throughout the flight he cranked the two hand wheels, one for the elevation of the radar and the other for its azimuth. The other person read off the range and passed the readings back to the main hut where they were recorded and reduced.

One of the particular challenges of the job in Antarctica was due to the large change in air temperature in the lowest layers of the atmosphere. This in turn caused a very large shift in the wind direction as the balloon rose through the lower atmosphere. Sometimes these direction changes caused the balloon to pass back and fly directly over the radar. When this occurred, one had to crank the azimuth wheel rapidly to move the radar completely round by 180° and then pick up the balloon on the other side. Occasionally this could happen several times during an ascent.

Wind-finding Radar

The Decca Radar Company in London had designed a brand new 3-cm wavelength, wind-finding radar to meet the special needs of the IGY. We were to be one of its first customers. Without this development there would have been no compact and convenient equipment for us to measure upper-atmosphere winds in the Antarctic, at the regularity required for the IGY programme.

Thus one of the more important things for us to do was to be trained in the operation and maintenance of that radar. The scientist who would take charge of the radar, David Tribble, and I therefore went through the radar maintenance course at Decca and spent many hours going over the equipment with its designer, Mr Clarke. We also had to work out a full set of spares for a piece of equipment which had never before been operational. The radar proved to be an outstanding success once David mastered its idiosyncrasies and solved some of the low temperature operating snags.

Glaciology

At the outset, I knew very little about glaciology. It was one of the disciplines of the IGY and someone had to look after it. Because of its obvious relation to weather, I inherited the responsibility.

Professor Gordon Manley at the Bedford College of the University of London was the person responsible for instructing me. Between us, we worked out a basic schedule of observations which could fit into our already overloaded programme. Later on, when sailing south on *Magga Dan*, I shared a cabin with Dr Hal Lister of the Trans-Antarctic Expedition (TAE). Hal was a professor of geography who had served as a glaciologist for two years on the British North Greenland Expedition. He taught me a great deal of the most practical aspects of the subject. When we arrived at Halley Bay, together we dug a small glaciological pit and put some of the theory into practice.

Jodrell Bank University of Manchester

One of the problems of scientific work in Antarctica is the lack of a good electrical earth. Particularly if you are sitting on top of an ice-shelf, you have no effective electrical contact with the earth. Such contact is essential for trouble-free radio operations and to minimize the mutual interference between various pieces of scientific equipment. Without a good earth, it is very difficult to isolate one piece of equipment from another. Without such isolation the measurements made on one piece of equipment get picked up by the other, sometimes actually precluding measurements.

The most serious sources of interference were generated by a powerful radar operated by our radio astronomers and by the ionospheric sounder. Both of these devices generated strongly interfering radio signals, as did the radio communications transmitter. In order to find out the nature of our problems, from 30 July to 4 August 1956, we brought together all the radio and radar equipment we would use, in

Cheshire at the Jodrell Bank Radio-Astronomy Observatory of the University of Manchester. With all these operating together, we could see precisely the extent of the mutual interference problem and, hopefully, work out the solutions. Our activities in Cheshire were orchestrated by Professor Bernard Lovell, FRS. It was an interesting visit and the first time I had seen the huge radio telescope the Professor had constructed.

A solution we came up with was elegant and relatively simple to implement. Every time the radio astronomy radar or the ionosonde transmitted its extremely short pulses of energy, we arranged automatically to turn-off the other equipment. Each of the sensitive receivers was fitted with a rapid-acting off-switch which was connected to the big radars. Thus every time the radar blasted away, it turned off all other sensitive equipments for that very short interval of time. The period of time was so short that the interruption was hardly noticed. We also had to set up a schedule for the operation of all the other mutually interfering equipment, such as the radio transmitter and the radio sondes, which did not operate with short pulses and did not lend themselves to the former solution. That it was possible so quickly to reach agreement on these complex and restricting schedules between all the different scientists, spoke volumes for their ability to cooperate, giving a little here and there for the benefit of others.

It should also be noted that all of the above measures would not have succeeded fully if our electricians had not practised the highest standards in design and installation of the electrical system at the base.

Data Reduction

Nature is not a temple but a workshop in which man is the labourer.

Ivan Sergeievich Turgenev 1818–1883.

One of the points stressed by the scientists at their meeting in Paris was the importance of preparing for the data reduction phase of the IGY by agreeing early on the formats to be used in presenting observations and the units to be used. However, it was not always easy to reach this agreement. The only problem we had was over the units to be used in reporting atmospheric radiation on the WMO (World Meteorological Organisation) forms which had been specially designed to minimise this problem. In observing radiation, some nations recorded their observations in Calories and others used Watts. The various nations had not decided on a standard before we sailed off to Antarctica. We had to wait a year before we could make a start filling in these WMO forms with our observations and in the meantime we followed the practice of the British Meteorological Office.

In fact the international community of scientists were very well organised for the flood of data which would be acquired during the IGY. However, there was a price to pay for those nations who already had in place well-organised systems. They had to make two sets of records – one following advanced national practice and the second following international IGY practice based on the lowest common denominator principle. By paying this small price, all nations benefited. We could all use each other's data more quickly and those who had not worked out their own data recording schemes could advance their national practice by adopting the WMO system.

We appreciated that, once we got home again, an immense amount of work would need to be done to analyse all the data and present it. This was a job for electronic computers, providing the observations were first put in a way which the computer could understand, and providing there were no mistakes in the data. The quantity of data we obtained was very large; we left Halley Bay in January 1959 with about ten tons of scientific records.

Every meteorological observation we made was first written down, then it was transcribed on to special forms and finally it was punched on to Holerith Cards, which could be fed directly into the computer located at the Meteorological Office in Harrow when we returned home. Each step in the transfer of data was checked and double checked. The Holerith cards, for example, were punched and then they were checked independently by a different person. Our meteorological observations were also transmitted immediately they were made to the radio station at Port Stanley so they could be used by weather forecasters. After the IGY, I discovered that weather data broadcasts made by Port Stanley did not reach the weather analysis centre set up by the USA at their Little America base until the IGY was nearly over. This was due to poor coordination which could have been avoided if Britain had sent one of their meteorologists to join in the multi-national team assembled at Little America in the Ross Sea.

The large amount of time scientists spend working on their data like this was a surprise to the support staff of the expedition. They saw it as a lot of hard, boring, clerical work. Nonetheless, our leader, Robin Smart and the support staff appreciated that it was a task they could help with, and they did so. For example, one of the diesel mechanics, Alf Amphlett, took on a major role punching the Holerith cards, the medical officer, Robin Smart, helped track balloons by radar, the cook, Malcolm Edwards, assisted with measurements of sea-ice thickness, one of the wireless operators, Henry Dyer, made sea-ice observations, and others too joined in to give a helping hand to the ever-busy scientific staff.

Packing Up

In preparing and executing a successful Antarctic expedition, no detail can be left to chance, particularly the proper packing of scientific equipment. The packing had to be designed safely to convey delicate, irreplaceable equipment half way round the world, through the tropical seas, and then cope with the special hazards of the Antarctic. We also had to remember that once it arrived, we ourselves had to hump it about and open up the crates.

When we were ready to pack up, I went with our stores officer to the East End of London, near the docks, to a company hired by the Crown Agents who specialised in packing almost anything to almost anywhere. There I supervised the packing of our equipment. We worked in a huge warehouse surrounded by every conceivable manner of goods being packed, from the complete contents of a house to highly specialized packing such as we required. They were also crating up great quantities of second-hand clothing to be sent for sale in the markets of the third world. It was a fascinating experience and a glimpse of activities normally taken for granted. It was also a pleasure to work with people who were so expert at their job and were eager to apply their wide experience and great skills to help us. As a result of this cooperation, almost all our equipment arrived in very good shape.

Tea with Her Majesty The Queen

On Tuesday 13 November 1956, just two days before our departure, all members of the Royal Society IGY Antarctic Expedition and their wives were presented to Her Majesty the Queen on the dockside of Butler's Wharf, as our ship was being loaded in the shadow of Tower Bridge. Then we sat down for tea with Her Majesty and her Lady in Waiting in the warehouse, which had been transformed into a royal teahouse for the occasion. Oonagh and I were fortunate enough to be placed at the same table as Her Majesty and enjoyed an informal chat with her, and a delicious tea.

My diary for that day read as follows:

'Today was a great occasion as Her Majesty the Queen came to inspect the *Magga Dan*. We were all presented to Her Majesty and Oonagh and I took tea at her table ... She was quite delightful and made us feel very much at ease with a word, a smile and interest for everyone.'

Chapter 2

The Voyage to Antarctica

Departure of the Magga Dan

The winds and the waves are always on the side of the ablest of navigators.

Edward Gibbon 1737–1794.

Our ship, the M. S. *Magga Dan*, sailed away from Butler's Wharf on the morning of Thursday 15 November 1956. I remember it being a mad scramble to drive myself across London with all my luggage in the jalopy, a venerable 1935 Morris. I parked the car nearby and left the key in it so that Oonagh could pick the car up later on in the day when her father brought her and Simon to wave goodbye. Simon was almost four months old. As the only baby seeing off the expeditions, photographs of Simon, Oonagh and her father on shore, and Joe on the ship, were plastered all over the three London evening papers the *Evening Standard*, *Evening News* and *Star* for 15 November 1956.

One last goodbye as Joe leans over the side of the ship to touch his baby son, Simon, held by his wife Oonagh. They would not see each other again for over two years. (This was published in the Evening Standard on 15 November 1956.)

There were two expeditions on board: our own, of course, the 21-man The Royal Society IGY Antarctic Expedition (RSIAE) led by Col. Robin Smart, RAMC and staffed by highly specialised scientists, sailing off for a two-year stint in Antarctica providing the UK contribution to the IGY, and the 12-man Commonwealth Trans-Antarctic Expedition (TAE) of seasoned polar travellers off for a year whilst they traversed the Antarctic continent. Not all the equipment and stores required by the Royal Society expedition could fit in the *Magga Dan*, so she was also supported by the supply ship M. V. *Tottan*, a Norwegian vessel under the able command of Captain Leif Jakobsen which set sail from London on November 17 and was waiting for us at Halley Bay when we arrived, such were the high ice-navigation skills of her Norwegian crew.

The *Magga Dan* was a new ship and sailed under the Danish Flag. The Captain of the *Magga Dan* was Hans Christian Petersen. The ship was specially designed for work in the pack-ice and had the highest possible rating from Lloyds of London for such ice-strengthened vessels. High above the deck, on the mast, there was a heated crow's nest for navigation through the pack ice. The nest was complete with controls, so the Captain himself could go up there and take complete control, to thread his way though ice-infested waters. From his perch, he could see the most promising route through the sea-ice or ice-bergs, and take immediate action to avoid hazards or to keep on the most promising track where the ice was thinnest.

The *Magga Dan* sailed from Butlers Wharf, London near Tower Bridge. Seeing us off in fine style were a number of dignitaries, including some members of the IGY Committee to whom the expedition reported. These well-wishers cruised down the Thames with us in the Port of London Authority Yacht, *St Katharine*.

I was installed in a cosy four-man cabin in an upper-berth of a two-tier bunk. My companions were meteorologist Andrew Blackie, glaciologist Hal Lister and Allan Rogers MD; the last two were from the TAE. Sharing a room with Hal was ideal for me because he was an experienced glaciologist and I was grateful for his advice in working out the final details of our modest glaciological programme. I certainly benefited from the way the members of the two expeditions were mixed together in the ship. I only wish that I had known at that time how much I would be required to learn about dentistry and medicine once we were isolated at Halley Bay, for it would have provided a sharp focus for the conversations I had with Allan.

I noted in my diary very favourable first impressions of the *Magga Dan*, although there was no room in the cabin for all our Antarctic clothing, so we stowed this in the corridors. The food was in the Danish style we soon got used to. Breakfast was served at 7:30 a.m. and 8:15 a.m., lunch at noon, tea at 3:00 p.m. and dinner at 5:00 p.m.

Having the last meal of the day so early took a little getting used to. From time to time, a few of us gathered in Robin Smart's tiny cabin for a gin-and-tonic before dinner. Then we took our dinner in the Officers' Mess presided over by Captain Petersen.

On the day before our departure, I was informed by the Port of London Meteorological Officer that the *Magga Dan* had been appointed a 'Selected Ship'. This was the designation bestowed by the Director of the Marine Branch of the Meteorological Office, Commander Frankom, on those merchant vessels which were considered responsible enough to make meteorological measurements. Normally this was a voluntary task undertaken by the British Merchant Marine. Merchant sailors received no remuneration for this invaluable work although, if the captain of a vessel did the tasks for several decades, he would be presented by Commander Frankom with a handsome recording barometer. Our case of course was a special one since the *Magga Dan*, a Danish vessel, carried five persons, Blackie, Burton, MacDowall, Tribble and Ward, seconded to the Royal Society Expedition from the Meteorological Office. It was understood that we would be making these important measurements, which in those days provided the main global network of weather observations for the oceans of the world. Accordingly, we commenced weather and sea temperature observations, at six-hourly intervals, on Friday 16 November 1956. For the meteorological team of the Royal Society expedition this event proved to be the first modest step in a daily routine of scientific observations which was to continue without a break until January 1959.

Getting to Know Each Other

The Expedition finally got together on the ship. The first impressions I received of my colleagues was that they were a 'happy crowd'. The voyage proved an ideal way to find out about each other, make friends and do the final planning. No one in the Royal Society expedition had ever been on a polar expedition before; we were first and foremost highly trained scientists, not polar travellers. On the ship we were able to talk with some of the seasoned travellers who were with the TAE, and also with the Danish sailors, several of whom had been to Antarctica before.

The members of TAE were going to their base at Shackleton and planned to traverse the continent from the Weddell Sea to the Ross Sea. We wasted no time in learning what we could from each other. I had many long chats with Hal and George Lowe, who was a fount of information on his speciality, photography. For George's helpful information, I traded part of the contents of the large bottle of ink I had brought with me. It turned out to be the only convenient bottle of ink on the ship, if not the only one. The ink was a last minute afterthought, bought on the eve of departure, which turned out to be invaluable.

It wasn't long before we felt urgently the need for more exercise. On November 17 I found a short length of rope and used my scouting skills to splice it into a ring for deck tennis. Four of us played for an hour that day and continued to play regularly for the rest of the voyage.

A gale blew up on November 18 and the ship soon started to roll. Ice-strengthened ships like ours roll like the very dickens because they cannot be fitted with bilge keels, which would cause ice to become trapped under the ship. As soon as the rolling got up to about 5 degrees, over half the party became affected so that only 40% of them were able to face the supper table and those of us who did so had little appetite. On the following day the rolling increased and all four members of my cabin were confined to bed. The gale intensified further on 19th and, even though the ship rolled to 35 degrees at one time, I and many others had become used to it. Until you get used to it, that degree of rolling is a little alarming. If you stand outside on the open deck, the first time it happens, you wonder whether you are going to fall off. At the peak of the storm the ship had to reduce the speed from 12 to 5 knots (22 to 9 kph) and change course slightly. This was not required for our safety but because the sea was coming over the side and might have damaged the two TAE aircraft we carried as deck cargo.

Madeira

It took us six days to reach Madeira from London. On the day before arrival, the ship's engines were stopped for one hour whilst some problem with the valves was repaired. I was on deck at the time the engines stopped and, at about the same time, happened to notice that the captain was also repairing a minor problem with one of the lifeboats! I was impressed by his prudence!

My first sight of the island, on the evening of November 21, was a delight. It was lit up like a Christmas tree because the inhabitants seem to leave all their lights on. It is a small, mountainous island with the peaks rising up to 6000 ft. (1829 m). All the way up the hills were terraced vineyards and banana plantations. We anchored at Funchal and went ashore first thing the following morning. Before going ashore, I received my mail from the hands of ships' agents, Blandy Bros.

It can get very boring, being confined to the narrow compass of a ship, so we all took the opportunity to do as much as possible in the five hours ashore. Andrew, George and I hired a big open taxi and took it to a point about half way up the mountain, to a large church called Monte. We had a coffee nearby and walked around. Everywhere you went you were pestered by hoards of small boys begging with their hands held out to you, accompanied by persistent calls for money. If you gave them anything, more and more beggars would arrive so the only thing to do was to be hard-hearted. We came down the mountain on one of their traditional sledges. They were pulled up hills by bullocks and then we climbed aboard and the whole thing slid down the cobble-stoned road guided by two guys, one on each side of the sledge. Half way down we stopped at a tiny café where we were joined by two other members. The five of us shared a bottle of wine and soaked up the local ambience. After a delicious lunch, we went to a wine cellar. In the wine cellar we had a lecture on the production of Madeira wine and purchased some samples. Some of us also purchased examples of the delightful lace made there. At the edge of the town there was an elegant lido where we took a swim in the 70°F (21°C) waters of their lovely pool, nestled on the rocky coast.

We all returned briefly to the ship to tidy up for a cocktail party

The Magga Dan in Funchal harbour, Madeira. For over 100 years, most British expeditions sailing off to Antarctica have called in at this tiny, beautiful island. It was a volcano aeons ago and boasts craggy 1500 m high mountains covered with a profusion of flowering plants and the home of hundreds of species of birds. Some of us swam here in the warm and crystal-clear waters, at a lido nestled on its precipitous scenic coast. In the evening, we were welcomed by a vibrant British community. Portugal, an ally of Britain since the 14th century, governs this charming island and the British influence is still strong. We bought some of the distinctive Madeiran fortified wine to warm up our Antarctic winters. Some of us sent off to our families examples of the delicate Madeiran lace, an industry started in the 1850s by Mrs Phelps, a British expatriate.

given by the British Consul at the local English Club, returning to the ship at 10 p.m. Many, however, did not get back to the ship until 5 a.m. the next morning. At 10:30 a.m. on November 22 we set sail for Montevideo, Uruguay.

En Route to Montevideo

During the 17 days it took to get to Montevideo, serious preparations were started for the scientific work of the expedition.

I was conscious that I had undertaken no practical instruction in the making and reduction of astronomical observations to determine true north, so as to provide the reference for making magnetic observations. I was familiar with the theory and I had read widely on the subject but I still felt that I had only mastered the tip of an iceberg. No one at the Eskdalemuir geomagnetic observatory was able to help because all they had to do themselves was to sight on a prominent feature of the landscape and then get its bearing from an ordnance survey map. The only difficulty they had was in transferring this reference to the underground chamber and this was one problem I did not face. However, they did lend me a theodolite to use. I erected it in the grounds of the observatory and mastered the way to set it up and became familiar with the controls, scales and optics. Since then I had obtained some pertinent material from the Royal Geographic Society and I now took the opportunity to study the techniques and the methods of correcting and reducing the observations. I also started studying the star charts showing the appearance of the night sky in the southern hemisphere and memorized the position of prominent stars.

By November 25 the sea temperature had risen to 75°F (24°C) and was still going up as we moved towards the equator. Preparations for its crossing were already being made in great secrecy by those who had previously crossed that line. Hal had made himself a wig from old pieces of rope and a skirt from a windsock but we still had no idea of his role or just what would happen at the Crossing of the Line ceremony. We wondered what they had planned for us as we sailed on through the tropical sea, leaning on the rail and watching the flying fish.

In groups of dozens these fish leaped out of the water and glided through the air for many yards at a time, usually about a foot or so over the waves. One morning, whilst walking round the deck, we found several who had tried to fly over the ship and we were able to examine them in more detail. Their wings are formed from two large fins and their tail fin is horizontal. Every now and again as they passed over the crest of a wave they gave themselves an additional thrust from their tail fin.

In the evenings several of us had taken to gathering together before dinner and chatting whilst sipping a glass of the Madeira we had bought in Funchal. At other times we cut each other's hair, which was getting very untidy.

The crossing of the line ceremony took place on November 29 and was celebrated in the traditional style. Just after lunch, King Neptune (the ship's bosun) with his Queen (Hal Lister) came aboard to the accompaniment of blasts from the ship's hooter and toy trumpets. Their court consisted of a herald (Vivian Fuchs), a doctor, two nurses, a barber, two bears, a bishop and lots of policemen to see that none of the subjects escaped. All participants dressed themselves up with zeal and looked just splendid. They gathered round a specially erected small swimming pool about 8 ft by 6 ft (2.6 m) and 3 ft deep (91 cm), which was to play a prominent part in the proceedings.

When the King and Queen were seated, the Herald called out our names and read out a list of the crimes with which we were accused. My crime was to leave my beautiful wife and child to escape the English winter and to befoul King Neptune's province with sea buckets and, moreover, to persuade four other met. men to do the same. I was promptly seized by the policemen and carried bodily struggling first to King Neptune, where I was forced to my knees, prescribed a dose of physic and fined eight drinks. The medicine was administered by the doctor aided by the nurses. Then the two bears, Bare Bum and Bare Tum, grabbed me for shaving. The ship's cook was the barber and he used a most revolting mixture of old soup for the shaving cream. I was then thrown into the pool and re-christened by the Bishop with the name of a fish. I was re-christened Pilchard.

As the Chief of Police, Robin Smart worked like a Trojan rounding up the subjects. After chasing one chap all round the ship's funnel, he sat down on the deck and said to the Doctor (John Lewis), 'Christ man, put that stethoscope on me and tell me whether I'm all right.' The proceedings were closed when we captured the ship's fire hoses and turned them on to the King and his court.

After cleaning up we were served a special dinner at which the Captain presented us all with certificates of participation. We all consumed too much beer and schnapps and sang songs in both Danish and English.

The construction of the non-magnetic hut would be one of the big challenges we would face at Halley Bay. So before reaching Montevideo, I started a study group of Fred Morris, Andrew, Jim Burton, David Tribble, Derek Ward, and myself to familiarize ourselves with the main features of its design, to make life easier for ourselves once we started to build it on the ice-shelf. As the only member of the design team on the ship who knew very much about the non-magnetic hut, I was anxious to share this information with the others who would

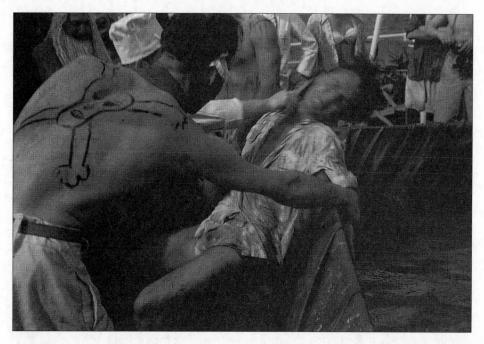

Ivor Beney's ordeal at the Crossing of the Line ceremony, performed as we crossed the equator into the Southern Hemisphere. King & Queen Neptune with their attendants boarded the ship. You were forcibly brought before the King who pronounced judgment on your sins, if you had not previously crossed the line. My sins were to have deserted my wife and three-month old child and then polluted King Neptune's domain with the bucket I used daily to measure the sea temperature. The ship's cook is enjoying his role as he shaves Ivor using a nasty shaving cream made from left-over soup. After being shaved, each victim was unceremoniously dumped into the pool and re-christened with the name of a fish.

assist in its construction. This was something we could easily do on the ship and it did prove to be a valuable preparatory exercise. It also gave me the opportunity to learn more about the many splendid qualities of the team assisting me.

During this part of the voyage we were sometimes treated to spectacular skyscapes and optical phenomena. On 25 November 1956, for example, Les Barclay and Len Constantine saw the rather rare phenomena called the green flash, a flash of green from the sun just as it disappears over the horizon.

With the air temperature hovering round 80ºF (26.7ºC), it was very pleasant on deck. One evening on the November 24, we all gathered on the boat deck for a slide show and talk given by the Captain. He spoke about sealing in East and West Greenland and the voyage to the Australian Antarctic base at Mawson in the *Kista Dan*, sister ship of the *Magga Dan*.

There were two passengers on the *Magga Dan* who were not a part of either expedition but came down to pursue their particular individual interests. There was a scientist with us who was interested in sea-ice, John Heap, and a BBC Correspondent, Donald Milner, who used the time on the voyage to edit a weekly news sheet which included contributions from several expedition members. John Heap made notes of sea ice conditions and left behind at Halley Bay sea-ice observing forms which Henry Dyer and others used whenever they had the chance to observe the sea-ice conditions off Halley Bay.

We spent a lot of time just looking at the horizon, though we continued with our daily games of deck tennis. Once I saw what can only be described as a flying eel. It was a long skinny fish with short wings near it head and tail. Then, suddenly, we noticed a whale just below the surface and right alongside the ship. It was about 15 ft. (4.57 m) long and lying partly on its side, so you could see the white colour of its belly. On another occasion, we discovered that a shark had eaten the ship's log, the gadget fitted with a propeller which trails behind the ship to measure its speed through the water. At other times the ship was accompanied by a large school of dolphins. There must have been about 100 of these splendid beasts swimming just ahead of our bows all the time, leaping out of the water as if they were running a hurdle race ahead of us.

About a week after crossing the equator, we were welcomed into the southern hemisphere by a solitary albatross. It was my first sight of this remarkable and large bird, which is never seen in the northern hemisphere. It sailed round the ship several times; a beautiful sight and one of effortless efficiency, as it glided around, banking, diving and climbing but never once flapping its wings.

We arrived in Montevideo very early in the morning of Sunday December 9. We had approached this famous city with eager anticipation as a welcome relief from the sometimes tedious confinement in a ship. The previous day I had noted how I was also looking forward to receiving some mail from home, the first for nearly a month, and how we were now looking forward to getting on with the job in Antarctica.

Montevideo

While I have been fumbling over books
And thinking about God and the Devil and all,
Other young men have been battling with the days
And others have been kissing the beautiful women.

Aldous Leonard Huxley 1894–1963.

As soon as we docked, the ship's agents, from a company called Gordon Firing, came aboard and assisted with currency and local arrangements. They also brought our eagerly awaited mail. I received over twenty pieces of mail from Oonagh alone and several people commented that I won the mail-received record.

The first thing we had to do was to participate in a press conference. Apparently there is still a substantial British presence in Uruguay and an abiding interest in British events. It was quite a lengthy affair, which resulted in a newspaper article. Some photos were taken including one, of a Señor MacDowall, which was published in a Montevideo newspaper.

As soon as possible I went ashore in the company of Andrew, George, Peter Weston, and Geoff Pratt where we took a 3-hour duration bus tour, sampled the famous Uruguayan steaks, and did a little shopping. For lunch we went to the Del Aguila restaurant, where I was astounded by size of the delicious 2 in. (5 cm) thick, 1 1/2 lb. (680 g) steak they served for a surprisingly low price. We took our evening meal at the Nogoro Hotel.

The bus tour of Montevideo first visited the fort at the top of the hill overlooking the city. It was also a lighthouse and contained a small museum. On the way through the suburbs, I was charmed by the colourful designs of the houses in some of the areas, particularly those along the beach. There were incredible contrasts in places. Alongside a beautiful new house you can find an obviously home-made, ill-kept shanty of abject poverty. As we went round the city, I formed the impression that the people were, on the whole, a happy bunch. The many Argentine visitors on the tour clearly and loudly appreciated the beauty of the girls, whom they regaled with calls and whistles of appreciation. We too thought them very attractive and that was perhaps why George opted not to return to the ship with the rest of us at the end of a very enjoyable five-course meal at the Nogoro hotel.

I purchased for Oonagh a bag made from the hides of veal calves and for Simon there was a tiny leather waistcoat. To get back to the boat, we had to pass by a police check point and were called into the little hut which sat by the side of the road leading to the docks. They did not do their job in a manner in which I had anticipated. The rather formidable-looking, heavily-armed policemen there turned out to be just as interested in the recipients of the gifts as anything else. They opened all our parcels and examined and admired each article in great detail and with obvious interest. It was about the recipients they questioned me and, possibly, since I was able to bring out a photograph of my wife and son, they let me through without further ado. I must say that I approved of their human interest approach so at the end of the examination I took a photograph of the two who obliged me with a smile and a wave.

We had a second day in Montevideo because we had to wait for the delivery of some spare parts needed by the *Tottan* when we met her at Halley Bay. We took our lunch again at the Del Aguila and this time my steak was 1 1/2 in. (3.8 cm) thick, and so I was able to finish it.

When we left on December 11 at 2:00 p.m., there were several very attractive girls waving the ship goodbye from the dockside. Apparently some expedition members had met them at a restaurant on their evenings ashore and this had led to brief liaisons. The South American ladies waving so merrily were certainly a very charming sight so I was glad now that I had joined the group who had opted out of visiting the night spots of Montevideo. Montevideo, and perhaps these charming ladies, must have left an enduring and favourable impression, for exactly six months later, on 11 June 1957, and in the middle of the Antarctic winter, one of the expedition members confided to me that he planned to leave the homeward bound ship at Montevideo.

In the 23 days of sailing from London we had covered about 6200 nautical miles (11,490 km) at an average speed of about 11 knots (20 kph). We still had about 3300 more nautical miles (6434 km) to cover which, in open water, could be accomplished in about 12 days of sailing. In fact it would take us about 20 more days because of a navigation error which led us into impenetrable sea-ice. At least our sea ice specialist, John Heap, should have been quite happy about that, but if so, he had the good sense to keep it to himself.

En Route for South Georgia

In the six days of our voyage to South Georgia we spent more time on preparations for some of the work we would need to do at Halley Bay. On arrival there, we would do our own unloading of the over 380 tons of equipment needed for our survival for two years and the facilities for the scientific work. First, we had to unload the two ships and organise the systematic dispersal of the stores to dumps round the main hut. Accordingly, I noted in my diary for December 14 that I spent the morning typing up stencils of the packing case numbers and stores dump lists so that, as the numbered boxes came off the ships, we could easily direct them to the appropriate one of the eleven stores dumps or to the designated building site. Based on our knowledge of prevailing winds and the location of the existing main hut built by the Advance party, we had some idea where the dumps should be situated and where the four new buildings should go. However, we left the final decision until we could consult the Advance Party by radio.

The five meteorologists on board continued their work of six-hourly weather observations. One task was to throw a canvas bucket over the side of the ship to measure the sea water temperature. Two days out of Montevideo, on the December 13, the sea temperature was 66°F (18.9°C) in the early morning but a few hours later it dropped to 58°F

(14.4°C) as we crossed the Subtropical Convergence Zone where the southward flowing and warmer waters meet more temperate currents flowing north. Three days later, on December 15 and exactly one month after leaving London, we entered the Antarctic by crossing the Antarctic Convergence Zone where Antarctic waters meet temperate waters. As we crossed over, the sea temperature dropped abruptly from 51°F (10.6°C) to 42°F (5.6°C). Shortly afterwards the air temperature dropped to 39°F (3.9°C). In this zone there is a great upwelling of the deeper nutrient-rich waters, which in turn support a tremendous increase in the population of birds, obvious to the most casual observer. The exceptional richness of the ocean near this zone is such that there was an increase in the bird population of at least one-hundred fold.

We were welcomed into Antarctica by some penguins. They were swimming away at a point which was about 400 miles (644 km) from the nearest land in South Georgia. Less welcome was a freshening wind which rose to a strong gale with Force 9 winds, which compelled the ship to heave-to for 12 hours. The *Magga Dan* was not able to resume course and speed until the next morning, December 16.

After less than a month of use, some of the equipment we were loaned for weather observations was cracking up. On December 12 I spent the morning repairing a barograph, a gadget which made a continuous recording of the air pressure, and which had decided to run eight times faster than normal. At the same time David Tribble, who later, under the stimulus of challenges of the Royal Society expedition, developed into an ingenious and original scientific instrument craftsman, was replacing the hinges on the Stevenson screen. The doors of this instrument enclosure were fitted with hinges containing steel pins, which were now completely rusted through by the action of the salty sea air.

Preparing for the scientific activity of Halley Bay, I spent part of December 16 working out the times of sunrise and sunset. This was the day we saw our first iceberg. It was about the size of four houses and looked impressive to me. Shortly afterward we passed by another one, which you could see on the ship's radar was 6 miles (9.7 km) away and 3/4 of a mile (1.2 km) long, and made the first one seem rather puny.

South Georgia and on to the Weddell Sea

We reached King Edward's Point, Grytviken, South Georgia on Monday 17 December 1956, five weeks after leaving Butler's Wharf in London. I noted at the time that I thought the island to be a beautiful one and, to my taste, would have been a great place for hill walking and climbing. I did not agree with Dr Hussey's view of the South Georgia scenery, as expressed in his book *South with Shackleton*. I did

Above, and below: *Magga Dan in Grytviken, South Georgia, the Atlantic gateway to Antarctica and our last port of call before plunging into the ice. It is an isolated mountainous island about 160 by 30 km in size and located about 1800 km east of Cape Horn. With many excellent harbours, it has been much exploited by whalers. The stark beauty of its snow-capped craggy mountains, glaciers, and iceberg-dotted sea does not appeal to everyone. When we visited in the summer, the population was about 1000 persons, mostly men. Joe MacDowall is shown in the lower picture.*

Shackleton's grave in South Georgia. Shackleton died on his way to Antarctica with Quest Expedition, 1921–22.

not find it at all depressing. The mountains rise sheer out of the green sea and are mostly snow capped and rugged. The highest mountain is the 9000 ft. (2743 m) high Mount Paget, that had not then been climbed. The sight of the mountains shrouded in cloud and occasionally piercing through a layer of cloud with glaciers coming down is quite unbelievably wonderful. Around the shores are multitudes of seals, elephant seals bask and penguins trot round while overhead wheel flocks of birds. The penguins are amusing to watch on shore but in the sea they are impressively efficient. They swim at high speed, dive deeply and pop up every now and then to take a breath of air.

At the government station there I met the meteorologist Danny Boreland and studied his weather charts of the area. Then we went to look at Shackleton's memorial cross on King Edward's Point. Later in the day Andrew, Hal and I walked round the bay to the whaling factory at its head. Then we visited Shackleton's grave.

In the evening the magistrate, Robert Spivey, invited us all to a magnificent party. With the members of two expeditions, ship's officer and residents invited, there must have been over 70 people crammed happily into his home and quaffing his champagne. For a few individuals, such as Fuchs and Spivey himself, the party was a reunion of those who had served together in various Falkland Island Dependencies Survey bases.

In South Georgia we were still about 1500 miles (2414 km) due north of our destination and were about to enter into the icy Weddell

Sea, which had the reputation of being a ship's graveyard capable of besetting and crushing ships even in midsummer, and was therefore the most dangerous phase of the journey. Up until 1956, recent British activity had been confined to the peninsular of Graham Land with no attempts to enter into the heart of the Weddell Sea.

On December 18 we entertained on board *Magga Dan* most of the British population of the island. On the next day, before we sailed for Leith, we took a tour of the operations of the whaling factory. My immediate impressions were of the revolting nature of the sights and smells, particularly the first few sniffs of the latter. Some whales had come in on the previous evening. On the huge wooden 'plan', which sloped down to the water, the body of a whale lay prone and was being dissected by sturdy Scandinavians wielding flensing knives, long poles terminating in curved, razor sharp blades. With the skill of long practice, they neatly sliced off the fat and skin of the whales and fed the pieces, for rendering down to oil, into large heated pots which were mostly below the plan with their lips jutting just above it. Then they cut up the meat aided by a large power-driven saw, as necessary. Antarctic skuas abounded and they gorged themselves so much that they had the greatest of difficulty in taking to the air in their overloaded state. It was a scene worthy of inclusion in Dante's Inferno. Having said that, and after touring other facilities and the laboratory, you had to recognize that the whole process was very efficient with little wasted of these magnificent beasts.

Sea Elephant on a beach in South Georgia.

Harpoon on the the bow of a Japanese whaler in South Georgia.

Some members of the expedition purchased Norwegian sweaters at the factory. Their quality was so good that they have given me over 40 years of regular wear. After making our purchases, we took in a Swedish film screened at the factory. Then I walked up a nearby hill for some fresh air and climbed up as far as the snow line. The ship then left for Leith for refuelling and to pick up our anthracite, which we were to use for cooking and heating.

Immediately before our departure from Leith at midday on December 20, I went off with Geoff Pratt to assist with an observation of the strength of gravity in the vicinity. The procedure took longer than anticipated and, as a consequence, we only just managed to get back to the ship before it took off again. Geoff used to work for British Petroleum and had prospected for oil in many parts of the world. When we got back to the ship, I was invited to see some of his large collection of superb photographic equipment.

As we passed close to the James Clarke granite rocks, I noted 30 icebergs in view. The weather worsened during the night and early on the morning of the following day, waves blown over the side of the ship in a SW gale damaged the tail of the de Havilland Otter aircraft on deck. The ship was hove-to again for that day.

While the Air Force guys were repairing the tail of the aircraft, smoke was noticed rising from an electrical winch which had become overheated due to an electrical fault. This could have been very serious since barrels of aviation fuel were lashed to that particular winch.

However, when alerted, the ship's crew dealt promptly with the problem.

Having experimented with cutting each other's hair, several of us decided to adopt a 'Convict 99' style by running the clippers all over it. One evening I asked Andrew to run the clippers over my head as a trial. It took far less time to cut this way, needed no maintenance and demanded little skill to execute. The style proved a most practical one, though it looked strange enough to cause a mild sensation at breakfast the next morning. The air temperature on that day was 33°F (0.6°C) and I was surprised to find that I hardly noticed the loss of my thatch. I concluded that its insulating value was not worth the time taken to maintain it and several of us kept the style for the rest of our stay in Antarctica.

On the eve of entering the Weddell Sea, on December 21, the weather, particularly the pattern of winds, was becoming of keener interest. For several days I had become concerned that the ship's radio operator had not been able to receive the weather reports available from South Africa. These would have allowed me to construct a weather chart showing the pattern of winds in the area to deduce something useful about their possible influence on sea-ice conditions. The operator was quite apologetic. He said that there were too many telegrams to send off for TAE members with reports to the BBC and other media. In the morning I therefore had a quiet word on the subject with Dr Fuchs. That evening I was able to prepare a weather chart. I thanked

Cutting up a whale on a 'plan' in South Georgia. The body of this whale had been brought on the previous day. They are butchering the whale on a plan, a raised wooden platform which slopes gently down into the harbour, so the body of the whales can be winched up. Heated cauldrons for rendering the fat lie below the plan with their tops just protruding above. It has to be admitted that this repellent process was a highly efficient one.

Vivian and showed the chart to the radio operator, to encourage him to provide us with a reasonable share of his time in the future.

The Icy Heart of the Weddell Sea

Shortly after noon on December 23, at latitude 60°S near South Thule in the South Sandwich Islands, we pushed through our first ice floes of heavy open pack ice about 4 ft. (1.22 m) thick, which broke up easily on impact. It was noticeable that the ocean swell had died away so it was pleasant cruising in a steady ship. Because of poor visibility, the ship was stopped at night to avoid the possibility of severe damage by running into a growler, or other heavy ice, which would be very difficult to spot in those conditions. We stopped once near a berg so that Geoff Pratt could climb on to it and attempt to make a gravity observation. When he got back on board, Geoff told me that the iceberg was moving too much for him to make a satisfactory observation.

Our discussions on the Royal Society expedition programme, to be conducted at Halley Bay, continued as we glided steadily through the calm sea. From time to time the whole ship shuddered as she broke through a piece of thicker ice. Our radio operator, Ron Evans, set up a meeting to work out the radio schedules, maintaining normal communications to the world with the minimum interference to the scientific programme. For the two-year period we were away, it was only possible to send a proper letter by normal mail about half a dozen times, and then only in December or January when ships visited us. For the rest of the year, we depended on the radio operators, Ron and Henry, to send or receive our messages. Each month we were entitled to send or receive about 100 words. At the end of that meeting, I noted that our radio operators seemed to have everything under control and that certainly proved to be the case.

We were entering the Weddell Sea, which was discovered in 1823 by the British naval officer James Weddell, the Master of the small sealer *Jane*, after he had been put on to half-pay at the end of the Napoleonic war. Weddell actually first named the sea after King George IV but the name was subsequently changed. I always thought that decision was very just, bearing in mind that George was only giving James half his pay at the time. He found the sea under remarkably ice-free conditions and was able to sail freely to latitude 74°15′S, longitude 34°16′W. He only turned back because of a lack of supplies. Since those days, the sea-ice of the Weddell Sea has acquired a fearsome reputation. The veteran US explorer Finn Ronne called it the 'hellhole' of the Antarctic, in an article he wrote in 1956 ('Antarctica' in the *IGY; American Geophysical Union Publication* No. 462; p. 22).

Shackleton's ship, the *Endurance* was trapped in the sea-ice of the

Weddell Sea on 18 January 1915. It was never released from this icy
grip and was finally crushed on 27 October and sank a month later.
As they drifted on the sea-ice, Shackleton's geologist, James Wordie,
made measurements of its movements. There is nothing like such
personal hard experiences to sharpen the edge of research. Later he
studied the ice reports made by the German ship *Deutschland* in 1912
when trapped in the Weddell Sea, the Argentine ship *General San
Martin*, and the photographs taken in December 1951 and January 1952
on flights from the Norwegian base Maudheim, located near Cap
Norvegia. No one was better qualified to advise on how to enter the
heart of the Weddell Sea when in 1955 James Wordie was Chairman
of the British National Committee for the International Geophysical
Year. He advised ships to enter the pack ice between the meridians
15° to 25° West longitude. He said that the ice would start near latitude
60°S and extend to 70°S with a shore lead providing an open channel
to the South.

The first British expedition to follow the footsteps of Shackleton
was the advance party of the Royal Society expedition, sailing in MV
Tottan in January 1956. By following Wordie's advice, they accomplished their passage through these treacherous waters in six days and
penetrated as far as 76° 40'S 27° 23'W on 3 January 1956, becoming
'the first Englishmen since that time to reach so far south in the
Weddell Sea'. (Ref. *RSIAE* Vol. 1, p 12). The route followed by the
Royal Society IGY Antarctic Expedition, advance party was as given
below:

Date	Latitude	Longitude
28 December 1955	*60° 19'S*	*29° 40'W*
29	*62° 55'S*	*24° 30'W*
30	*65° 25'S*	*20° 00'W*
31	*67° 10'S*	*15° 00'W*
01 January 1956	*70° 30'S*	*13° 10'W*
02	*73° 40'S*	*21° 05'W*
03	*76° 31'S*	*27° 23'W*
(Ref. Wordie 1956, *Nature*, Vol. 177, pp. 598–600, March 31)		

If you look at a map, you will see that it is tempting when leaving
South Georgia to set a course directly for Cap Norvegia. If this is
done, one ends up about 200 miles (322 km) to the west of Wordie's
recommended course, where the ice is heavier and more extensive. The
TAE ship MV *Theron* found this out to her cost in 1955/6 when she
took 36 days to penetrate through to the area reached by the Royal
Society expedition in six days. Unfortunately, we too were about to
discover the same thing due to a failure of the ship's navigation
equipment.

Singing Christmas carols on board Magga Dan *on 24 December 1956. Seated were Andrew Blackie, Hal Lister, Jim Burton, John Heap, and Peter Weston; standing were Bill Bellchambers, George Hemmen, Derek Ward, Robin Smart, and Malcolm Edwards.*

The problems of the future alluded to above were happily hidden, casting no pall on our Christmas spirit. As is customary in Denmark, on the evening of December 24, whilst the ship was stopped, we sat down with the Captain and officers for a real Danish Christmas dinner of rice pudding, goose with all the trimmings and fruit salad. The singing, speeches and general jollifications continued until about 5 a.m., by which time the ship was moving again steadily and rapidly south.

Christmas Day was quiet, contrasting with the activity of the previous day. Many members of the expedition had carried presents from their loved ones back home, and our celebration was tinged with the sadness of separation from loved ones and the keen recollection of previous Christmas Days with them. Parcels were opened and in many cases replies of thanks were sent or at least reflected on. The broadcast of the Queen's speech was received in the ship's lounge and a special edition of the BBC programme, 'Calling Antarctica'. The expedition received a special personal message from Her Majesty, which took four hours in transit instead of the four days it normally took for us to receive a personal message from home, half way round the world away and passing from one radio station to the next. We had decorated our cabin. All our Christmas cards were on display with photographs of our families. There was tinsel hanging round the room and Allan Rogers brought out a miniature Christmas tree he had been saving for the occasion.

On Boxing Day, the First Mate of the ship, Bill Peterson, was taken

by John Lewis for a flight in the TAE Auster. Whilst the ship was
stationary, in order to complete the routine meteorological observation,
I went out in a small boat and made measurements of the sea
temperature well away from the contamination of the *Magga Dan.*
The flight reported good ice conditions to our SE for at least 60 miles
(97 km). These good sailing conditions continued on until December
28, when, in the evening, we met a wall of solid, impenetrable pack
ice. We heard that the two USA ships, *Staten Island* and *Wyandotte*
were stuck in the ice ahead of us near Cap Norvegia, on their way to
the US base Ellsworth at the head of the Weddell Sea.

It was then that we discovered that the repeater for the gyro compass
was 15° in error, so that the ship had been sailing too far to the west
by that amount. The error was finally confirmed in the discrepancy
between the dead reckoning position of the ship and the result of sun
shots, but it was first noticed by one of the Royal Society expedition
meteorologists when logging the wind direction. We immediately
pointed it out to the ship's duty officer who took further action. As
far as I could ascertain, this error had continued since December 26
and was probably due to the electrical power being interrupted whilst
the ship turned through 15°. The net result was that we had inadver-
tently strayed into the same region where heavy pack ice held up the
TAE ship *Theron* one year ago and at least 80 miles (129 km) to the
west of the intended track on the western limit of that advised by
James Wordie. On December 29 I noted that we had to retrace our
tracks by going to the north and east and that we pushed slowly
through close pack ice all day. There were many icebergs to be seen
from the ship and many long dismal faces to be seen on her. I felt
sorry for Dr Fuchs, who keenly felt the problems that had occurred
last year and led to the difficulties eventually faced by the TAE Advance
party. He had intended to sail this year on the recommended track,
now well to the east of us. It was ironic that he should once again
land up in the area of *Theron's* problems.

In the evening of that day we had a discussion in the lounge on
the unloading at Halley Bay. Amongst other things it was decided that
a *sine qua non* of unloading would be that no equipment was ever to
be left out on the sea-ice, but moved directly from the ship to the
base and the safety of the ice-shelf.

On the night of December 30 we were twice trapped in between
ice floes, from 11:30 p.m. (on 29th) to 5:00 a.m. and again from
1:00 p.m. to 5:00 p.m. Each time we had to go over the side of the
ship wielding iron poles and the one precious ice chisel, the only one
the *Magga Dan* carried. The method of freeing a ship from the icy
grip of sea-ice is to open a channel along one side of the ship, releasing
the pressure and letting float up some of the ice trapped under the
ship and holding it up. Each time the whole process took about five

hours to complete. The ice freed from the side is pushed to the stern of the ship, where the wash from the slowly turning prop can drive it further astern. With so few poles, it was a slow job. When we returned from Halley Bay on the *Tottan* in January 1959, we learnt the correct way to do this job but the *Magga Dan* just did not have enough equipment, too few poles and no dynamite. I noted in my diary at the time that no ship should venture into the Weddell Sea without a supply of at least 50 chisel-headed poles with wooden handles and some crowbars about 10 ft. (3 m) long. After seeing how it was done on the *Tottan* two years later, I would add dynamite to the list. Both expeditions were over the side of the ship doing this work. I was particularly proud of the way the Royal Society expedition members worked. Clearly, they were no strangers to cooperating harmoniously and systematically in long periods of very hard work and with good humour. Some members of the ship's crew made a similar comment to me. In appreciation of our efforts on the ice, a day or two later, on New Year's Eve, I was pressed by some of the ship's officers to have several small tots of Danish *aqua-vitae*, drunk in their style in one gulp like a medicine.

As a result of this work, we had a good day's run to the ESE on December 31 so we could enjoy a delicious New Year's Eve dinner with an appropriate celebration and good spirits.

The New Year 1957 opened with a good day's run due south through mixed and rotten pack ice. The ice thickened on the following day, at times it was 10 ft. (3 m) thick. Despite a slight retracing of our steps at 3:00 a.m., we were making good progress. We were heartened to hear that our stores ship, *Tottan*, was only 25 miles (40 km) away. It was a beautiful day with brilliant sun at midnight producing wonderful effects, subtle changes in the colours of the ice, which sparkled as if tiny jewels had been sprinkled on it. It was our first experience of having to wear sunglasses at midnight.

In the afternoon of 2 January 1957, as we were encountering increasingly heavy ice, John Lewis and Bill Petersen did another ice reconnaissance in the Auster aircraft. This flight confirmed the presence of a wide shore lead, as predicted by Wordie, and it assisted both *Tottan* and *Magga Dan* to take the easiest route to that lead. The *Tottan* was very close to the shore lead but we still had 25 miles (40 km) to go through close heavy pack and this took us until 6:00 a.m. the following morning, when we came out into a wide shore lead.

This was my first experience of the spectacularly beautiful sight of the dazzling white cliffs of Antarctica with their blue shadows, fringed with sea ice and with its dark blue-black sea in the foreground. Particularly when the sun is low at midnight, the ice can take on a bewildering array of delicate hues and when cracks and indentations of the ice shelf take up a very special shade of blue, the deeper the

crevasse the darker the hue. On the other hand there are times when the continent deserves the title 'white desert' but not today, when the sun is shining brightly stimulating this display of nature's grandeur.

On January 3 we were sailing at full speed down the Caird Coast, discovered by Shackleton in 1915. We were about five miles (8 km) off the ice cliffs. Appropriately enough, on this day we heard that James Wordie had been awarded the KBE by H. M. the Queen in her New Years Honours list. And our own Alf Amphlett, our diesel mechanic, had been awarded the BEM for his work supporting an expedition to Christmas Island.

As it was clear that we would soon reach Halley Bay, most of us completed our packing.

At 2120 GMT (7:20 p.m. Halley Bay local time) on 4 January 1957 we arrived at Halley Bay in perfect weather. We put our watches forward one hour and decided to start unloading at 6:00 a.m. the next day.

Above and opposite: Our first view of the Antarctic continent. In the background lies the ice-shelf, or barrier which fringed the coast near Cap Norvegia at about 71°S 15°W. In the foreground lies the heavy hummocked sea ice we took many days to penetrate. Between the two lies a broad shore lead. We followed Tottan into this shore lead, and on to Halley Bay, about 800 km to the right of the picture. (The author is shown here).

References

The UK Contribution to the IGY 1957–58, 1957, The Royal Society, London.

'Antarctica' in the IGY; *American Geophysical Union Publication* No. 462; p. 22.

RSIAE 1960, Vol. 1, p 12, The Royal Society.

Wordie 1956, *Nature*, Vol. 177, pp. 598–600, March 31.

Ronne 1956, 'Antarctica' in the *IGY; American Geophysical Union Publication* No. 462; p. 22.

Frank Press and Gilbert Dewart, 'Extent of the Antarctic Continent', *Science* Vol. 129, No. 3347, p. 462, 20 February 1959.

Chapter 3

At Halley Bay off the
Caird Coast in Coats Land

January 1957

When we arrived at Halley Bay on 4 January 1957, we had the inestimable convenience and comfort of a large living hut whilst we constructed a major geophysical observatory capable of meeting the UK commitment to the IGY. Four major structures had now to be built, fitted with their scientific equipment and made ready to run for the commencement of the IGY less than six months away. But before we could do anything, some 400 tons (406 metric tons) of equipment and stores had to be unloaded from our two ships, the *Magga Dan* and *Tottan*. There was no time to lose with this vital stage, because we knew that we only had a few short weeks left of the summer weather favourable for extensive outdoor construction. For the next few weeks I rarely had more than five hours sleep a night and sometimes worked right through the night.

Welcome to Halley Bay by six members of the ten-man advance party on the left, and two members of the crew of Tottan on the right, who arrived at Halley Bay shortly beforehand.

Magga Dan and Tottan tied up to the sea-ice in Halley Bay. Mountain peaks about a hundred metres below the surface of the sea created this cosy cleft in the ice front. High cliffs on each side of the bay provided some protection. Shackleton's expedition was the first to report this feature. They called it Glacier Bay in 1915, just before the Endurance was trapped in the sea-ice. Alf Amphlett is shown here driving a tractor down the 1 in 10 slope from the ice-shelf to the sea-ice.

The main living hut was 128 ft. (39 m) long and 27 ft. (8 m) wide. It provided accommodation for up to 24 men in two dormitories fitted with bunk beds, one above the other. The engineers at the Crown Agents had excelled themselves in its design. The advance party, who constructed it in 1956, had spared no pains to make it as attractive as possible. We were all particularly impressed by the craftsmanship and taste exhibited by the design and decor of the lounge. It was a long room done in the old English style, complete with a small bar at one end, an anthracite stove in the middle, and a record player at the other end with a library of books and records. The beams in the roof were stained dark brown and carved skilfully to give that 'olde' look. When we arrived, Gus Watson was seated behind the bar like a genial mine host with his ample whiskers smartly waxed. This was to become our cinema, church, pub, cafe, library, etc. and was always a cosy place of relaxation and recreation. We never forgot the dedication and skill of the advance party for this haven and in particular the imagination and talent of the two carpenters who created it, Doug Prior and Johnny Raymond.

In planning for unloading, whilst the ship was fighting through the ice and in radio discussions with the advance party, we had developed a detailed plan for the location of the various buildings and stores dumps. When we arrived at the base upon the ice-shelf, the advance party had already put up signs marking the location of the generator shed, non-magnetic hut, balloon shed, radio astronomy hut (twinkle hut) and Decca radar. When we landed, the first thing we did was to

add signs showing the disposition of eleven stores dumps, coal here, food there, etc. These dumps were all marked with long bamboo stakes distinctively flagged so that stores could be located even when buried under the ample snowfall of the area, 3 ft. (91 cm) a year plus any snow drift effects. Eventually the food boxes and the stock of chemicals for the generation of hydrogen were raised above the surface on Dexion platforms, a great convenience, delaying for a year the burial by drifting snow.

Unloading each day continued from 6:00 a.m. to 8:00 p.m., starting on Saturday January 5. Our three Ferguson diesel tractors and one TAE Muskeg over-snow caterpillar tractor were available to pull the sledges over the 3 km of sea-ice, followed by 2.4 km up the 1-in-10 drift slope to the top of the ice-shelf. As delivered, the tractors were equipped with half-tracks but they were eventually converted to full-tracks by the fourth day of unloading. The conversion doubled the load pulled by the tractors from six drums of fuel oil per load to 12 drums (2465 kg).

The tractors were not in brilliant condition when we arrived. Little or no maintenance had been performed and they had been driven hard by almost everyone on the base. They had worked extremely hard in adverse conditions. Consequently, in the first day or so, Alf Amphlett and Ivor Beney had to do a number of repairs to keep them going. It was not until the following summer that we were in a position to give them the extensive overhaul needed to make them fit to do the unloading the following year. Although they were not designed for

Unloading – a view from the ships looking east towards the base. The tractor on the left is returning with an empty sledge to pick up another load. The one on the right is on its way up to the base. The ice cliffs on the right are about 30 metres high. Eighteen months later, hundreds of metres of the cliff in the right foreground split off from the ice-shelf and floated away as an iceberg.

Ivor Beney delivering a load to a stores dump near the base. The contents of each case were known from the numbers painted on the side. The boxes were then distributed to one of 11 dumps we had set up, according to the category of its contents: food, fuel, building material, scientific stores, tools, etc. Each dump was set up in a line across the prevailing wind, marked with flagged bamboo poles so that we could still find them when the cases were completely buried under the snow.

Antarctic conditions, the Ferguson tractors eventually did the job required of them. Particularly when we saw the splendid way the TAE Muskeg vehicle performed on snow, it was not easy to understand why we were lumbered with these three particular tractors. I guess the reason was that they were one of the standard items of equipment for the FIDS bases up the Antarctic peninsular of Graham Land, where rocky or mixed conditions prevailed. However, from the time Shackleton discovered this region of the Antarctic, it has been known that this coast consists of nothing but snow and ice. Therefore we found it hard to understand why more appropriate vehicles had not been purchased.

On this first day, working from 6:00 a.m. to 9:30 p.m., we only managed to move 35 tons of stores up to the base. It was mainly anthracite, which we burnt at the rate of 25 tons per year. Soft snow which had fallen recently made the surfaces so bad that the tractors were continually bogging down. When that happened, you first untied the sledge and moved the tractor ahead to a better surface and then continued with a longer tow rope. If that did not work, you had to dig it out. The tractors had not yet been fitted with their full tracks. Ivor Beney, one of our diesel mechanics from the Royal Engineers, had his own technique to keep a tractor going in poor conditions. He jumped up and down in the seat whilst singing at the top of his voice. The following day we managed to move 45 tons, including the Decca Radar and the sledge foundation, which was pulled up to the base by the Muskeg vehicle. It took three of us 2 1/2 hours to assemble the

radar and 1 1/2 hours to put the mounting sledge together. As we mastered the problems of unloading, the load moved up to the base rose each day to level off at about 60 tons per day. On the sixth day, January 11, we had unloaded the *Magga Dan* and commenced on the *Tottan.*

Although we were all bronzed from our sea voyage, we were by no means accustomed to the fierce sun of the Antarctic ice shelf, which, for three months of the year, came at you 24 hours a day from all directions, reflected by the blindingly white snow surface. Parts of the face, such as under the chin or nose, became exposed for the first time. To avoid snow blindness, it was essential to wear the special snow goggles we were issued with, which completely covered the whole eye and filtered out sufficient of the harmful UV radiation. Those who tried it, soon found by bitter experience that normal sunglasses just do not do the job. During the unloading, several persons got touches of snow blindness and two of them were incapacitated for two days, requiring medication for the acute discomfort involved. Whilst working hard on the stores dumps, snow goggles steamed up and, when it was necessary to refer to those stores lists we had prepared in the ship, one was tempted to push the goggles up to the top of one's head. Tedious as it may be, this detailed careful work checking case numbers made it possible, over the two years, to find anything needed from among the 11 stores dumps in the long lines which were later buried under the snow. This damaging power of the sun was one of the more tedious aspects of the Antarctic summer, particularly when you had detailed scientific work to perform, like reading the dials of a theodolite or

After working a 7-day week, for 12 hours a day of unloading or building, Robin Smart and Jim Burton savour their one-can-of-beer-a-week ration. They are shown in the lounge of the hut built in the previous year by an advance party. We had 400 tons of stores to unload, four new large huts to build and equip with a wide variety of scientific equipment, before the end of the brief period of weather suitable for outside work. From January to April, therefore, we worked these long hours to ensure the Halley Bay geophysical observatory would be up and running for the start of the IGY on 1 July 1957.

thermometers, the latter being a three-hourly chore for the meteorologists. The same was true when you had to make repairs to outdoor equipment such as fixing a tractor problem, replacing the worn out brushes of the radiation fluxplate or one of the innumerable precise jobs so necessary to keep up the schedule of observations.

The changing of the guard at Halley Bay occurred on January 8, when the responsibilities of the base passed from the Advance Party to the Main Party led by Colonel Robin Smart, RAMC. At the same time my four colleagues and I took over from David Limbert responsibilities for the meteorological programme, which we would soon expand considerably. On the following day I worked up some of the ozone observations, a task which I had taken over from Dr Stan Evans.

Way to the east of Halley Bay in October 1956, our advance party had spotted the miraged indications of a mountain range. With the exceptional clarity of the atmosphere, we knew the mountains could easily be hundreds of miles away. They had been called by our expedition the Tottan Mountains. On January 11, John Lewis of the TAE piloted the de Havilland Otter towards them and found they lay 230 miles (370 km) away on a bearing of 210° in the Norwegian territory of Antarctica. The Norwegians christened them the Tottanfjella. They rose to a height of 9200 ft. (2804 m). As he flew past them and 250 miles (402 km) from the sea, George Lowe spotted two snow petrels flying round the top of a 7000 ft. (2134 m) peak. (Ref. Fuchs and Hillary, *The Crossing of Antarctica*, p. 68).

On January 12 our ten-man advance party plus the 16 TAE members sailed off south for Shackleton Base. As the ship departed, we were reminded that we would soon be dependent on the radio for our letters to and from home. Then we would only be able to send and receive one brief 'air letter' per month containing about 100 words. The messages from home were sent to the Postmaster at Port Stanley. He opened them and sent them on to us over the radio. In return, we radioed our message to Port Stanley, where it was put in an air letter mailed off to our families. On February 17 I received my first two of these air letters. The amount of such traffic was limited because, when the radio was transmitting, several parts of the scientific programme could not operate. We would later realize that for about two or three months in the middle of winter, we would not receive any of these letters at all because of the winter break in the sea link between South America and Port Stanley. In January 1959 we stopped in South Georgia on our way home and were quite astounded and surprised to meet so many people there who knew so much about us and our families, with the details of our doings over two years. Clearly they had been sharing the contents of our monthly letters as they were sent to and from us like the instalments of a real live soap opera.

We sometimes also got messages via 'ham' or amateur radio operators. On January 7, I received a message from Les Hill with the call sign of G8KS. As he lived near London, I gave him Oonagh's phone number and on January 9 Les read me out her reply.

Royal Society Expedition
Builds up Shackleton Base

When they arrived at Shackleton on 12 January 1957, the ten members of our homeward-bound advance party made a welcome input to the building programme of Fuchs' Trans-Antarctic Expedition. During the 14 days they were there, they made a major contribution to the construction of four new buildings, an aircraft workshop, emergency stores hut, hydrogen generating hut and a vehicle stores hut. Amongst other things they also cured the interference emanating from the electrical generators, installed a hot water system, erected chimneys and assisted with the electrical wiring system. Knowing of their performance at Halley Bay, I could just imagine how much this seasoned team could accomplish in two weeks of flat-out work at Shackleton.

Tottan

On January 12 we went on board the *Tottan* and met her Norwegian crew for the first time. The ship and crew had already captured my imagination for its superior performance in fighting through the formidable ice of the Weddell Sea in the summers of both 1955/6 and 1956/7. This year, she had beaten the more modern and larger *Magga Dan* to Halley Bay. I formed a very favourable impression of the captain and crew of the *Tottan,* which showed all the signs of being a happy and efficient ship with a delightful captain.

January 13 was our last long day of unloading when we moved about 60 tons of oil drums, and tins of caustic soda and shredded aluminium for the generation of hydrogen. *Tottan* sailed away at 3:00 a.m. the following morning. We marked the end of unloading by starting work the next day two hours later than usual at 8:20 a.m.

Base Routine

Throughout the unloading period we rose at 5:45 a.m. and had a cup of coffee with bread and cheese. Our bread was quite superb and nothing like the mass-produced impostor, then the only type available in England. Bread was usually baked by Malcolm or Len but, in addition, Gwynne Thomas occasionally baked it. His father was a Welsh baker and it was his recipe I used when I joined the evening baking roster in 1958. From 8:00 to 8:30 a.m. we returned to the mess for a full English-style breakfast. At 10:30 a.m. we had a 15-minute break with cocoa, bovril, ovaltine or horlicks. The main meal was taken at 12:30 to 1:45 p.m. and was the largest of the day. A typical lunch started with a bowl of soup followed by tinned steak, tinned potatoes, peas and carrots, and finished off with apple pie topped with a slice of cheese. At 3:30 p.m. we were back for a drink of tea or coffee. At 5:30 p.m. we took another three-course meal and finally a drink at 8:00 p.m. None of us put any weight on as we burnt all this food off during the 15-hour days of physical activity.

During most lunch breaks I made an ozone observation. The observation took half an hour, with another period in the evening needed to reduce the observations. After the evening meal, there was always some scientific work to do.

Every nine days, each person undertook what was called 'gash' duties. They left off their normal tasks and took their turn cleaning up the lounge, dining room, corridors and workshop, assisting the cook, cleaning out the garbage, doing all the washing up, getting rid of waste water, which you carried out of the hut, bucket by bucket to a gash pit 20 yards (18 m) outside, filling up the three water tanks with clean snow, attending to the stoves, bringing in food from the stores dumps, etc. Two persons were required to do this and no one was exempted save the two cooks, who were continually involved in some of these onerous tasks.

In fact it did provide a not entirely unwelcome change from normal duties and associates. I noted that I did my first gash duty with Robin Smart and the next one with Ivor Beney. Prompted by the notes in my diary for the period, I remember how I enjoyed chatting with them as we swept up and cleaned. Later in the year, as we settled in, only one person was required for gash duties so that we only did this chore every 18 days. There were some general duties which needed a much bigger effort, such as taking out the 40-gallon drums we used for our toilets and refilling the anthracite store in the hut with fresh supplies from the coal dump outside.

Building the Observatory at Halley Bay

The first two buildings were erected at the same time, the non-magnetic hut and the generator shed. One of the carpenters, Fred Morris, was in charge of the former and Ken Amy was the carpenter in charge of the latter.

Four of the five meteorologists assisted in the construction of the non-magnetic hut, leaving one to look after routine surface observations and other tasks. Once the exterior was completed on January 28, our carpenter, Fred Morris, and the meteorological team moved on to erect the balloon shed. They returned to finish off the floor and inside of the non-magnetic hut on February 12. Finally the radio echo hut and the remote stations were built and a number of large antenna arrays were set up.

The two carpenters, Fred Morris and Ken Amy, directed most of this important activity and the scientists provided the less skilled labour. In many ways it was a happy phase of the expedition, with everyone busy, working hard and harmoniously together, with palpable evidence of achievement clear from each day's work, as more structures broke the skyline and problems were overcome. The one task that gave us most difficulty was the application of roofing felt to the outside of buildings in the prevailing low temperatures.

The most challenging building was the non-magnetic hut, of a unique design. It was the first time such sophisticated, continuous recordings had been made of the earth's magnetic field from a floating ice-shelf. To ensure there was no interference with the normal earth's magnetic field, the hut had to be entirely free from any magnetic materials. The materials used, aluminium, brass and copper fittings, the sand, cement, bricks and marble, were all tested for freedom from magnetic properties at Eskdalemuir Observatory in Scotland. We commenced construction immediately *Tottan* left on January 14. The task took the five of us a total of 51 man-days to complete.

After selecting the site for the non-magnetic hut, I first determined the direction of the earth's magnetic field over two days and then lined the axis of the hut in the magnetic meridian. The first day of construction was taken up in measurements, laying out the site, marking where the piles for the sensitive instruments were to be driven, assembly of equipment and erection of the pile driver. The following

A view of Royal Society Base, Halley Bay in February 1957. The generator shed in the foreground is almost completed. Just to the right of it is the main hut, built the previous year and now almost engulfed in snow. Hidden behind the main hut, work has commenced on the construction of the radio echo hut and in the distance is the long line of the food dump. An all-sky camera to photograph the aurora is the dark object on the left of the picture. A Stevenson screen for measuring the temperature of the air is the small white, box-like structure in the middle.

day we commenced driving the first pile and it took us all day to drive one telegraph pole 18 ft. (5.49 m) into the ice shelf to provide a firm, vibration-free foundation. The business end of the the pile driver had to be wound up by hand and then dropped on to the top of the pile. It was a slow and exhausting job. For the next day, we rigged up a tractor winch to haul the massive driving weight up and we used the tractor to move the rig. So the second pile took only 1 1/2 hours to drive. Ten more were driven on the next day and pile-driving was completed on the third day. When we measured up the tops of the piles, we were satisfied to find that no pile was out of position by

Jim Burton and Fred Morris driving the pile foundations for the non-magnetic hut. We drove wooden telegraph poles 6 metres into the compacted snow, to provide the necessary stability for the delicate and sensitive geomagnetic instruments. Eventually, the instruments will be mounted on top of these piles whilst the structure of the hut will be entirely separate and built on a platform made from the planks of wood laid on the surface and shown in the foreground. The stock of anthracite used for cooking and heating in the main hut is shown in the left background of the picture.

more that 3 inches (8 cm). That was well within specifications for the trouble-free fitting to proceed with a frame round the piles. This last job was quickly and expertly done by Fred.

The next phase of construction was to level the grillage which supported the semicircular roof arches. On top of this were laid the 57 floor joists and base for the roof arches. This phase took another three days.

Whilst all this building work proceeded apace, some elements of the scientific programme were continued, the regular meteorological observations and my ozone observations. On Saturday January 19, for example, I spent much of the day working on the ozone spectro-photometer whilst at regular intervals the surface meteorological measurements were made.

Birthdays were always an occasion for special celebration and a contribution for each person's birthday was kindly provided by the Royal Society. It was David Tribble's birthday on January 20. At dinner there was a special cake and a tot of whisky all round for the birthday toast. David had already completed the construction of the radar and was working in the team building, the non-magnetic hut. We were all about to start on the construction of the balloon shed.

David was the meteorologist who developed considerable talent for constructing various ingenious and useful devices, which he created in a den he made for himself in an unused recess of the attic of the main hut. In his den he had a little workshop where he also grew various

Jim Burton, Joe Mac-Dowall and Fred Morris (carpenter in charge of the building) standing in front of the completed non-magnetic hut. David Tribble and Derek Ward also formed part of the team which built this hut.

plants, including marigolds. The soil came from England and the whaling factory in South Georgia contributed the fertilizer. The marigolds were grown by the light of electric lamps, so they were rather lanky specimens, but the flower had the same rich colour as if it had been grown in a normal garden. He also initiated a systematic photographic study of sastrugi on the snow surface near the base, thus making a significant contribution to the glaciological studies of the expedition.

On January 28 many of us waited up to welcome the MS *Magga Dan* back to Halley Bay, on her way home with the advance parties of the Royal Society expedition and TAE. She arrived at 1:30 a.m., consequently I stayed up all night, going off again the following day to work on the balloon shed. The sea-ice in the bay had broken off to the drift slope so there was no room for the ship to come alongside. She laid her bow against the shelf and we climbed aboard from a rope ladder, and then she lay off for a while for fear of bumping into some large blocks of ice. We handed over our mail, said goodbye to our friends, and welcomed Peter Jeffries, a new member for our meteorological group transferred from the TAE advance party.

Clearly the TAE advance party had had a tough winter at Shackleton. They had not been able to build their hut before the fierce conditions of the Antarctic winter set in and they spent the time living inside a Snocat crate 21 × 9 × 8 ft. (6.40 × 2.74 × 2.44 m) in size. Furthermore, the previous year their ship had left before their stores had been taken up to the camp site and 300 tons were still left on the sea-ice. It was only possible for the eight men in the party to bring a small proportion of this up to the ice-shelf and that fortunately provided sufficient for them to survive the year. (Ref. Fuchs & Hillary, *The Crossing of Antarctica*, Cassell, pp. 49–59).

Some Living Routines

By this time we had established our regular routines. Every ten days, for example, two persons had a bath and dhobi (laundry) evening. I was paired with Andrew and we took it in turns to go first. It was my first bath since leaving the UK two months earlier and held on Saturday January 19, when I repaired to the relative privacy and pleasures of the bathroom. Usually those on gash duty had done their job well so both the bathroom tanks were full. But if not, the first steps were taken on the roof of the hut where blocks of snow were cut and fed into the bath water tank. Then you went into the workshop alongside the bathroom and lit the anthracite stove to heat the water. Having washed your clothes and bed linen in the electric clothes washer, you luxuriated in the pleasures of soaking in a tub of hot water. The only problem was that after all this luxury and warmth,

you had to empty the bath, bucket by painful bucket, and dispose of it in a gash pit which lay outside the back door of the hut.

However, the hardship of this less-than-ideal end to a beautiful evening in the hot tub may have stimulated consideration of the mechanics of gash pits in the ice-shelf. But for whatever reason, later in 1957 we hit on the idea of creating a gash pit directly under the bath. After discussing this with Robin and others, by means of a few test runs, we soon found this could be done without creating any problems.

My first bath night was on a Saturday and that was the night on which we also showed the full-length feature film, *Trinidad.* These Saturday evenings were the main social gathering of the week. It was also the day on which the week's chocolate ration was distributed, together with one can of beer per person. In addition, after the film, the 21 of us shared one bottle of Scotch whisky, which was set out on the bar for those who liked a tot. Every Sunday morning there was a short religious service, after which a bottle of gin was available to share. This après-worship social gathering was followed by lunch and possibly a ski run down to Emperor and Halley bays. We had another regular gathering on Wednesday evenings when the weekly bottle of rum was put out.

On several occasions we held scientific discussions where some members prepared in advance and others joined in. These proved very successful. Many members of the expedition were enthusiastic photog-

Joe MacDowall with an Emperor Penguin chick which had wandered up to our base from the rookery 3 km away. On the left is the main hut, built only one year ago and now almost engulfed by snow accumulation.

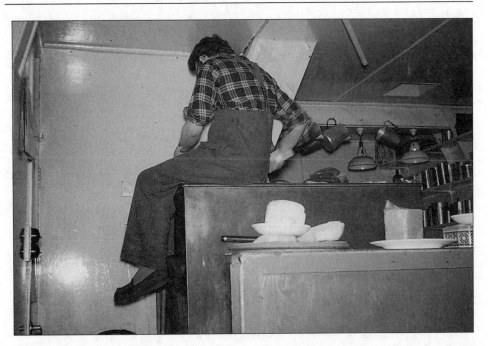

Les Barclay doing his 'gash' duty and assisting with the innumerable domestic tasks in the hut. He is sitting on top of the copper tank used for our water supply. Part of the gash duty was to keep this topped up with clean snow.

raphers, who had brought with them all the necessary equipment to process colour films. Derek Ward was one of the scientists who was also an enthusiastic and accomplished photographer. One Saturday evening, January 26, he gave a slide show of the many fine pictures he had taken since we had left London.

February 1957

The building phase of the expedition continued through January and February. By February 11 the exterior of the balloon shed was completed and some of us returned to complete the inside of the non-magnetic hut. The balloon shed was equipped with a 10 ft (3 m) -high roller blind garage-style door, through which the inflated balloon was launched. In addition, it was fitted with a large trapdoor in the roof which proved to be too heavy for use. On February 5 we did a great deal of heavy work on the balloon shed. First we had to haul up to the roof the two leaves of the hatch and then we had to erect the 1200-lb. (544 kg) Gill hydrogen generator which still lay on its side. For the job I rigged up a times-four block and tackle to assist six of us in its erection and movement to place. I spent the rest of that day assembling a multitude of pipes and gauges on to this splendid beast, which proved to be so reliable in routine use, once we mastered its idiosyncrasies.

For much of February the summer weather continued. However,

there were several periods of severe snow-drifting, which would greatly have set back the building programme if we had not pushed on with it so quickly. Although the weather was clearly deteriorating, we still experienced days like February 6, when the air temperature was 20°F (−6.7°C) and we worked outside with our shirt sleeves rolled up. The challenge of building in these conditions was to get the exterior sound- and snow-proof before the snow drift conditions commenced.

We were well aware of what can happen, as in the case of the TAE advance party at Shackleton Base. The ability of snow drift to enter through the tiniest crack was dramatically illustrated on February 13 in the non-magnetic hut after a moderate gale. The exterior was complete but there was a tiny, unnoticed hole through which had been forced into the interior of the hut a pile of snow six feet high. All this had to be shovelled out before we could continue work. During nine months of the year, moderate gales sometimes occurred every few days. Thus the immense difficulties of building at Halley Bay can be appreciated, except during the brief summer season. Our diligence and speed of building had stood us in good stead. From now on, in the poor building days, we could make a start unpacking our scientific stores and gradually expanding the scientific component of our work.

On February 7 & 8 I opened packing cases of meteorological stores. I got out the Holerith cards for recording our observations in a machine-readable format, unpacked the sunshine recorder, found it damaged and repaired it, and then I did a test of the new radiation instruments. The following day I laid out a new set of accumulation stakes, because the ones used last year were becoming affected by the great increase in the size of our encampment, which caused drifting snow to exaggerate the natural rate of snow accumulation.

From time to time, responding to Donald Milner's requests, I took out the BBC tape recorder and gave a brief report on happenings and developments. I did this on January 17 and again ten days later. On February 13 I made a special recording of the start-up of the new Meadows-MacFarlane diesel-driven electrical generators in their re-cently constructed generator shed.

On February 14 we celebrated Fred's birthday. Those of us who were lucky enough to work alongside him, building the non-magnetic hut and the balloon shed, developed an admiration for his carpentry skills and his particular brand of cheerful energy, to say nothing of his very own attitudes to life. Our huts were superbly crafted by Boulton & Paul and were made of precut timbers. As far as possible they had been preassembled in the UK before being packed up. All the pieces were carefully labelled so that almost anyone could then assemble them like a jigsaw puzzle. Being a trained craftsman, that was not the way Fred usually worked, so we were occasionally treated to a few pithy comments from Fred on something which for him was an unnecessary complication and slowed him down. We learnt from him how to measure twice and cut once and how to hammer in nails, and screws too, without damaging the surrounding wood. The first time I saw Fred hammer nails into floor boards, I was astounded by the speed at which he worked. It was something to be wondered at and clearly the result of years of practice. The nails seemed to flow in a stream from one hand while the hammer moved so quickly as to become blurred, but it never missed the target. Some of us will always be grateful to him for teaching us something of a craft which was of use to us for the rest of our lives. I was particularly grateful to Fred for his training in skew nailing, a trick I have used in the many wooden structures I have built in my homes. I pay silent homage to him every time I cut my timber after carefully measuring it twice.

Throughout the building phase of the expedition, both our carpenters, Fred and Ken, were at the centre of a maelstrom of activity. When the building was done, however, the amount of work they had to do dropped off dramatically, whilst the scientists switched over from their earlier role as unskilled construction labourers. This was a difficult transition for the carpenters to accomplish and it was a great credit to them that they did adapt. On the other hand, the scientific staff just moved into another busy period but one they were trained for and happy in accomplishing.

There was another gale with snowfall on February 15, which reduced the visibility to about 100 yards (91 m). Derek and I went out together in it, to collect a specific case from a stores dump. Thanks to the organized system we had used for the dumps, it only took us 15 minutes to locate it and return to the hut. There had been a great deal of snow-drifting near most huts, as well as other obstructions. Some of the building supplies had been left outside near huts and became deeply buried under snow drifts. So on the following day we all went outside to extricate this building material, which had become buried under about 4 ft. (1.22 m) of drifted snow.

I was on gash duty on February 18, after which I started to put up the synchronome clock, a precise pendulum clock which is designed to generate the timing signals for the chart recorders. The task kept me up until 1:30 a.m. the next morning. It actually took me three more days to get that clock up and working properly, until I discovered that the manufacturer had not aligned the instrument correctly on its base board. You had to tilt the whole case slightly in order to keep the innards level, so the case of the clock always looked slightly crooked.

For some time now, I had become concerned about the location of our 35 ft. (11 m) high meteorological tower, used to measure the wind direction and speed, at the regulation height above the surface. This latest storm convinced me that a new tower would have to be erected, which was further away from the enlarged encampment. I started construction right away on February 22 and finished it on the 27th after four days of work, since I was on gash duty for one of the days.

The following day, after laying some of the necessary cables between the new tower and the meteorological office, the sun was setting and we were treated to one of those almost magical displays of delicate colours which changed from minute to minute as the sun set. At one time the whole mast was bathed in a gleaming golden hue as if some giant hand had gilded it for our pleasure. It certainly looked better than the usual shiny grey of the Dexion struts. It was snowing again on March 1 when I completed the job of laying the nine cables from the tower to the hut for the wind, temperature and humidity measuring equipment it carried at several levels above the surface.

On the same day Jim Burton injured his hand and had his arm in a sling. Jim was an irrepressible cheery, cricket-loving Yorkshireman of indefatigable energy, usually bursting with rude health as he busied himself with his meteorological duties. As if he did not have enough to do, from time to time he edited six editions of the publication of our paper, the *Halley Comet*.

March 1957

Our two radio astronomers were still busy building their very extensive set-up. Having completed their hut, on March 4 Philip Brenan took some sledges off to build their remote aerials for the observations of the scintillations of a radio star. The meteorologists David Tribble and Derek Ward went with him to give a hand in constructing the three large yagi arrays. The aerials worked at 60 Mc/s, observing scintillations of a radio source in Centaurus. They were believed to be due to irregularities in the ionosphere at a height of 100 to 200 km above the surface and moving at several hundred metres per second. Each array consisted of six elements fixed to each of five long poles which pointed skywards and they were spaced one kilometre apart. Back at the base, Robin Smart assisted in the building up of the huts later placed at the remote sites. They were erected on a sledge foundation and then pulled into place by tractor.

The other piece of radio astronomy hardware comprised a large rotating radar set operating at 70 Mc/s and designed to track aurora and meteors. David Cansfield and Len Constantine assisted the astronomer, David Harrison to build this radar.

By the first week in March we were firmly into the winter style of weather, with a prolonged gale blowing up every few days, sometimes with snow. Most of the time however we were concerned with the installation of our scientific equipment. Several pieces of radiation equipment were installed, also a fluxplate radiometer and temperature measuring equipment at two levels on the new tower. I also rewired the meteorological office and installed a direct current (DC) power supply for the time-marking circuits and small motors. The DC power came from a bank of lead acid accumulators in the attic above the meteorological office. On March 12 Andrew and Derek commenced the installation of our cloud searchlight, a vertically pointing searchlight some distance from the hut which enables you to measure the height of the clouds.

After a few windy days, March 15 was a beautiful day with sunshine and very little wind. I fitted four more guy wires to the almost completed tower and secured them to dead-men buried in the snow. I took a number of photos and at night did a spectroscopic observation of total ozone in the atmosphere using the light of the moon. There was an auroral display that night.

On March 26 I made a determination of our latitude from the elevation of the sun; the result was 75°30′58″S. On March 30 I did another fix using a star, Delta Serpens. On the following night, I determined the azimuth of the magnetic fixed mark for the geomagnetic observations as 0°02′24″. On April 9 I did another shot using the sun and the result agreed with the star shot. I remember feeling at the time that the preparation work on the ship had paid off and I was rapidly becoming more confident with the astronomical part of the geomagnetic work.

April 1957

Derek Ward ties a radar reflector to a hydrogen-filled balloon in the balloon shed during a storm.

As a result of the continued hard work through March, we were ready on April 1 to conduct the first balloon ascent, which went to a height

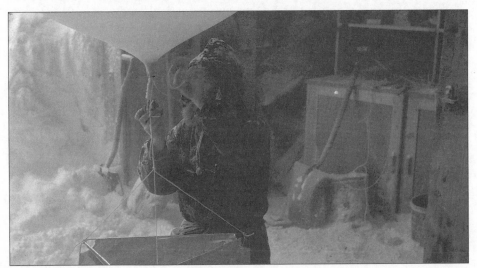

of 66,000 ft. (20 km). Amongst other things, we had brought into the hut 400 radio sondes, ready for launching two a day from the commencement of the IGY. We tried another ascent the next day but the water used to generate hydrogen was too cold and it nearly froze. Then a gale blew up and Jim and I went out to measure the snow stakes, which we had forgotten about on 1st because of the excitement in launching our first balloon. Peter Jeffries later worked on the Gill hydrogen generator to solve some problems with its operation. The whole meteorological team were now deeply involved in building up the scientific programme, with wind-finding ascents going on most days and learning how to operate efficiently the Gill hydrogen generator. The first time we used it we took one and a half hours but by April 10 we had brought this down to ten minutes.

Derek phones his colleagues back in the main hut to let them know the instant the radio sonde is launched.

Terrestrial Magnetism

Continuous observations of the earth's magnetic field at Halley Bay were crucial both for their own sake and to support several other elements of the IGY research programme. In particular, the auroral, ionospheric and radio astronomy researches depended on obtaining concurrent geomagnetic observations.

Terrestrial magnetism has a long history of its utility to mankind, first for navigation and more recently in support of a wide range of services, such as world-wide radio telecommunications. The ability of

Peter Jeffries runs out into the storm to launch the balloon-borne radio sonde and radar reflector, which are just about to be whipped away by an easterly gale force wind.

a magnet to provide directional guidance has been know since Peter Peregrinus recorded his experimental work on magnetism in the 13th century, and possibly earlier. This almost magical property of a magnet to guide one round the oceans of the world was known for centuries before 1600, when a Fellow of St John's College, Cambridge and physician to Queen Elizabeth I, William Gilbert, discovered that the earth was, in effect, a great magnet, and he gave impetus to further studies in terrestrial magnetism. We now know that the field has its origin in the movements of the molten core of the earth. Then we discovered that the regular small daily changes in the field were due to electrical currents of tens of thousands of amperes flowing in the ionised layers of the atmosphere hundreds of kilometres above our heads. Under magnetically disturbed conditions, the magnitude of the currents increases ten-fold. In much more recent years, it has been appreciated that the transient rapid changes also had their source in the ionosphere under the disturbance of solar flares, immense explosions on the sun. The solar explosions fire off ions and electrons which then enter the earth's atmosphere at speeds far exceeding those of meteors and result in the aurora, disruptions to radio communications, and magnetic storms.

The genesis of the earth's magnetic field and its variations provide an awe-inspiring picture of the way we are under the complex influence of titanic forces ranging from the very core of planet earth, deep beneath our feet, on the one hand, to those which stoke the fires of the sun. This is, of course, one of the reasons why those of us studying the subject were so fascinated by it. And perhaps why my colleagues and I were content spending hours on end checking and recording long series of closely written figures, in what casual observers of our activity could only perceive as a tedious grind.

Installing Geomagnetic Recorders

Finally, on April 3, I reached the stage of being able to commence the installation of the La Cour magnetic variometers inside the non-magnetic hut.

Research into terrestrial magnetism rests on continuous observations of the three components of the earth's magnetic field, viz. the Horizontal, Declination, and Vertical components. A set of variometers therefore consists of three separate instruments, one for each component. Variometers need to be sensitive to the constant small changes in the magnetic field. This is called the 'Normal' set of variometers. Because the first moments of a magnetic storm can involve very large changes in the magnetic field, it is also necessary to employ a second 'Insensitive' or 'Storm' set of instruments with about one-fifth of the sensitivity of the normal recorder.

Thus a complete set of the two variometers comprised six instruments, which I had now to set up. The three instruments of the normal recorder were set up in one room and the storm recorder in an adjacent room of the non-magnetic hut. Both sets used photographic recording on to a slowly revolving drum to provide a continuous record of the three components of the field.

With great care I took out the quartz fibre for the horizontal component of the Normal Recorder and suspended the magnet from it. To measure the horizontal component, the fibre was twisted until it forced the magnet to lie at right angles to the horizontal component of the field. This was achieved by using, as a reference, a thread I strung along the direction of magnetic north and running down the centre of the hut. A tiny mirror was fixed to the magnet and this directed to the recorder drum a beam of light from a projector, once you had everything set up correctly.

Then I fixed a series of small reflecting prisms to a bar to provide a fan of beams from the magnet so that, as the spot of light went off the top of the recording drum, another recording spot of light would appear at the bottom of the record, so obviating the problem of going off scale for moderate magnetic storms.

The declination, or the direction of the horizontal component was observed by suspending a magnet from a fine quartz fibre with negligible torsion so that it was almost completely free to align itself with the direction of the field.

The third instrument in the trio was designed to measure the vertical component of the earth's magnetic field. It comprised a small magnet supported on knife edges, which rested on a polished agate surface so that it could see-saw with negligible friction. When I first set up the magnet, its north end settled lower than the south end. If this was not corrected, the instrument would also be sensitive to changes in the strength of the horizontal field as well as the vertical field. So I ground down the north end until the magnet was perfectly horizontal. I placed a lamp above the magnet and looked at its reflection on the roof until I was satisfied. Then I generated a strong horizontal field near the magnet using a coil of wire and confirmed the magnet did not move when this field was switched on. Satisfied, I moved on to the adjustment of the series of reflectors producing the fan-beam for multiple recording of moderate storms.

It took another three weeks to complete the full installation of the magnetic variometers, and then we were ready for continuous recording of the three components of the earth's magnetic field.

Then on April 26, Andrew and I started to use the three absolute instruments to establish the baseline for the continuous recording. We were both elated now that we had brought two major programmes of the IGY to the verge of operational readiness, over two months before the start of the IGY. Recognising this point, on April 23, I wrote a scientific talk on the subject for the BBC.

Andrew and I shared the geomagnetic observing programme and it was a very well-balanced partnership. Andrew was a self-confident and good humoured Scottish scientist, who had several years of experience at the Middle Eastern bases of the Meteorological Office, in addition to his geomagnetic skills. He was the deputy leader of the meteorological/geomagnetic group, in whom I had great confidence.

Now that the cardinal elements of our programme were established, I set up various ancillary programmes. For example, to measure the temperature of the ice shelf, I dug a 40 ft. (12 m) hole and on April 28 David Tribble made and installed in it several thermocouples to measure the temperatures below the snow surface.

Throughout April we continued to send up a daily balloon carrying a radar reflector and tracked it with the radar. Practice made us more confident as we rapidly improved our skills and developed more confidence in the procedures. In May, we added a radio sonde on a 30 m long piece of string under the radar reflector and were then able to measure the temperature and humidity structure of the atmosphere, in addition to the wind velocity. Apart from some troubling teething problems with the radar, which persisted through much of June, by the end of May, we were confident of our ability to undertake the full IGY programme and were able to attend to some of the secondary programmes. Twice-daily balloon soundings of the atmosphere were commenced on 21 June 1957, nine days ahead of the starting date of the IGY. They were continued for more than 18 months.

Two men were required to operate the radar. The leader and medical officer, Robin Smart, volunteered to assist one of the meteorologists with the work and this was a tremendous help to our team. As they tracked the balloon on its upward path through the atmosphere, the radar operators passed the range, azimuth and elevation back to the main hut by telephone. In the hut, others plotted the observations on a plotting table and from that worked out the minute-by-minute movement of the balloon and hence the direction and speed of the upper-air winds.

The IGY and Meteorology

The IGY was enthusiastically embraced by meteorologists and they were very well prepared, both in terms of equipment and organizational skills. It has turned out they were right in believing it would be the best way to accelerate the realization of the dream of mankind to be able to make more accurate weather forecasts. Progress to date had been painfully slow, notwithstanding the efforts expended, so that for many in the population forecasts were the regular butt of bad jokes.

As a result of his discovery of the jet stream in 1927, the German meteorologist, Dr J. Georgi, proposed the Second International Polar Year, which was held in 1932–33. For meteorological progress it was 25 years too soon. The results of that exercise were thought at the time to have been rather disappointing since the current radio-sounding, wind-finding and radiation equipment had not been developed or was not deployed in the required extensive network.

In the intervening years, great efforts were made, so that when the IGY dawned, the world had ready the required observing systems plus the tools to analyse the immense quantities of data gathered. Thus the stimulus of the IGY brought forward these forecasting improvements as the power of electronic computers combined with the expanded network and scope of observations. The IGY triggered an upsurge in radiation and energy balance observations in a broad variety of circumstances, required for more atmospheric modelling, and launched the sattelite age, which provided a synoptic view of global weather. With the explosion in air travel, this came only just in time to support the new requirements to run airline systems with the necessary precision, to say nothing of the expanded calls on weather forecasting services demanded by the sophisticated agricultural and industrial systems that had grown up in the northern hemisphere.

Ionospheric Physics and the IGY

The ionospheric and meteorological programmes were conducted in the main hut. The activity of the meteorologists described above, as they toiled to build up the full IGY programme, was mirrored by the diligence of the ionospheric physics team of Bill Bellchambers, Les Barclay and David Cansfield. Their branch of science had important applications to the maintenance and improvement of world-wide radio communications, particularly important in those days just before the launch of the first artificial earth-orbiting satellites.

The subject of their study was the layers of ionised gas well above the surface of the earth, right out of the reach of aeroplanes or balloons. Natural movements of these conducting layers through the existing earth's magnetic field generate an additional magnetic field which is detected near the surface of the earth as a magnetic disturbance. Consequently its existence was proposed by Balfour Stewart in 1882 to account for the observed small variations of the earth's magnetic field. The self-taught genius Oliver Heaviside also postulated the existence of such a layer from his mathematical analysis of radio wave propagation. Its existence was supported when Marconi demonstrated the practicability of world wide radio communication to points below the horizon of a transmitting station, suggesting that the radio waves were being reflected back to earth by a conducting layer high up beyond the reach of man. The Nobel Laureate and Fellow of St John's College, Cambridge, Sir Edward Appleton, was the British scientist who finally proved beyond doubt the existence of this ionosphere by reflecting radio waves from it and systematically probing the layers.

Two particularly important layers were actually found. The lower one is called the 'E' or Heaviside layer, which at Halley Bay we found to extend from a height of 80 km, and the 'F' or Appleton layer, which had its maximum strength at a height of about 430 km above Halley Bay. The E layer allows the extensive propagation of longer radio wavelengths whilst the F layer provides the means for short-wave transmissions to circle the globe from one point on it. Forty years after the dawn of the satellite age, the ionosphere was still enabling the short-wave transmissions of the BBC to reach a world-wide audience for no charge by the creator of the facility.

As soon as the unloading phase of the expedition was complete, Bill's team erected a 78 ft. (24 m) mast which supported the system of ionospheric aerials. The erection of a mast this size by a small team of amateur mast-erectors would be quite an achievement in temperate climates, but to do it in Antarctic conditions was something else. A problem proved to be the way the snow lay round the aerials in large, drift-induced mounds, resulting in differential subsidence exaggerating the rate of sinking between the mast and guys. Further, the snow found its way into the hollow centre of the mast, where it melted and re-froze, splitting the seam of the mast and weakening it. Despite its weakened condition, the mast lasted until 13 August 1958, when it buckled at the base and then on 26 October 1958 it collapsed completely. Fortunately the team was able to erect a new set of aerials before the the the 78 ft. (24 m) mast finally subsided.

Installed in the main hut was the necessary electronic equipment. The ionosonde comprised a large radio transmitter used to fire upwards a beam of radio waves for reflection back by the ionosphere. The frequency of the waves swept over the short-wave band from 0.7 to 25.0 MHz in a period of five minutes at hourly intervals. The reflections up to a height of 100 km were recorded on a film which provided a thorough sounding of the ionosphere by showing the height of reflecting layers versus the frequency of the wave reflected. Two other devices measured the absorption of the ionosphere and its movement. Absorption at either 2.2 or 4.0 MHz radiation was observed using equipment which was designed by the Cavendish Laboratory in Cambridge.

On April 1, three months before the commencement of the IGY, we were able to start regular soundings of the ionosphere. The measurements of absorption of radio waves in passing through the ionosphere began on May 2, followed by ionospheric drift observations on May 8.

An interesting bonus from the careful analysis of the ionospheric records was an independent determination of the height of the ice-shelf on which we were sitting. The ionospheric signals showed a series of interference fringes consistent with a weak reflection from the bottom of the ice-shelf at a depth of 150 m below the surface. This may be compared with the figure of 143 m I determined by measuring the elevation of our base above sea-level and applying the principle of hydrostatic balance to a reasonable model of the change in the density of the ice-shelf, based on observations to a depth of about 40 ft. (12.2 m).

Auroral Observations

The expedition's auroral observer was Dr Gwynne Thomas, a Welsh scientist who had been just as busy as the rest of the party with unloading and building. He could not see any aurora until the beginning of March, when the sun started to set for long enough.

The genesis of the aurora was summarized by the US scientist Sydney Chapman as follows: 'The aurora is the only visible manifestation on the earth of a complicated series of phenomena that originate from disturbances in the internal and upper layers of the sun. Immense clouds or streams or wisps of gas at very low density are ejected from the sun; the gas consists mostly of atomic hydrogen.' When this stream enters into the atmosphere, the first thing we detect is the aurora, which is followed by magnetic storms and disruption to radio communications. Auroral displays range in brightness from that of the Milky Way to more brilliant than moonlit cumulus clouds. (Ref. Sydney Chapman et al. 1956, *IGY Instruction Manual, Aurora and Airglow*, Vol. 4 Part II, p. 89, Pergamon Press).

When considering its establishment, the desired location for an observatory at Halley Bay was near the zone of maximum auroral frequency. Since no previous observations of aurora had been made in this region of the Weddell Sea, the precise location of the zone was uncertain. The US scientists Vestine and Snyder had used magnetic data to make an estimate of its position and this was the best guidance available. (Ref. Vestine and Snyder, 1945, *Terr. Magn. Atmos. Elect.*, 50, 105–124). That is why the Royal Society specified the base should be set up on the eastern coast of the Weddell Sea 'South of 75°S' latitude. Our final location was a compromise of many factors including logistics, but it turned out to be ideal for observing aurora under both quiet and active conditions. Sitting just to the north of the zone, we were able to observe the 'quiet arc' of the aurora to the south on almost every clear night and see its full development during magnetic storms.

Gwynne was ready to commence scientific work on April 1, three months ahead of schedule. His first observations were made on the night of April 1/2. The aurora appeared above the southern horizon at 2200 UT (8:00 p.m. local time). It gradually moved overhead and then shimmered in the zenith for over an hour. The evening's display culminated in a spectacular flaming form at 0100 UT, which finally disappeared an hour later.

Taking Stock of Progress

April was the month when the days drew rapidly to a close and we prepared ourselves for the three months of Antarctic night to follow. Mid-April was therefore a good time to take stock of our achievements to date. I spent April 17 filling three long tapes with recordings for the BBC. I also noted that it was our coldest day to date −30°F (−34.4°C). Some of our equipment was feeling the cold and playing up. On April 20 the aspirated thermometer seized up and had to be repaired. I also found the oil in the levelling screws froze on the theodolite. I stripped the screw threads of all traces of oil and solved the problem.

Sunday April 21 was Easter and also the Queen's Birthday. We declared a holiday of sorts with a slightly reduced programme. Jim Burton, Bill Bellchambers and Len Constantine took the opportunity to ski 13 miles (21 km) to the south of the base on that day. A delicious roast of pork was served that evening and a tot of port all round to conclude.

EMPEROR PENGUINS

Ubi bene ibi patria.
(He makes his home where the living is best).

Up to 20,000 Emperor Penguins lived in a rookery at Emperor Bay, one and a half miles (2.4 km) south-west of Halley Bay and three miles (45.8 km) from the base. During the summer, they were away at sea but returned in the autumn for breeding in the depths of the Antarctic winter, with temperatures dropping to −40° to −50°C and winds gusting regularly up to 30 m/s (108 kph). At the beginning of

With heads down from sun and cold wind, Gwynne and Joe pay a social call on our neighbours at Emperor Bay. The Emperor Penguin (Aptenodytes forsteri) is the largest of the penguin family, reaching a height of 4 ft (120 cm). Their short feathers, in a dense fur-like mat, provide a superb waterproof and insulating layer. This flightless bird dives into the sea and uses wings to propel itself rapidly in pursuit of fish, steering adroitly with webbed feet.

April, as soon as the days became shorter, the birds returned to the rookery. About 1000 would return in the first week of April and the remainder by the end of the month. As you stood at the top of the cliff, you could see them marching steadily home in a long line from the nearest big break in the sea ice.

The socializing began as soon as they were gathered together in the rookery at Emperor Bay. As they became quite hectically amorous, they undoubtedly warmed up their long winter nights.

It was believed that penguins were the most primitive of living birds and that the Emperor might be the most primitive penguin. They are certainly the most remarkable in their ability to hatch out their eggs without the benefit of a nest, exposed to the depths of the Antarctic winter. For 63 days they balance the 12-by-8 cm egg on the top of their feet and cradle it in the warm folds of flesh and feathers at the base of their abdomen, in what is like an inverted pouch. At the same time they crinkle up their toes to raise the soles of the feet from the cold sea-ice surface. They are therefore constrained, for the time being, to shuffle round on their heels and toes.

A view of the Emperor Penguin rookery in the Spring of 1958, looking east from the seaward side of the bay. Most of the birds here will probably be females caring for their small chicks. One adult, in the middle foreground, is in the process of feeding her chick with the regurgitated sea-food she gorged on in the Weddell Sea, whilst her hungry mate was left back at the rookery incubating the egg through the winter. Now it is the males' turn to feed in the sea, providing they can find suitable openings through the sea ice. Usually, the birds find their way into the sea via the cracks in the sea ice created by the effect of frequent winter storms, but not always. In some years the sea-ice is impenetrable; the females' foraging is not successful and the chicks die.

Above: *Two friends admire each other's offspring.*

Below: *Feeding time at the rookery.*

In December the chicks were about three months old and beginning to form into crèches. With about 20,000 birds, the droppings lie thick on the sea ice. Soon, when temperatures rise or on calm sunny days, the ice will melt producing conditions reminiscent of a fouled farm-yard. Once the birds exhaust the clean areas of their rookery, some of them will move away and up to the ice shelf.

But that is only part of the remarkable story. The egg is, of course, laid by the female, in the midwinter dark days of June or July, but she then passes it over to the male for the 63-day incubation period. As soon as the transfer is safely accomplished, she retraces her footsteps and heads north to find open water. She gorges herself in the sea, filling her stomach with the food necessary to feed the chick when it emerges two months later. On returning in August or September, I would like to believe that the family is unerringly reunited and the chick is passed back to Mum who feeds it with regurgitated food. In fact I do not believe it has yet been established that the mother always locates her own offspring.

May 1957

There was a snow cave near the downwind door of the main hut. It was dug by our advance party into one of the deep drifts thrown up by the hut. They were recovering some of their stores which became deeply buried under the drift. In 1956, David Limbert used the cave to keep the hydrogen generating equipment and filled small balloons for wind-finding ascents. We took over the vacant cave for our main glaciological pit. It provided protection from the elements whilst digging and studying the layers of accumulated snow in controlled and optimum lighting conditions. As we dug down, it was not too difficult to discern the annual layers of accumulation and measure the snowfall which had accumulated in years gone by.

The snow at the bottom of the pit, at a depth of 30 ft. (9.1 m), fell 15 years earlier in 1943. In that particular year snow accumulation was 4% greater than normal. A 140 cm layer of snow accumulated which was frequently marked by wind crusts. The weather prevailing at the time of deposition leaves its signature imprinted and affects the quality of the deposits. Surfaces exposed to strong winds become smoothed and partly glazed and appear buried as wind-crusts. The summer season from December to February particularly leaves quite unmistakable signs on the snow surface. During this period of relatively gale-free weather, combined with 24 hours of solar radiation, a meta-morphosis of the surface takes place. There is evaporation and the layer becomes coarse-grained and loosely packed. In some years there is melting, so the lower layers become soaked with melt-water which later refreezes. The winter deposits retain the relatively fine grain size of 0.2 to 0.5 mm in diameter and have the consistency of rock salt with a density of between 0.3 and 0.5 g/cc.

Digging the pit commenced in May and continued through June in the depths of the Antarctic winter. The consistency of the packed snow, called firn or névé, was rather similar to rock salt or a sandstone, softer at the top but gradually hardening with depth as a result of the compression from the upper layers. About 9 ft. (2.74 m) beneath the surface, you had to chop the firn out with an ice pick and then shovel the fragments into a bucket which was then hauled to the top with a rope. The work became progressively more difficult with depth. The width of the pit had to be sufficient to swing an ice pick but not too wide to preclude climbing up and down by wedging your body between the two opposing walls, using a chimney-climbing technique.

I was acutely aware of this crucial width, having been caught out once before when digging a pit. I had dug down to about eight feet (2.44 m) in depth using a shovel. The firn was not hard enough to require the use of an ice pick. I had been throwing the firn directly out of the pit. I had dug as deep as I wanted and in any case it was nearly time for lunch. So I threw the shovel out and tried to follow. After several futile attempts, I soon found that it was quite difficult to escape and I felt suitably chastened, if not foolish. In fact I never did succeed unaided in extricating myself. I was still struggling to escape when a colleague passed nearby and I was able to call for his help and make his day a more merry one.

Because of the Emperor's unique characteristics, scientists were keen to study their embryos, which can provide clues to the provenance or origin of the species and its early development. In pursuit of that objective, Robin and Bill went off to spend the night at Emperor Bay on May 15, the first of a series of visits they made during May to July.

Their object can be stated simply enough: it was to collect a series of embryos starting as soon as possible after conception. When they got down to the bay, however, they found that 20,000 birds only had one thing on their mind and they were pursuing that with great gusto and very little discrimination for the sex of potential partners. We could not easily recognise the sex of penguins but assumed they could. But, if so, their ability had a distinct hit or miss quality about it. Finally they marked the successful partners and, in subsequent visits, endeavoured to find the resulting eggs.

Altogether a series of 25 embryos were collected and subsequently returned for analysis by Professor F O'Gorman at the University College, Cork. On receipt of the specimens, he noted, 'As collecting has to be made in the depths of the Antarctic winter, ... the difficulties were considerable. It might have been expected that much of the material would return badly fixed and useless for histological purposes. It says a great deal for the skill and enthusiasm of the collectors that so much of the material arrived so well preserved.' In his discussion of the results of this work, Professor O'Gorman seemed to be optimistic that the Halley Bay embryo collection would indeed confirm that the Emperor is the most primitive penguin. (Ref. *RSIAE*, 1964, Vol. 4, pp. 353–363).

We all regularly visited the rookery. I believe we drew strength from the visits, contemplating the wonderfully attractive if mysterious way nature arranged affairs for one of her most remarkable species. I certainly did. In the autumn, when they gathered on the sea-ice of Emperor Bay, they were all in splendid condition, sleek and fat with a colourful glowing plumage. As one of the few animals with no requirement to protect a home or nesting place, the Emperor Penguin usually maintained a cool, dignified mien when approached, unlike lesser penguins who got in a great state of agitation when you came near. By breeding in mid-winter, they had no enemies to contend with and their chicks were free to grow without the fear of a skua snapping them up.

In mid-winter they huddled together for warmth, moving continually, amiably and slowly so that all got their fair share of the warmth in the centre or the frigid conditions on the upwind side of the gathering. Whilst mother fed her chicks, the males went for longer walks in the vicinity, sometimes visiting the base three miles (5 km) away. They moved most rapidly on their stomach, propelled by feet and wings.

Typically, when you took a walk on the sea-ice you might see a group of penguins a mile (1.6 km) or so away. They saw you at the same time and made a bee-line for you, moving quickly on their bellies. A few metres away from you, they stood up and looked at you. After a few minutes of mutual examination, they appreciated that you were rather uninteresting. They would then abruptly turn away from you and toboggan away as fast as they had come.

Once the chicks were old enough, they were collected together into one large crêche so the adults were free to wander about, returning to feed them from time to time. Once the bulky grey plumage of chicks started to moult, showing the more attractive white and black adult plumage, the chick started to think about wider horizons. The regurgitations they took directly from mum's throat were becoming boring and sparse, no doubt. They started by climbing up the cliffs of the ice-shelf until they overlooked the open sea 100 ft. (30 m) below. As the days grew longer and warmer and the chicks got hungrier and braver, they very slowly edged closer and closer to the cliff edge of Penguin Leap. Finally they had no option but to plunge into the water way below. Within a few minutes of entering the sea, they recovered their composure while deep inside them an instinctive ability took over and away they swam. They were in their preferred element at last, where they would find all the food they needed and were beginning to crave.

Final Preparations for the IGY

During May and June the final preparations were made for the commencement of the IGY on July 1. After that, the amount of routine work for my meteorological and geomagnetic team would more than double. As I read my diary for the period, I can recall vividly the sense of urgency and mounting excitement in the air. Though we were ahead of schedule, we still had a number of important tasks to complete and more practice was required.

The launching and tracking of the weather balloons, followed by the reduction of the results, was a skilled team exercise involving five people in unbroken physical and mental effort. Two of them were busy for three and a half hours, two more for two and a half hours, and the two men in the radar were busy for the one hour duration of the ascent. Practice was needed for us to learn to work together and each individual had to polish his skills and adapt them to the special conditions. There were only six persons in the group, one of whom was recovering from night duty. If it had not been for the volunteer efforts of others in the expedition, the projected schedule of twice-daily ascents would not have been possible. Robin in 1957 and Bert in 1958 regularly worked in the radar whilst Alf and Gwynne also contributed their time to make the programme succeed.

It could be regarded as a *non sequitur* to set the size of the meteorological party at six people and at the same time specify a twice-daily radiosonde programme. That the expedition did achieve its objective reflects all the more credit on those who made this possible once they were in the field at Halley Bay.

Great efforts had been made by the designers and manufacturers of our meteorological instruments to adapt them, but the fact remained that nearly all of the equipment we used, versatile though it was, had not originally been designed for operation to the extremes common in Antarctica. We therefore had to solve innumerable problems for ourselves.

As the temperature fell, we began to experience a number of problems in operating the radar, which persisted on and off until the end of June. The effect of low temperatures on the rotating horn gave us some problems to solve, and so did the directional drives. Electronic malfunctions which occurred in the last few days of June were cured when an additional 500 W of thermostatically controlled heating was fitted to the cabin. We also had to get used to the exceptionally rapid change in the wind direction as the balloon passed through the lowest layers of the atmosphere. This was to be a characteristic of winter atmospheric conditions and due to a very rapid change in the air temperature in those layers.

Low temperatures and the absence of warming sunlight was causing most of the rubber balloons to burst before reaching a height of 15 km. In the following year we were able to get the balloons to go up an additional 10 km by soaking them for hours in a mixture of lubricating oil and Avtur (aviation turbine fuel), a trick we learnt from the US expedition at the South Pole.

When I visited Australia in 1959, I discovered that many of the little but troubling problems we encountered had been solved by the Australians. In addition to their relative proximity to Antarctica, they had the advantage over us in that, in more recent times, they had an unrivalled continuous record of mounting Antarctic expeditions. In the pre-IGY period they were the only country with a scientific base on the main core of the continent. During that period British expeditions had been confined to relatively small parties on the peninsula of Graham Land and north of the Antarctic circle.

Before the IGY started, there was much I still had to do in May and June, in addition to standing in the regular shifts of the met. programme, doing the ozone observations and digging the glaciological pit. I was spending a good part of my time on the final setting up of the geomagnetic programme, involving both inside and outside work. I was either adjusting the instruments in the hut or working just outside it with my theodolite pointing at the heavens to determine the direction of true north and the exact latitude and longitude of the base as it moved slowly seaward. I found that the whole base was moving westward at 320 metres per year and at the same time was rotating by about a quarter of a degree per year.

May 30 was the day Robin showed me a signal from the Royal Society which approved my appointment as Leader of the whole

expedition for next year, taking over from Robin after he returned
home. I felt greatly moved at the trust placed in me and the honour
of that appointment. It gave me great pleasure to accept. As I noted
in my diary at the time, I was very happy working at Halley Bay and
would certainly do my best to see that year also went well for us all.

Earlier in that day I dug out the front door of the main hut to
provide an easier route to the balloon shed with the hot water for
generating hydrogen. Previously we had used the back door and this
meant we had to negotiate a major drift slope on the way to the
balloon-filling shed. That too was only a temporary expedient as it
had to be dug out repeatedly. Later in the year, a heated tank was
installed in the generator shed itself, so the job could be done on the
spot.

June 1957

I had already run the seismographs at a location near the hut but it
was too noisy. Finally, on June 7, I dug a cave at the bottom of the
glaciological pit 30 ft. (9.1 m) below the surface and set up a base for
them with a marble slab left over from the geomagnetic installations.
There the sensitive instrument was insulated from local disturbances
and well away from any traffic. This was the last programme to be
implemented before the start of the IGY in three weeks' time.

Derek developed the seismograms, or the photographic records
showing the tiny movements of the instrument. When I analysed the
seismogram he gave me for June 8, I found recorded a small earthquake,
which I inferred had occurred in the South Sandwich Islands some
1500 miles (2414 km) to our north.

On June 13 Robin was very late back from one of his trips to
Emperor Bay to observe the shenanigans of the penguins. We were
now in the depths of midwinter with 24 hours of darkness each day.
Several people had noticed his absence and we were concerned. Obviously you need to be careful walking round in winter darkness. So
I went off to look for him. On that calm day, I navigated by noting
the direction of the sastrugi which were sculpted in the snow surface
by the relatively steady strong east winds of a few days ago. As is so
often the case in these situations, he returned to base just ten minutes
after I left. We must have passed each other by in the Antarctic winter
darkness. So Robin turned back to catch me, which he did when I
was halfway to Emperor Bay. It was a windless day with an air
temperature of −20°C. I was so warm as I strode along with him that
I took off my gloves. In a week's time it would be Midwinter's Day.

On June 17 we had a strong gale, the third gale of the month. For
38 hours the wind blew with gale force, peaking at a steady 54 knots,
or just over 100 kilometres per hour (kph) for a whole hour. When

it was gusting up to 77 knots (143 kph), I was blown off my feet and, even when lying there on the ground, could feel the thrusting and pulsing force of the wind trying to tumble me along. The snow seemed to be everywhere, penetrating into the hut through the tiniest crack, including some which may have been opened up since the last gale occurred six days before. With cold air forced through every crevice, the hut was cooled and the electrical generators overloaded. Later in the day, when the wind dropped suddenly, we went outside to the dump and dug out two more anthracite stoves for the main hut. We installed them in the radio sonde room and the darkroom. It was so cold in the meteorological office that the anthracite stove there was lit for the first time that day.

Len Constantine carving a turkey for our Midwinter's Day feast on 21 June 1957. One of the most significant annual celebrations in Antarctica is held on Midwinter's Day. It is an antidote for cabin fever or the depressing effects of the prolonged absence of the sun. We were celebrating the fact that in about three weeks' time we would see the sun again.

Midwinter's Day

On Midwinter's Eve I opened a parcel prepared by Oonagh seven months before. It was just delightful to read the letter written so long ago. What a pleasant change from the 100-words-per-month air letters I had been surviving on since arriving here; the ration for the number of words was actually set at 60, but she usually managed to fit in 100 words. Oonagh's midwinter package for us contained a number of paper hats and hooters, which we blew in a cacophony of celebration after the dinner. The Midwinter's Day feast on June 21 was sweetened by a hamper sent to us by the Royal Society. Amongst other things, it contained sherry and port for the

dinner and other goodies. Robin unintentionally provided some gratuitous entertainment after dinner and just before we went into the
lounge for a film show. He brought out the gift he had received of a
cigarette lighter. When he used it to light up his after-dinner cigarette,
the whole machine burst into flames.

The first edition of the *Halley Comet* was issued on Midwinter's
Day. The publication contained a message from Robin congratulating
the editors, Jim Burton and David Cansfield, on its production. It
contained several contributions holding promise for the future. Bill
wrote an article on the ionosphere and I did one on meteorology and
the IGY. Malcolm composed an interesting piece on the wines of
France, to which the editors added some appropriate verses. Robin
wrote an entertaining piece called 'Scotia in Antarctica'. It was written
in support of his following thesis: 'There is, of course, no doubt in
the mind of any reasonable person that COATS LAND is historically,
culturally, by right of discovery, and by old ties of friendship, Scottish.'
Support for this view was set out with good humour, using carefully
selected quotations from Mill and Shackleton. (Ref. Mill, H R, *The
Siege of the South Pole; Sir Ernest Shackleton, South*, p. 497). At the
risk of finding himself on permanent gash duty, Jim demurred in a
similar vein. He also quoted from an impressive, selective list of
publications in support of his view that those explorers were in fact
English residents. And Weddell himself was a Yorkshireman. Jim and
David produced five more editions during the expedition, maintaining
a very high standard in its production.

We had a holiday on Sunday June 30, the eve of the IGY. In the
lounge after dinner we held another enjoyable scientific discussion.
Several of us prepared a brief account of our Antarctic scientific interests
and the programme of the IGY, and many others joined in.

Nations Working in Antarctica for the IGY

On the eve of the commencement of the IGY, ten other nations had
also set up bases on the Antarctic continent. A final list of twelve
participating nations included Argentina, Australia, Belgium (1958
only), Chile, France, Japan (1957 only), New Zealand, Norway, Spain,
UK, USA and USSR. The largest and most comprehensive effort was
mounted by USA, followed closely by USSR.

The USA air-lifted a station to the South Pole and called it
Amundsen-Scott base. They set up a Weather Central on the Ross
Sea side of the continent. The main Russian base at Mirny opened in
the area claimed by Australia. They also set up Sovietskaya station at
the pole of inaccessibility and Vostok base adjacent to the south
geomagnetic pole. There was also a USSR base called Komsomolskaya
at 74°5'S 97°29'E.

The Australian scientific presence in Antarctica was already quite large before the IGY started. It was based on a permanent station at Mawson complete with dozens of huts and a substantial aviation group. Australia already pursued a broad range of scientific disciplines in Antarctica, which they expanded. For the IGY, they set up an additional base at Vestfold Hills called Davis, plus an unmanned inland station.

The UK had two institutions running Antarctic bases. The Royal Society, as the nation's premier scientific body, was responsible for the geophysical observatory at Halley Bay dedicated to IGY studies. This was complemented by the Falkland Islands Dependencies Survey (FIDS) which ran a number of small bases orientated towards geographic survey and geological discovery, largely north of the Antarctic Circle. To the maximum extent possible, FIDS bases did include some geophysical studies for the IGY.

Our nearest neighbours, for the full duration of the IGY, were the Norwegians to the north near Cap Norvegia and the USA base Ellsworth to our south at Vahsel Bay, adjacent to the TAE at Shackleton, which closed in December 1957, one year before the end of the IGY.

References

Fuchs & Hillary 1958, *The Crossing of Antarctica*, Cassell, pp. 49–59, 68.

Sydney Chapman et al. 1956, *IGY Instruction Manual, Aurora and Airglow*, Vol. 4 Part II, p. 89, Pergamon Press.

Vestine, E H and Snyder, E J, 1945, *Terr. Magn. Atmos. Elect.*, 50, 105–124.

RSIAE, 1964, Vol. 4, pp. 353–363.

Mill, H R, *The Siege of the South Pole; Sir Ernest Shackleton, South*, p. 497.

Chapter 4

The IGY Commences –
1 July 1957

Winter Living and Scientific
Observing Routines

Before the hut became buried in 1957, access to it was a problem during the gales which occurred frequently for nine months of the year. At these times, it was almost impossible to keep the outer doors of the hut drift-proof. Each time you used them, you were faced with a problem of clearing the snow and ensuring the door closed properly and remained drift-proof. With the complete burial of the hut, access actually became easier as we were then able to use a roof hatch. The hatch was 2 ft. 3 in. (69 cm) square and was originally constructed by the auroral observer. It was cut through the roof on the downwind side of the ridge and looked rather like a small chimney sticking up above the roof. It was found that, providing the hatch was kept a foot (30 cm) above the prevailing snow surface, it could be left open the

The generator shed is almost buried after one winter.

The radio echo hut too was buried and, for some reason we never fathomed, this small hut was the only one which threw up a drift about a metre higher than itself.

whole time, even when the hut became completely buried. In late 1958, I adapted the idea by building a shaft up from the rear door of the hut which was large enough to accommodate the removal of large items of equipment in preparation for our departure.

On the first day of the IGY, 1 July 1957, I was on what we called 'M' meteorological observing duty. In this division of labour you covered all the surface observations from 10:00 a.m. local time in the morning to 3:00 p.m. in the afternoon. Then you had a break until you commenced night duty from 11:00 p.m. until 9:00 a.m. the next morning. Whilst on duty, every three hours you went outside the main hut to do a complete weather observation of the clouds, precipitation, visibility, temperatures, humidity, winds, etc. logging these in the big red books which now reside in the Meteorological Office Library in Bracknell, UK. In addition to that, you went down to the balloon-filling shed to generate hydrogen and fill the balloon. Then you returned to the hut to plot out winds and continue with the three-hourly weather observations.

On July 2 I slept in after night duty. During the evening upper air sounding, I assisted in the radar tracking the balloon as it ascended through the atmosphere. On the third day I covered the observations from 10:00 a.m. to 10:00 p.m. local time and also assisted with the radio sonde ascent, this time working inside the hut. After three days of slightly different duties, the pattern repeated itself. Interspersed in that regular pattern of scientific work was the assignment of gash

or domestic duties, which by now had settled down to once every 18
days.

You may ask: how did the scientists of the world come to agree to
commit 20,000 to 40,000 people, in 67 different nations round the
world, to undertake this type of observing schedule in about 4000
locations over the whole globe? Of this number, 2000 stations were
formally designated and numbered by the IGY organizing committee,
CSAGI. Halley Bay was given the number 'A989' by CSAGI and
'89–022' by the World Meteorological Office (WMO). How did so
many people become convinced it was all worth while and how did
we, at Halley Bay, come to the same conclusion? What led up to this,
the largest, most complex and most comprehensive international scientific undertaking thus far conceived? Were all agreed with the idea
or was it the subject of some controversy?

Writing 40 years after the event, it is clear the IGY exceeded
scientific expectations and also made a contribution to the conduct of
international affairs. An appreciation of the IGY was conducted by
the USA Congress in 1973 (Ref. *The Political Legacy of the International
Geophysical Year*, by the Committee on Foreign Affairs, US House of
Representatives, November 1973). Whilst searching for assessments of
the IGY, they were unable to find any negative comments. On the
other hand, they had no difficulty in finding evidence to support the
view that the IGY was 'the single most significant peacetime activity
of mankind since the Renaissance and the Copernican revolution.' (Dr
Hugh Odishaw, NSF-NAS Hearings: IGY Report). Sydney Chapman,
the former Sedleian Professor of Natural Philosophy in the University
of Oxford, said that the IGY opened up 'a new era in the history of
the human race.' Clearly Prince Philip had been right on the eve of
the IGY when he said, 'At the same time it (the IGY) may well help
solve the real problem – the conflict of ideas.' Nor was Pope Pius XII
disappointed in his hope that the IGY would be an effort likely to
contribute to peace and cooperation amongst all peoples and their
material well-being (S. Chapman, The IGY, *Nature* 175, 8 January
1956, p. 56).

At the beginning of July, we were right in the dark depths of the
Antarctic winter. We had not seen the sun since May 2, when it finally
set with a prolonged and magnificent crimson sunset. Over the whole
winter period, only 24% of the days were cloud free. It seemed as
though on a majority of clear nights we had an auroral display. Every
15 minutes of the night Gwynne Thomas poked his head out of the
roof hatch to note the forms of the aurora and measure their dimen-
sions. Early in the evening, when you looked to the south, you saw
a white band just above the southern horizon. This was what we saw
90% of the time from 9:00 p.m. to 6:00 a.m. local time. During
about one-third of the time, an active display developed with the

aurora taking on several forms, occasionally brilliant, which rose to cover the whole sky.

One night in July, I walked away from the bright lights near the hut and lay on my back looking up at the magnificent show, wondering at its majesty and conscious that it was sent to us by a sun we had not seen for over 50 days. It was nice to know we were not being neglected by the sun.

The display started with the familiar white arc in the south which rose in elevation whilst its lower border sharpened and the whole display brightened markedly. Then rays appeared cutting across the arc and spread in from one or both ends, and also showed the red colouration due to nitrogen. At times these rays moved rapidly, changing their bearing by 30° in 10 seconds. Then the display rose to cover the whole sky, for hours showing a variety of forms and coloured from white to greenish-white and sometimes red. Then, in its most active phase, we would be treated to the flaming form of display when waves of red colouration pulsated to the zenith on both the north and south sides of the sky. It was highly evocative of a sky which had burst into flames.

Optical phenomena involving the moon were also displayed in mid-winter. On July 8 there were several forms of lunar optical displays due to clouds of ice crystals and atmospheric water vapour. We were treated to a display of lunar rings with arcs and mock moons or a lunar parhelion. Most of these splendid displays are caused by the refraction of light, from sun or moon, by the ice crystals in the atmosphere. These are prismatic in a variety of forms. The type of display depends on the particular crystal forms present and their variety. The crystals comprise two main prismatic shapes capable of refracting light with angles of 60° or 90° between adjacent faces. The 60° prisms bend the light by 22° and separate it into the colours of rainbow. The 90° prisms refract the light by 46°. Thus a collection of randomly distributed ice crystals create a concentration of light at angles of 22° and 46° from either the moon or sun, forming small and large halos tinged with red on the side nearest the moon or sun.

The phenomenon of diffraction by water droplets is responsible for the formation of corona round the moon or sun. These take the form of rings of various sizes round the sun. The size of the ring depends on the size distribution of the droplets concerned. With this phenomenon, the inner part of the rings are tinged with blue. The phenomenon we witnessed on July 8 presaged the strong SW winds with snow which fell two days later.

As a consequence, on July 11, I had to dig out the entrance to the glaciological and seismic pit. The door was buried beneath 5 ft. (1.5 m) of snow drift. As a bonus, I found at the bottom of the pit one of our treasured ice axes which had been missing for some time. That evening it stopped snowing and the clouds cleared to reveal a beautiful full moon surrounded by a corona, due to the moist air still present. I returned to the hut and worked on the seismic records, which revealed the occurrence of an earthquake in Persia.

From mid-July we were moving into the coldest period of the year. The weather caused innumerable problems with the outdoor equipment. Several times the rotating horn to the Decca radar seized up or broke. Finally on July 20 we used up the last of the spares provided. David Tribble, with Alf's help, managed to fabricate one and got the machine operational again.

Snow drift was a continual problem, affecting access to the non-magnetic hut. The stepped, felt-faced doors were quite effective once they were closed, but as soon as they were opened, drift got into the area near the hinges and rapidly stopped you closing it. Then more drift got in and so on until you just had to take the time out to clean the whole door of every scrap of snow. It was very difficult to do that whilst it was still snowing, particularly when you were working in the dark with the snow blowing in your face. On one occasion I was reduced to entering the hut via the window used to sight on the fixed mark.

Coldest Day of the Year

The coldest day of the year was on July 29. The air temperature was −50.6°C (59.1°F) and there was a 16-knot (24 kph) wind. On that very day, the wind measuring equipment failed. It was fitted to the top of a 30 ft. (9.14 m) tower. I therefore climbed the tower to disconnect and remove the anemometer with the assistance of Jim Burton. Later on Derek helped me install a replacement. Under these conditions, tasks taking a few minutes in temperate climates become quite a challenge. Most jobs of this type just cannot be done whilst wearing the bulky gloves required to counter Antarctic conditions. Some of the more fiddley things are even difficult to accomplish when wearing chamois leather or silk gloves. Too often there is nothing for it but bare hands and that is what I had to use at the top of the tower, causing frostbite in two fingers. It was only superficial but still intensely painful as the fingers thawed out.

Electric motors stopped and had to be repaired. That too was a delicate task with the inherent risk of getting frostbite. We depended on these for continuous recordings of air temperature at two levels on the meteorological mast and to monitor the net exchange of radiation with the ventilated fluxplate radiometer.

The fluxplate radiometer showed that in the depths of the winter, in June 1957, the surface was losing, by radiation alone, some 27 watts of power from every square metre. In summer, during January 1958 the flow was reversed as 33 watts arrived by means of radiation on every square metre of the snow surface. Thus, from an area of 166 metres square, 1000 horsepower (746 kW) was being radiated away in midwinter. This is the power which provides the motivation to drive the winds and weather systems. It was the first time radiation flux measurements had been made in Antarctica continuously for a whole year. Without such data, quantitative models of the atmosphere cannot be constructed, making it implausible to expect that even the power of modern computers could forecast the weather with accuracy. Consequently, before the IGY, when attempting to make forecasts, it was a case of 'garbage in, garbage out' for huge areas of the world.

In the early hours of Sunday July 14 I came off night duty and went to bed until the afternoon. Outside it was considered to be an inviting day but was notable because the twilight of high noon was the brightest we had seen for a long time. However, it was still extremely cold outside with a 10-knot (19 kph) wind out of the east and an air temperature of –36ºC. The invitation of the twilight encouraged a large party to go down to the bay for some needed exercise. For some in the party, it was a welcome break from a week's routine of scientific work inside the hut. Rising late, I missed the excursion although I had had plenty of fresh air the previous night, going outside every three hours to do the meteorological observations, and walking over to the balloon shed to launch a balloon. I noted at the time that the conditions were pleasant with little or no wind and an air temperature of –35ºC. The wind was much stronger in the afternoon so, when they returned from their walk to the bay, several persons had superficial frost bites on their face or ears.

There was more excitement on July 30 when we recorded the strongest sustained wind of 56 knots (104 kph). Drifting snow reduced visibility to five yards (4.6 m) and the wind was so strong that gusts were able to blow you down. I was on duty for part of the day and went over to the non-magnetic hut while Andrew followed me. At one stage a gust blew both of us down. As soon as we left the main hut, we caught hold of one of the stout ropes strung from wooden posts linking the various huts together, for use in these extreme conditions. The non-magnetic hut was 100 yards (91 m) from the main hut. Walking there with a visibility of less than five yards (4.6 m) would have been risky. Unfortunately, the rope ended at the last post, a few metres away from the door of the non-magnetic hut. At the last guide post, I still could not see any sign of the non-magnetic hut through the swirling snow drift driven by a fierce east wind. I took off into the whiteout in what I judged to be the right direction and managed to find the door successfully.

Shortly afterwards, when Andrew did not arrive, I figured that he had to have reached the end of the guide rope but must have taken off in the wrong direction and was still wandering around lost. I went outside again to find him. Starting from the last guide post, I took off into the swirling snow drift just to the right of the hut. In navigating unaided outside in these conditions, one is helped by the relative steadiness in the wind direction. This allows you to maintain a steady course by keeping your orientation with respect to the wind. You can do this by the feel of the wind on your body or by observing the movement of the snow over the surface. In the absence of wind, you can do the same by observing the orientation of the sastrugi on the snow surface carved by the last storm. Using the comparatively steady wind direction as a reference, I searched in a straight line for about a dozen paces and then returned to the safety of the guide line and took off again in another direction. After negotiating a steep drift caused by the hut, a hint of his welcome form suddenly appeared out of the pervasive whiteness of the swirling snow. Not only had he lost his bearings, but he had also tripped over the snow drift, rolled to the bottom and was still disorientated. When I found him, he was gathering his wits, cleaning his glasses, and very relieved to see me appear on the scene.

The month of July therefore was a testing time for both men and equipment. It was the first month of full-scale observations. We were very busy curing innumerable bugs that had to be driven out of the systems. July was the first time we had used the Gill hydrogen generator twice a day and we did have a few problems to iron out. We were still having to carry the water for the job from the main hut. On July 31, however, with the assistance of Alf and Ivor, an electrically heated tank was fitted into the balloon shed itself, obviating one of our most unpleasant chores.

Health in Antarctica

Antarctica is a very healthy place to live. No longer is one prone to suffer from many of the accustomed wide range of bacteriological and virus diseases which beset the physical well-being of the rest of the world. We were remarkably healthy at Halley Bay. The only trouble was that we caught a slight cold every now and then – usually after we had put our head into a kit bag to find something we needed. Although we did not know it at the time, when we packed up to go south in 1956, we were taking cold viruses with us in the dust and air of our kit bags. Dandruff, too, was no longer a common complaint.

However, no one or nowhere is immune to the condition called anxiety hysteria. Its roots lie deep in the brain and are more easy to recognise in others than in oneself, It is very difficult to combat. It is caused by stress and the things which may stress one person can have little effect on another, such is the infinite variety in the makeup of individuals. A cure may not be possible without changing the condition of life, which in our case was possible once a year or so. The power of the brain is such that the symptoms of the condition are manifest in a wide range of distressing physical conditions and they must be treated very seriously, as I discovered at first hand treating a patient whilst Robin was away on a sledging trip. The physical effects will usually remain chronic until the root cause of the anxiety is removed, which in our case occurred as soon as the relief ship arrived and, when it did, the recovery was almost magically rapid. In this regard we were fortunate because a certain and immediate cure for this increasingly common complaint is not normally available.

Many Antarctic expeditions have noted the effects of the long dark winter period. Cabin fever can set in and it is all too easy to become depressed or fed up with your companions. In addition to the adverse effects of the environment, some of us were conscious of the lack of any air letters for two months. They did not start coming through again until August. This was due to the winter break in sea communications between Montevideo and Port Stanley. None of us were entirely free of the pervasive influence of winter. For those expeditions dedicated to travel, it must be particularly difficult to cope with enforced inactivity. A scientific expedition like ours was more fortunate in having a tough, demanding schedule of observations to be made year round. We never had too much time to think about ourselves or our situation. There were always more jobs to do and that made the time seem to pass by more quickly.

Having said that, there were a few more grumbles and gripes, which soon subsided with the return of the sun in August. The onerous schedule of work did occasion comments on the futility of making observations which no one ever again looked at. In reply, I could always point to the exceptional IGY effort already made in setting up data centres. We were encouraged by the news we had from London that David Limbert's observations made in 1956 had just been published, and this too reassured us greatly.

The support staff faced a greater challenge in that the amount of work they had to do dropped off markedly. As a result, in some cases, their peace of mind if not their health suffered. The most content were those able to find tasks within the scientific programme for their abundant talents and energies. Happily, many did just that, volunteering their services for various scientific tasks such as observing the sea-ice cover, measuring the thickness of sea-ice in Halley Bay, assisting in the radar, punching Holerith cards, baking bread, and continuing to be alert for other ways they could assist.

Social relationships had a bearing on the contentment and health of the expedition. If a man becomes isolated, he can suffer considerable mental anguish, which may be difficult to spot in its early stages, until it has developed into something more serious. One must have the sensitivity to spot and sort out such situations before they can give trouble. The social fabric of our expedition proved to be congenial and adaptable. Small social groups started to form as soon as we set sail in *Magga Dan*. Once we settled at Halley Bay, it became plain to me that these little groups were rather dynamic. For a few days, the same three or four persons might sit and chat together at their coffee break and then, for no apparent reason, a slightly different grouping would emerge quite naturally. From time to time an individual became isolated. Whenever that occurred, I made a point of chatting with him, gradually encouraging him back into the main stream.

August 1957

With less than two weeks to go for the return of the sun, the days were brightening up rapidly and we felt the need to get out. Earlier in the year there had never been much time to go far from the base. The most we did was to walk to the bays and back. The only journey to date had been taken in April 1957, when Bill, Jim and Len took a day trip by ski south from base for 13 miles (21 km), to a point on the ice cliffs overlooking the sea. Whilst there, Jim planted a bamboo stake so that he would be able to measure the rate of snow accumulation on a subsequent journey.

Now that so many of the bugs had been driven out of our equipment and we became more efficient, there was time to look forward to more travel as a break from the tedium of the base. The keenest in this regard were those whose tasks kept them cooped up in the hut. Although during the course of their duties they got more than their ration of fresh air and exercise, some of the meteorologists also joined in trips from the base.

In the winter evenings, several persons gathered together after dinner planning future trips. Equipment and rations were weighed out and details planned. If we were to do any travelling that year, something had to be done about a man-hauling sledge. The best we had was two damaged, 6 ft. (1.82 m) -long sledges. These were converted into one good, man-hauling sledge 10 1/2 ft. (3.20 m) long. Bill Bellchambers and others worked hard on its construction in our little workshop during the winter evenings in their precious free moments. To make the longer runners, they had to glue together two pairs of runners from the damaged sledges, shape them and refurbish the complete structure. The reconstructed sledge served well, covering over 200 miles (322 km) during five journeys taken in 1957 to points up to 32 miles (51 km) away from the base. We were not able to obtain a new man-hauling sledge until the relief ship came to us in January 1958.

Sunday and Monday August 4 and 5 were noticeably warmer at about −18°C. That was 10°C warmer than most of the preceding month. I went skiing on Sunday and again on the Monday with Bill, David Harrison, and Robin. We went to Emperor Bay to look at the penguins. There were no chicks yet but the expectant parents were rather peevish. This brief warmer interlude did not continue for long. After a few days it cooled off again so that the average temperature of August turned out to be several degrees cooler than July, despite the return of the sun on August 12.

In preparation for the sun's return, Fred and Ivor constructed and installed a new mounting table for the solar radiation instruments. It was fixed to the roof and raised several feet above it. First I installed a sunshine recorder, which measured the duration of sunshine by using a glass sphere as a lens to focus the sunlight on to a card. When the sun shone, its focussed image burnt a hole in the card. As the sun moved, so did its image and a line was burnt in the card. By measuring the length of the burn, you measured the duration of sunshine each day.

If you look at the results of our observations, published from 1960 to 1964 in four huge volumes, you can see how the sun was last above the horizon on April 30 and returned on August 12. It was strong enough to burn a hole in the card for just 12 minutes on August 14. Alongside the sunshine recorder, I set up two Moll solarimeters, which measured the amount of radiation in the wave band 0.3 to 3.0 micrometers, selected by the glass domes of the instruments. One instrument measured the radiation coming directly from the sun plus the diffuse radiation from sky or clouds. The other just measured the diffuse radiation of sky plus clouds, the direct solar radiation being cut off by a shade ring.

Each Moll solarimeter we used actually measured the elevation in temperature caused by solar radiation falling on a 14x10 mm horizontal surface painted black, by comparison with the temperature of a large piece of brass which was kept shaded from the sun in the body of the instrument. Another type of instrument used in the USA was called the Eppley. It did the same job but measured the temperature difference between black- and white-painted horizontal surfaces. (Ref. *Annals of the IGY*, Vol. V, Part IV, *Radiation Instruments*; Pergamon Press). Both instruments were protected by glass domes which conveniently filtered out the effect of long-wave radiation from water vapour in the atmosphere. The glass filter ensured the instrument only responded to solar radiation.

For the first few days after the return of the sun, I kept an eye on the functioning of the new radiation installation and noticed that hoar frost was forming on the instruments, possibly affecting their records. The problem arose at that time of the year because of the thermal inversion in the very lowest levels of the atmosphere. There was a rapid rise in air temperature with height, with a consequent increase in the amount of water vapour in the atmosphere above the surface. Under these conditions, water vapour was driven down and deposited on any surface in the form of hoar frost.

The extent of the rapid change of temperature and humidity in the lowest layers can be appreciated if one looks at our air temperature measurements made on a tower at heights of 1.4 and 8 m above the surface. The daily average on August 12, at a height of 1.4 m, was −47.3°C but 6.6 m higher up, it was −42.6°C. (Ref. *RSIAE*, vol. IV, pp. 74–84; The Royal Society 1964). I pointed out the hoar frost problem to David Tribble and he set his ingenious mind in motion. After a few trials, he skilfully installed a modicum of electrical heating to the observing table, judiciously arranged to be just sufficient to drive off the frost without affecting the measurements in any way. Later in the month, on August 31, the excessive hoar frost deposits on two rhombic aerials caused them to collapse under the weight of ice deposited.

On August 16, I had the opportunity to try out the new, longer man-hauling sledge Bill had built. I was on gash duty and used it to collect blocks of snow for our three water tanks. It was an enormous improvement over the two wrecks from which it had been constructed. It carried much greater loads with relative ease. This was appreciated since we now collected snow for the water tanks further away from sources of possible contamination. We had found that an accumulation of diesel contamination affected the water supply. The tank was cleaned out and we started collecting much further away from the generator shed.

After making recordings over a period of two days for Donald Milner of the BBC, on August 19 we made direct contact with London and passed the resulting recordings over.

Our personal contact with family and friends at the time was very poor. It was not until August 23 that I received the three air letters which had been held up during their route to us by air, sea and radio. Oonagh, as usual, had done a splendid job of compressing just the right news into the constraints of 100 words, which could be read out on the open radio. As a consequence, I immediately sent her a brief telegram of thanks and appreciation. Later in the year, when the cost of such telegrams to family and friends was added up, I found that they had cost me much more than I could afford out of my slender civil service pay packet. As a consequence, I had to increase the monthly deduction I paid to the Royal Society in London for the pleasure of being able to send a telegram to celebrate the birthday of family members.

A Skiing Accident

On or about August 19, Robin fell very hard whilst skiing. He was carrying a camera at the time and the fall drove it hard into his side just below the rib cage. I later discovered that he knew at the time he had severely bruised his liver and possibly damaged one of his bile ducts. Robin made light of the occurrence but he rested in bed for a while after this accident and may have hoped that he had recovered. Future events showed that he had not, by any means, but the severe, life-threatening problems which later clearly emerged did not show themselves until the middle of September.

Seismic Work

In the last week of August, I was also busy analysing the seismic records or seismograms. The Willmore seismograph failed earlier in August. As I repaired it, I took the opportunity to examine the mechanism more closely. The business end consisted of three heavy weights which were suspended on springs. Each weight was constrained so that it could only move in one of three directions at right angles to each other. Thus one of the weights could move along a north-south line, the other east-west and the third up-and-down. Consequently, when the ground moved under the influence of an arriving earth tremor, the inertia of the weights caused them to swing on their springs so that you could then sense the movement of the earth, measure its direction and precisely time the arrival of the tremors, which were usually far too minute to be noticeable, unaided by such sensitive detectors.

The vibrations from an earthquake spread round the world in all directions, coming to you by various recognisable paths or phases. Some travel on the surface of the earth, others go more directly to you penetrating through the crust and deep into the earth's mantle, yet others go deeper and get reflected back to you via the earth's core, and so on. The speed of transmission along each path is a known characteristic. Therefore, by noting the different arrival times for each route, it is quite possible to deduce the distance to the source of the earthquake. Using the record of two or more stations, you can pinpoint the earthquake and find out how deep it is below the surface.

I measured the times of arrival of the various phases and, using an agreed code, transmitted the observations off to Dr Stonley at Cambridge University, who in turn passed these on to the IGY data centres and the 11 observatories round the world who had specially requested this information from Halley Bay. As I looked at the seismograms in

August, I concluded that it would be best to set the recording drum to rotate at twice the present speed, increasing it to 60 mm per minute and making it easier to measure times of arrival and recognise the various characteristics of the phases. Before doing so, I discussed the idea with Derek, who was responsible for the photographic processing. He understood and saw no problem with the idea, so it was adopted for the remainder of the IGY.

On August 29 I started on a tour of meteorological observing duty. As I went out to record the weather that night, I also noted the splendid aurora, which moved to the zenith of the sky at about 9.45 p.m. local time and seemed to cover most the heavens. There was another display on the following night. As you looked up, it seemed as though you were inside a massive flower looking out of it with the petals pulsating and changing in form and colour continually. The display of stars too was a particularly brilliant one, extending from horizon to horizon, something you never saw at home.

That Little Skiing Accident has Bigger Implications

As I cheerfully went about my duties at the end of August, I had no idea how life could be turned upside down in a few short weeks. I was absorbed with the work and the conditions which kept both body and mind active and fully alive. The tremendous variety and challenge in the work appealed to me and I could not have been more happy with the qualities of my colleagues. Time and again in my diary I recorded contentment with my lot and admiration for all my companions, their sterling qualities and skills. It was to be my great privilege to lead them in 1958 after Robin's departure, though he would be greatly missed by all of us.

Although my bunk was just a few feet above his, I had no more idea than anyone else how serious his fall had been. After a few days of rest he seemed to have recovered. On September 4, I noted in my diary that Robin had completely recovered. But I was wrong, he had not, as I was to find out when I was abruptly catapulted from a familiar routine into a full time, untrained nurse fighting for the life he knew was then at risk. Never in my life was I to experience such a sudden change of circumstances or to have to learn to cope so rapidly with the mysteries of the human body and its life forces.

Bill, Jim, and David Harrison loaded the new sledge for a two-day trip on August 31. Securely lashed to the sledge were a double-walled pyramid tent weighing 60 lb. (27 kg), primus stove, sleeping bags, and FIDS sledging rations. Ropes were attached to the sledge terminating in a harness for the shoulders, which was made of lampwick for greater comfort in hauling. They set off to the east and got to a point 14 miles

(22.5 km) from the base, where there were some quite distinct hills on the ice-shelf. The weather was just great for the trip.

September 1957

The sun had wasted no time in returning to us and already there were seven hours of sunshine on Sunday September 1, a great start to the month. As was our custom, Sunday commenced with an interdenominational service based on the British Army shortened version of the prayer book. Five of us participated on that Sunday in the cosy lounge so skilfully constructed by the carpenters of the advance party. We sang the hymns better than usual, I noted. Those attending always enjoyed the event though we often had a little difficulty hitting the right notes or setting the pitch at the beginning. Sometimes we started on too high a pitch and had to fudge it halfway through, giving cause for comment by those who had hoped to sleep in that morning and did not exactly welcome our singing as the joyful sound it was intended to be. In an attempt to minimise problems, Les Barclay and I used to go over the hymns the night before. There were one or two which we could always cope with but we could hardly sing those every Sunday. The balance we aimed at, but did not always hit, was variety within our slender capacities for song. After the service, the sociability of the occasion was supported by a single bottle of gin, which was left open on the bar at that time.

Fortified by a social drink that Sunday, I went outside to repair the ventilating motor of the fluxplate radiometer, or total radiation fluxmeter, which had just failed. This particular instrument was one in which I had a personal interest. It was a design that I had developed whilst working at Kew Observatory, one of the first things I did after graduation. The instrument was based on a design originated by the USA engineers Gier and Dunkle, (Ref. MacDowall, J; 1955; Total-Radiation Fluxmeter; *Met. Mag.* 84, 65). Until Gier and Dunkle provided their original and elegant solution, no one had been able to figure out how the measurements could be made using equipment simple enough for worldwide use, 24 hours a day and 7 days a week, in all weathers. Since the atmospheric heat engine was sustained or driven by the power of the total radiation flux, no accurate understanding of the atmosphere could be achieved without precise and extensive measurements. By the same token, no computer could be expected to provide an accurate weather forecast until accurate observations were available.

The radiometer gave more trouble on September 5 when I was on night duty. The blower was not working properly and it was covered in hoar frost. I discussed the problem with Alf and he assisted by giving the motor a complete overhaul, which had to be repeated at regular intervals.

The problems Andrew and I had in gaining access to the non-magnetic hut were finally solved on September 2. Now that we were fully acclimatised to Antarctic conditions, we considered it a beautiful day. It was sunny all day with a 10 kt (19 kph) wind and a temperature of –36°C. We went over to the non-magnetic hut, dug out the door and built a porch with a hatch opening at the top. From then on entering was a breeze in all weathers.

There was another magnetic storm on the evening of September 4, presaged by a magnificent auroral display. At 10:10 p.m., on my way over to the generator shed to fill and launch a balloon, I saw the most splendid display. Way up in the zenith a corona was coloured yellow, red and green and looking as though a monster star shell had burst above us.

On September 6 I found that recordings were too faint from the normal H variometer. I went over to the non-magnetic hut and made the necessary adjustments. It was such an improvement to be able to gain access through the new porch.

We Face Up to a Medical Emergency

Philosophy, like medicine, has plenty of drugs, few good remedies, and hardly any specific cures.

Sébastien Roch Nicholas Chamfort 1740–1794.

Robin retired to bed again on September 7 and then on 10th he had a relapse followed by a very serious attack on 16th, when I commenced looking after him full time. He told me to read up the relevant parts of the medical text book written by Hamilton Bailey. He said that if the internal injuries did not heal up or became patched by the greater omentum, then I should be prepared to drain the abdomen. He said that he wished that we had a stock of Vitamin K, which would assist with the healing of internal injuries.

Accordingly, I pored over his text books and reviewed the meagre stock of surgical instruments, just in case his worst fears were justified and I had to drain his abdomen. A full report was passed to the Royal Society in London and they arranged for medical advice from one of the foremost British experts in the field, Professor Rosenheim. I sent to Dr Rosenheim the fullest details of Robin's condition. The treatment we were giving in Fowler's position and the measures to reduce the chances of thrombosis were confirmed as fully appropriate. He then told me that if Robin was in his care at a London hospital, he would receive exactly the same treatment as I was providing at Halley Bay.

For a period Robin was totally incapacitated and could no longer hide the seriousness of his state of health. As his deputy, I took over all his duties and became his full-time nurse, attending to all his bodily needs, keeping a log of his pulse rate, respiration, and temperature, at hourly intervals during times of crisis.

Clearly his internal injuries had never cleared up and had possibly been leaking poisons into his abdomen these last few weeks since his fall. He was confined to bed on a liquid diet but he had to be nursed in a special position, called Fowler's position, so that the corrosive poisons, leaking into his abdominal cavity, drained downwards. The advice I received was to place a padded bar across the bed under his knees and to prop up his back. The idea was to make him as comfortable as possible sitting up in bed, with his knees up. First I sat Robin up in a comfortable position and then we built the padded bar for his knees and the support for his back.

In attempting to cure his internal injuries, his blood had become prone to clotting, therefore in this constrained position, there was an enhanced risk of thrombosis, particularly in the legs. In nursing him therefore, I watched carefully for indications of clotting and tried to prevent this by instituting a regime of regular massage and exercise designed to help avoid the dangers of blood clots. Robin was worried about this possibility and said that he would like to get his hands on some Heparin, a drug which can help avoid blood clots. Later he did in fact get a small clot in one leg, which cleared up with the assistance of some massage and exercise.

The London specialist stressed with me the crucial importance of keeping Robin in good spirits and in an optimistic frame of mind. I did this by spending many hours with him. Occasionally, when he felt stronger, we chatted about our many mutual interests whilst watching keenly his state of health.

Alarmingly, his condition deteriorated rapidly on September 16, 29 days after his fall and on the sixth day after his second return to bed. Robin had some sort of crisis at 1:30 p.m. He called out and was nearly unconscious, pale and with a rapid pulse. His pulse was up to 120 per minute and pounding in his ears. After several very distressing minutes the condition subsided. After about two hours I left him for about ten minutes, to be rapidly recalled at the onset of a similar but slightly less severe attack. His pulse rate eventually dropped to normal over a period of several hours, but at times was unsteady. During his first attack, Robin had a distinct feeling of something flooding warmth from his stomach to his toes. I stayed by his bed until 11 p.m. when I was a little more confident of his chances of recovery.

The crisis I had just observed in Robin was a quite remarkable experience. Before it occurred, I was not too optimistic. He did look quite dreadful and was in considerable distress. But after the crisis, there was something different in his appearance which made me much more optimistic.

At the time of his fall, he thought that either the liver or one of

his bile ducts was damaged, but not the duct from the gall bladder
to the intestines. A few days before he had thought the greater
omentum had moved over. Today he believed that either a bruised
area under the liver sac had burst or there was an extensive leakage of
bile, suggested by a tightening of the abdomen. There were no signs
of extensive, internal haemorrhage. Alternatively, it was a coincidental
or triggered heart attack. Some premonition of this had been felt on
return from Emperor Bay recently, when his pulse rate remained at
100 per minute for an a excessive period, and this he considered as
evidence of heart strain.

On the following morning he was still in a bad way but improved,
with less yellowing of the whites of his eyes, giving me fewer fears for
his eventual recovery. He said that he needed some doses of Vitamin
K to encourage clotting at the site of the internal injuries. Of course
this might also have increased the probability of thrombosis occurring
in his legs, so it was perhaps just as well we did not have this particular
drug at Halley Bay.

In fact it was not until September 17 that I really did believe he
would get better. On September 16 no one would have given much
for his chances. At the time, Robin was convinced death was near at
hand. His mental anguish was very considerable over his wife, mother
and daughter. I did everything possible to reassure him. After the crisis
had occurred, Professor Rosenheim indicated he was sure of Robin's
eventual recovery.

It was perhaps unfortunate that Robin's worst crisis actually occurred
when our radio operator was talking to the Trans-Antarctic Expedition
at Shackleton Base. So they were the first to get the news and this
was spread far and wide at a time when Robin's state was at its worst
and he was openly predicting his own demise. Although we never
actually requested assistance beyond medical advice, both TAE and
the US Expedition at Ellsworth offered help should the situation
require it.

There was no privacy possible at our base and there could be no
secret about his state and what he believed might occur. What was
happening was plain and in the open for all to see and hear. Consequently, not only did Robin's spirits need keeping up but also those
of all members of the expedition. Maintenance of the expedition
members' morale immediately became a high priority for my attention.

On the evening of the 17th there was another regular schedule of
radio contact with the TAE at Shackleton. Their leader, Dr Vivian
Fuchs, said that he had decided TAE would fly Dr Allan Rogers up
to see Robin. They would do this as soon as possible and bring some
of the needed drugs with them. When Robin was informed of this
generous and gratuitous offer of a mercy flight from Shackleton, he
was noticeably relieved. Witnessing the effect on Robin, I could

appreciate how much this moral support contributed to his eventual recovery even though, as it turned out, Allan never did arrive before we had nursed Robin well on the way to full recovery. In fact when they finally met, Robin looked in better physical condition than Allan, such were the unexpected turns and twists of fate in Antarctica.

It is very difficult for a doctor when he is sick. Inevitably their mind goes into overdrive, worrying about all the horrible things that just might happen. I knew full well the enormous importance of inspiring in him faith and an optimistic spirit. I gathered from what he told me many years later, as we walked together across the countryside of Northern France, that I did succeed. He said that the confidence I exuded nurtured in him the will to live. He said this inspiration, combined with my nursing care, actually saved his life.

Robin's Would-be Saviours had to Save Themselves

On September 20, Flight Lieutenant Gordon Haslop took off in the TAE Auster with Dr Rogers in their errand of mercy. They took off at 3:30 p.m. and flew under a clear blue sky. The 220-mile (354 km) flight should have taken one hour. They had still not arrived seven hours later. Just when it looked as though we had recovered from the crisis caused by Robin's fall, we were to be faced with another which would occupy our thoughts for the rest of the month.

Gordon missed us and landed 40 miles (64 km) to the north before he ran out of fuel. The weather was almost perfect at the time, with a few scattered clouds over the sea. We could hear the radio of the plane in flight as they spoke to Shackleton and sent off a news reports to the UK media reporting on their errand of mercy.

When they became overdue, we lit a bonfire from a pile of wood 12 ft. (3.66 m) high soaked in Avtur. The flames went up to 25 ft. (7.72 m) but to no avail. After they had landed, we heard the conversation between Haslop and Squadron Leader John Lewis in Shackleton. Because he never saw us, Gordon naturally thought he was still to our south but John had been carefully tracking his flight and knew he had to be to our north. At the time he passed by us, he thought he was flying two miles off the ice-shelf and spotted neither us nor the penguin rookery. On September 21, Lewis ordered Gordon to take off and fly south. Because of deteriorating weather, he later modified that message to, 'If the weather improves, take off and fly south.' Bad weather meant that they were not able to do so for another nine days and in the meantime had to live in a cave dug into the snow.

On September 22 a gale was blowing and there was a radio blackout preventing contact with the downed plane. Bill, Alf, Jim, and David

Harrison were preparing to go north with a tractor having a radius of action of 80 miles (129 km). Robin's abdomen had improved but he was very worried about the possibility of thrombosis in the legs. The gale continued on the following day and Robin developed a thrombosis in one leg. Accordingly, Robin also sent the following request for Heparin to Finn Ronne, leader of the USA Base at Ellsworth, 50 miles from Shackleton: 'To Ronne Ellsworth. Our request for Heparin passed to you via Shackleton for patient recovering from superficial split right lobe of liver with haematoma discharge on September 16. Abdominal symptoms now cleared up but slight venous thrombosis of legs. Smart.'

We never did get any drugs in time to be of use. Maybe that was just as well. We never had Vitamin K and when the Heparin arrived, it was no longer essential. If we had used the former early on, then its use would have increased the risk of thrombosis.

After a careful study of the records we made of radio contacts with the TAE mercy flight and of the winds at 5000 ft. (1524 m), the height at which the plane was flying, I worked out that it had to be about 40 miles (64 km) to our north. By 23rd our ground party was ready to go at a moment's notice and we offered to send it north to the plane. Dr Fuchs sent the following reply: 'Thanks for the ground party suggestion but not necessary. Allan and Gordon have survival rations for 25 days. Auster can take off in 20 knots (37 kph) wind but useless until drift goes. We cannot expect to hear from them until weather improves as they will be conserving their battery. They may be drifted up but should be able to start. We believe they are 25 to 60 miles (40 to 97 km) up the coast.' On 24th he added, 'If you send a ground party they should have a small sledge to man-haul back if tractor breaks down. We ought to decide on the use of such a party when the weather breaks. How many men will you send? The plane is within one mile of ice cliff edge.' Bunny was told that the party would be of four and radio equipped. We asked for details of their plans and said that the ground party would not leave until Shackleton thought this to be desirable or necessary. They were also told that we had been 12 miles (19 km) up the the coast and that far at least was suitable for tractors. On speaking to Fuchs at night, he said that he now thought the aircraft was 70 miles (113 km) to our north. He said he was in fact more certain of this than one is normally in these cases. He also said that the Auster lay to the north of a large glacier to our north, one which he had flown over. We found it difficult to see how Gordon could have flown over that feature without noticing.

On 25th the weather showed signs of future improvement but was still poor and we had a lot of snow. I heard from Finn Ronne at Ellsworth and he said he was ready to rescue the TAE party as soon as the weather was better. The air crew at Shackleton were not yet ready to fly, but should be before the weather improved.

When I went up to the non-magnetic hut on 26th, I found the porch we had constructed full of snow. There was a small crack in the porch and that provided just enough for the drifting snow to come in and fill the porch with snow. It was another gale day here but on 27th I heard they were now prepared to fly from Shackleton when the weather was right. They would bring the necessary fuel with them and radio beacons to conduct the search from here.

The wind continued to blow at gale force on 28th. There was a gale at Shackleton too but they were now ready to fly. The forecast from Port Stanley gave 5/8th of cloud for the following day, which should provide conditions good enough for flying. The continual strain of anticipation followed by disappointment was affecting all of us at the base. We were now concerned for the fate of two doctors and the pilot of the Auster. Robin was still confined to his bed but he said that he hoped to be able to rise the next day. If so, that could ease everyone's concern.

To get a better appreciation of how Gordon and Allan might be coping in their hole in the snow 40 miles (64 km) away, I worked out the windchill factors for the period of their exposure. When they landed, the wind chill factor was 2400, at which point life in temporary shelters was judged to be dangerous. On the next day it had dropped to 2000 and conditions continued to improve to below 1400, a level where exposed flesh does not freeze.

On Sunday 29th the weather was cloudy, calm and very warm for the season. The de Havilland of Canada Otter had been test-flown at Shackleton. Further radio transmissions had been received from the Auster with the news that both men were all right and the plane was too. They were told to sit tight until the Otter came for them with additional fuel and assistance. Robin was still not able to get out of bed; maybe he would tomorrow. It was so warm that I worked outside bareheaded and without gloves whilst digging out the back door of the hut, which had become completely buried again during the recent storm. We saw the first sunset for many days.

We marked out a runway for the Otter aircraft, whose arrival was eagerly anticipated. Robin managed to get out of bed for the first time for part of the day. He put on a brave face and I was probably the only one who really knew how bad he still felt. The Otter took off from Shackleton on 30th but had to turn back.

October 1957

Finally, the TAE Otter flew over the base in the afternoon of October 1. It circled, took a pass over the Dawson-Lambton glacier, and finally landed at 3:30 p.m. They refuelled and took off again at 4:30 p.m. They found the Auster 58 nautical miles (107 km) north. Allan and

Gordon were quite fit but very, very thirsty. The first thing Allan did when he came into the hut was to grab hold of a jug of orange juice sitting on the bar and drain it to the bottom. Robin was up to meet the party and now seemed to be recovering rapidly.

The weather deteriorated on October 2 so the visitors were not able to leave. A local flight was made and the radios were tested. It was noticed that some of the ice was moving south in the vicinity of the McDonald Ice Rumples 7 miles (11 km) to our north-east. That evening we had a special film show for our visitors and afterwards there was an extra special issue of beer for all. During the day, Allan gave me instructions in the technique of intravenous injection of Heparin for the treatment of Robin's thrombosis.

On October 3 we could not get the Auster aircraft started. That was probably a good thing because we heard later that the weather conditions had deteriorated at Shackleton later in the day. In the evening we had another film show and beer issue.

Our welcome visitors finally left today, October 4. There seems to be little doubt that the members of both expeditions were greatly stimulated by recent events. No element of our scientific programme was affected significantly. The meteorologists certainly had to take on a greater load, as I was pressed into service nursing Robin full-time through the days of his crisis. Several others did a great deal of preparatory work to set up a rescue ground party and all worked with a will to set up the runway etc. The point was certainly driven home that the addition of an airborne element to an expedition can be a two-edged sword. Yes, it can provide a tremendous addition to your capability, but the price you pay for this can too easily be quite high.

However, the misfortune of the TAE Auster failing to spot our base as they flew by it on September 20 had clearly made an impact on the TAE. It turned what would normally be expected to be a relatively speedy operation, involving only two persons, into a significant effort involving two aircraft and many people. It also raised the possibility of additional efforts being stimulated in the nearby USA base at Ellsworth, where the personnel inevitably became concerned. During his discussion with the TAE, Robin therefore suggested to Bunny Fuchs that two members of the Royal Society Expedition be loaned to them, thereby accelerating the TAE programme. The two persons selected, Fred Morris and Ivor Beney, were both towers of skill and strength, tempered by the challenges of their recent experiences in building and maintaining the base at Halley Bay.

John Lewis and Ralph Lenton flew up to Halley Bay on October 5 and took Fred and Ivor back with them to Shackleton. Later on Fred also served at the TAE southern outpost of South Ice. At Shackleton, they made short work of innumerable tasks that had to be accomplished before TAE set off on its historic journey. When I spoke at length to Fred and Ivor on their return to Halley Bay, I heard the full details and was proud of what they had accomplished at both Shackleton and South Ice. I believed that any delays due to TAE's bad luck on the Auster flight on September 20 had been more than made up for by the achievements, from October to December, of these two stalwarts from the Royal Society Expedition. As Hal Lister put it in a letter to me dated 12 November 1957, 'Your Ivor and Fred have been working hard helping us out and, quite unforeseen, they are a tonic, since they are fresh and bright, and new faces are so welcome.'

Scientifically speaking, spring was the season of the year when the ozone observations were of particular interest. In writing about this, Dr G. M. B. Dobson said, 'One of the more interesting results on atmospheric ozone which came out of the IGY was the discovery of the peculiar annual variation of ozone at Halley Bay ... The annual variation of ozone at Spitzbergen was fairly well known, so assuming a six-months difference, we knew what to expect. However, when the monthly telegrams from Halley Bay began to arrive and were plotted alongside the Spitzbergen curve, the values for September and October 1956 were about 150 units lower than was expected.' When I had worked in Oxford, I had learnt this directly from Dr Dobson and knew he was waiting anxiously for my measurements, particularly at this time of year. I therefore spared no efforts to obtain ozone measurement whenever the weather permitted. I managed to get a complete sequence, through the whole year, by using the moonlight in winter and the sun in summer. It was the first time successful measurements had been made at Halley Bay using moonlight. By the end of the IGY, we had three years of observations and developed a high degree of confidence in them. From this Dr Dobson concluded, 'The winter vortex over the South Pole was maintained late into the spring and that this kept the ozone values low. When it suddenly broke up in November both the ozone values and the stratosphere temperatures rose very suddenly.' (Ref. Dobson, G M B, 1968; *Applied Optics*, Vol. 7 No.3).

The sequence of measurements at Halley Bay proved to be one of the most comprehensive in Antarctica and provided the base line for the discovery of the 'ozone hole' which developed recently as a result of atmospheric pollution. Throughout the first two weeks of October the weather was quite good and I was able to make many observations of ozone and also to take out the theodolite for astronomical fixes, keeping track of the movement of the ice-shelf and the direction of true north for the geomagnetic records.

The Dawn of the Satellite Era

Radio signals from Sputnik I, the USSR artificial earth satellite, were heard on October 7 on 20 Mc/s. I was a little surprised by the tremendous impact this had on the general public, who seemed to have no idea it was coming. They were not expecting it to happen. However, we were well aware that both USA and USSR had formally announced the launching of satellites as a part of their contribution to the IGY. We were also aware that both were racing to be the first in space. The element of competition was clear when I was in Paris listening to those two countries unfolding details of their satellite programmes for the IGY. In this sense the IGY was the stimulus which ushered in the new epoch of the space era and the founding of an industry which grew to conduct $50 billion per year after 40 years of growth.

Since June we had been conducting two radio soundings of the atmosphere per day, measuring its temperature, humidity and wind structure to heights of between 20 and 30 km. After doing an inventory of our stocks, I found that we had been using our store of chemicals for hydrogen production more rapidly than anticipated. One reason for this was the need to use larger radar reflectors, which were heavier and needed more hydrogen to lift them. If we went on in this way, we would run out before the end of the IGY. I therefore decided that we would be prudent to cut out one ascent per week. This had a social benefit in that it allowed all the meteorologists to attend the regular Saturday evening film show, the social highlight of the week.

At 7:30 a.m. on October 14, Robin, Bill, and David Harrison took off with the sledge, tent, etc. for a trip to the McDonald Ice Rumples. This was a rather disturbed area, where we believed the ice-shelf to be grounded so it was lifted up as it moved over a subsurface hill. The most marked feature of the area we called the 'Gin Bottle', which was about 6 miles (9.7 km) from the base. The party returned at 3:00 p.m. the next day. This particular, short trip was omitted from the list of sledging journeys listed in the expedition's sledging report. (Ref. *RSIAE*, Vol. 4 p. 330).

We had some good weather in the second half of October. I was able to do several astronomical fixes. The weather was even good enough to make ozone observations of the 'Umkehr-Effect'. (Ref. IGY *Ozone Instruction Manual* Vol. 5 Part 1, *Annals of the IGY*, Pergamon Press). Such a series allows one to infer the vertical distribution of ozone in the stratosphere.

On October 18 it was a particularly good day so several of us went to visit the bays. I was on gash duty but managed to join some of them in a trip to Emperor Bay. Andrew and I took photos of penguins.

Meanwhile nearby, Robin was looking at a seal hole when up popped a seal's head. Robin promptly tapped him on the nose. In the photograph taken of the occasion, it was quite clear the animal was a Leopard Seal, a beast quite capable of killing a man. At that time of the year they cruise in the sea just off the ice edge. When they see a penguin, they can come out at high speed and catch them. They can do just the same with a man and they can out-run him on land. You could also see them catching penguins in the sea. Fortunately this particular leopard must have been rather surprised as he promptly disappeared after Robin's tap.

Bill went fishing at Halley Bay. He had no luck either with the fish or in sounding the bottom of the sea there. With 600 ft. (183 m) of line out, he still did not reach the bottom.

There was an almost complete eclipse of the sun on October 23. At 05:00:30 U T (3:00 a.m. local time) the eclipse was at its maximum when only a sliver of the lower edge of the sun was visible. Vestiges of the corona were visible even though it was not a completed eclipse. We were all outside watching this impressive scene.

When we went inside the hut, Robin asked me to have a look at one of his teeth that was giving him trouble. It was about the third time I had acted as his dentist. He showed me the tooth and I examined it, describing to him what I saw. He said that it needed to have the decay drilled out and filled, so that is what I did. I took hold of his dental drill, fitted in an appropriate bit and very, very carefully drilled away at the blackened rotten part of the tooth until it was all gone leaving a clean sound tooth. As I went through this step by step, Robin guided my actions because I was still learning what to do. When the tooth was all clean and dry, I mixed up a plastic dental filling, which I believe was called De Trey's dental cement, and I filled the cavity. Then I changed places with Robin and he treated one of my teeth which had been giving me trouble.

Another Leopard Seal was seen by David Tribble and David Harrison on October 24 when they were walking near the ice edge at Emperor Bay. It followed them along the ice edge but did not attempt to attack them.

We went to the stores dumps on October 25 and built two new Dexion platforms. Three of the old dumps were dug out and restocked on to the new platform, It was very pleasant working outside in the sunshine with the temperature at −25°C. Later on that day, I made a shot of the sun for latitude, longitude, and azimuth of the fixed mark.

On the 26th, the brushes of electric motors needed refurbishing yet again. I took down the two aspiration motors on the meteorological tower and the blower motor on the fluxplate radiometer. I stripped them down and replaced or reseated their brushes, as Alf had taught me, and I reinstalled them.

We had a particularly pleasant social evening after the film show that Saturday. Bill and others talked animatedly about their recent sledging journeys.

There was another equipment failure to be dealt with on Sunday October 27. A spring on the Dobson spectrophotometer broke and it took me several hours to fix. After two more observations it broke again, so I had to strip the equipment down once again. This time I found that two small but important washers had not been supplied with the equipment. I found some replacements and this time was more successful.

On 27th and 29th I was operating the radar during the evening balloon ascents. It was quite noticeable that these night-time ascents were now rising to much greater heights. It was on the eve of 24-hour sunlight so that the balloons were now being warmed by the sun's rays and therefore not bursting so prematurely.

On Wednesday October 30 the sun was up for 24 hours and would not set again for three and a half months. We noted the event with our weekly Wednesday tot of rum. A pleasant evening was enlivened by conversation amongst Robin, Bill, Henry, Alf, David Harrison, and myself. Henry told us something about the sledging journey he took with Len from September 15 to 21. It was the longest to date. Instead of using a tent, they had built two igloos and slept in them for both legs of the journey. The farthest point reached was 31 miles (50 km) from base to a point at the very edge of the Dawson-Lambton Glacier due south of us.

On the 31st, I spent much of the day tidying up the seismic observation for the month. Peter Jeffries and I also had a discussion on ways to solve the occasional failures we experienced with the windmill-driven switches on radio sondes. We came to the conclusion that it might be worth trying the use of the smaller radar reflector, which might not reduce the rate of ascent so much at the top of the ascent where we experienced the problem. We tried it that night and it did seem to work.

November 1957

On November 1, Robin, Bill, Jim, and David Harrison left on a man-hauling sledging trip at 6:15 a.m. on a course of 120°. They reached a point 32 miles (51 km) from base where the ice was very disturbed and just on the edge of the Dawson-Lambton Glacier. I spent much of the day finishing off the month's seismic work, coding the observations up and sending them off to London by radio.

Every now and then Jim Burton, assisted by David Cansfield, produced our own newspaper, the *Halley Comet*. The second issue was published on the 2nd. The editorial dedicated the issue to the departure of the TAE on their historic journey and the onset of spring with its welcome return of the sun, open seas and migrating birds. In the issue we bade the TAE *bon voyage*.

The following day there was some discussion about the content of the paper, which, like all good journalism, was spiced with elements of controversy. My admiration for Jim's abilities was heightened by yet another example of his talents and capacities. In addition to his heavy meteorological work load and his glaciological studies conducted during several man-hauling sledging trips, here he was producing a newspaper several times a year. For this issue I prepared a short article on the magnetic field at Halley Bay and Robin wrote an article on the Emperor Penguin.

On November 5 I learnt that my appointment as next year's Leader had been publicly announced. I received several telegrams of congratulations and a message in the BBC programme 'Calling Antarctica'. The announcement was published in the *Sunday Express* on November 3, and in the *Times*, and *Guardian* on 4th. The *Times* also published my photo and so did the *Illustrated London News* on the 9th. There was a photo of Oonagh and Simon in some of the London evening papers. The *Evening News* of November 4 christened her the 'Ice Widow'. The photo of Oonagh and Simon on the November 6 issue of the *Star* was a very happy one.

On 6th, at our regular Wednesday evening gathering over a tot of rum, Alf, Robin, Bill, and I had a very pleasant series of conversations. Despite the previous late night I was up the next morning at 6.30 a.m. to make a series of ozone observations. In the afternoon I shot the sun to measure the azimuth of the fixed mark used for geomagnetic observations, which I repeated on the 8th. On 9th I discovered a problem with the theodolite which affected yesterday's readings, so I repeated them and also measured the latitude and longitude of the base.

There was a gale blowing on the 10th; it was a good day for inside work. Stimulated by hearing that Oonagh had sent me a 50-page letter for Christmas, I spent much of the day writing my reply to send back to her. I also made a start with some other annual reports. The gale continued on the 11th whilst I pored over the seismograms and got that work up to date.

The gale subsided by the 12th, so David Tribble and I fitted a wooden tube through the drift at the north end of the non-magnetic hut. With this fitted, I was able to sight on the fixed mark without first having to dig out the window. I also dug down to the entrance of the seismic cave, which was under 6 ft. (1.83 m) of snow. Then I constructed a new roof and entrance at the new level.

It was all hands to the pump on November 14 for a coal heave. The whole expedition turned out on a fine day. We dug down to the store of anthracite and carried 200 bags of it into the hut.

The blazing sun and high temperatures we enjoyed for the past few days caused a problem on 15th at the non-magnetic hut, which was leaking. Snow driven into the roof was dripping inside. To prevent any problems entirely, I fitted a tent of closely woven cotton material over the instruments. The material I used was Ventile, the same fabric used for our anoraks. On 17th I went into the roof of the hut and found snow and ice which had been driven inside and was causing the problem. By then the weather had deteriorated, slowing the rate of dripping water.

The gale continued on 18th so I spent some time indoors conducting the ozone monthly tests and preparing a talk on the subject for the scientific discussion we were going to hold on the following Wednesday.

On the 19th we found the gale had driven so much snow into the balloon shed that we set to digging again. The wind was blowing at 48 knots (89 kph) when we launched both balloons today, but we did manage to launch them successfully.

We had a very fine scientific discussion on Wednesday November 20. One of the Radio Astronomers, Philip Brenan, was particularly interesting. He said that he thought the layers causing radio star scintillations lay at a height of about 1500 km.

On November 23 I was on gash duty, which in a way was quite fortuitous. Two days previously I spent much of the day outside on a clear warm day. I measured the baseline of the movement stakes and then did an azimuth shot. As I worked away sighting at the sun with a theodolite, I must have pushed my sun goggles off once too often and was now suffering a mild dose of sunstroke. Not enough to incapacitate me but I couldn't see properly, so it did make it very difficult to do close work.

There was another splendid summer day on the 25th. Soon we expect TAE to fly up the 220 miles (354 km) from Shackleton with both their aeroplanes. They will leave the Auster behind for us to send back on our relief ship. We spent the day digging out the Auster crate and dragged it over to the area we had marked off for the landing strip.

I went down to Emperor Bay on the afternoon of the 26th. I took a number of photos and made a tape recording of the scene for Donald Milner of the BBC. The south-westerly wind had blown some sea-ice in but there was still a wide shore lead.

During the day I typed up most of my annual report on glaciology. Robin, Bill, Jim and I had a good evening of conversation after the rum ration available in the bar on Wednesday November 27. The subject was history.

On 28th it was snowing, with those large flakes common in temperate climates. I spent much of the day analysing seismograms. I was pleased to hear from Derek that he now feels better working the normal meteorological roster. At his own request, he had worked on night duty continuously for part of the winter.

Philip and Les returned on November 30 from a two-day trip to the Gin Bottle, where they had done some surveying. I spent that Saturday tiding up the monthly reports. After the weekly film show, there was a good informal discussion on the subject of Communism versus Christianity.

We expect to receive the visitors from Shackleton Base tomorrow.

December 1957

The TAE party did not arrive on December 1 as expected, because it snowed all day. I spent the day writing the annual seismological report. I did some more writing on the 2nd, this time for the Christmas Edition of the *Halley Comet*. I wrote on the subject of the Halley Bay Ice-shelf.

The snow storm continued through the 3rd. I went over to the non-magnetic hut to remove the stuffing from the boxes round the instrument foundations. As the snow compacted, the piers had risen through the floor of the non-magnetic hut and I needed to see whether this might cause more serious trouble as the frame round the piles fouled the floor joists. If so, that would be the first job I would give Fred when he returned from Shackleton.

In the continuing foul weather on 4th, the balloon we were launching broke away this morning and had to be repeated. At 8:45 p.m., Jim, Les, and David Harrison returned from a man-hauling trip they took to an ice hill at a point 14 miles (23 km) away on a bearing of 070°. Whilst away, they planted several stakes to measure snow accumulation and mapped some pronounced undulations of the ice shelf.

December 5 was another filthy day. Derek made a very good job of improving our technique for generating hydrogen. In more temperate climates the balloon was filled until a certain measured free lift was observed and this was the standard Meteorological Office procedure we used to follow. However, free lift is a function of the temperature of the hydrogen, which cools later on in the flight. He improved the rates of ascent by ignoring free lift and used careful measurements of the quantity of chemicals employed.

Back in the main hut that day, David Tribble was making a step-function improvement in our living conditions. He installed drains under the bath and kitchen sink. We had been mulling over the idea for some time and done tests. The system worked perfectly and obviated the need to dispose of all our waste water by the bucket.

At last on 6th, the weather showed signs of improving. I went out to the rear of the hut and dug out the entrance to the seismic pit and found it had been perfectly soundly sealed. Ken Amy started to shore up the foundations of the generator shed under the generators. The problem was due to the tremendous amount of heat created by the generators running continuously. Over the year, more and more snow had been melted under the hut. If something was not done soon, the hut and generators could subside into the huge hole below.

On 7th the weather turned foul again. I went into the seismological pit and readjusted the seismographs so they were more heavily damped. As a consequence, on the following day I found the records were much improved.

On 8th the weather had improved sufficiently for me to do ozone measurements and also sun shots for latitude, longitude and azimuth. The better weather also brought our TAE visitors on the 9th, returning to us Fred and Ivor. We were very glad to see them back again and have the use of their unequalled skills. There were several important jobs waiting to be done by them, particularly the foundations of the generator shed and the piles of the non-magnetic hut.

In the afternoon of December 9, John Lewis took me for a flight in the Otter aircraft. We set off inland on a bearing of 120° magnetic to the coast proper 35 nautical miles (65 km) away. At that point there are ice falls preceded by lenticular holes which look like icebergs embedded in the floating ice-shelf after calving from ice-falls on the coast proper. From the vantage point of the aeroplane, you can see that we sit on a triangular piece of ice-shelf meeting the snow-covered land of the coast on a front of about 100 miles (161 km). Where the coast joins the ice-shelf, there are more ice cliffs, about 100 ft. (30 m) high in places, and not unlike the cliffs of the ice-shelf. The disturbed area is not large in extent and there are many paths through to higher ground, which looks undisturbed though undulating slightly. From the air, our ice-shelf looks deceptively like sea-ice. When we returned from this flight, John Lewis said to me that he thought Gordon might have followed this line of the coast, mistaking our shelf for sea-ice, when flying to us in September with Allan Rogers. That would certainly explain a lot but we may never know for certain.

I was also on gash duty that day and I cleaned out the drinking water tank. In the evening we stayed up very late talking with our friends of the TAE and welcoming back Fred and Ivor, who had been absent and missed by us for nearly three months.

Our visitors left on December 13, just ahead of a brief spell of bad weather. The weather cleared up on the following day giving us a perfect calm and sunny day. Although it was Saturday on the 14th, the regular social gathering was relatively quiet as it had been declared a World Meteorological Interval (WMI). This meant that we sent up a second balloon that evening, a practice normally avoided on Saturday evenings to conserve stores and allow the meteorological team to participate fully in the only social event of the week.

On Sunday morning December 15, I went out to help generate hydrogen. Later on I calibrated the Dobson ozone spectrophotometer in weather conditions favourable for that task.

In preparation for the arrival of our relief ship, we held a digging party on the 16th to recover the bridging timbers from stores dump Number 5. These were heavy pieces of timber designed to provide a bridge for the tractors and sledges over cracks or gaps in the sea-ice. They had lain untouched for a year and were found buried under 5 ft. (1.5 m) of snow. Once the timbers were exposed at the bottom of the huge hole we had excavated, they were attached to the tractor winch and hauled up to the surface. We continued to dig on the 17th and 18th to raise deeply buried stores dumps and move the precious cases to the present snow level about 5 ft. (1.5 m) higher.

Andrew was at the helm of the radar during an exceptional radio sonde ascent on December 18. Because of marked changes in the wind direction with height that day, the balloon went overhead the radar five times during the hour-long flight. Every time this happened, he had to swing the whole radar round 180° by rapidly winding the hand-driven azimuth control wheel of the radar.

Over the last few days of sunshine, Bill and I had been using solar power to shift snow. Bill sprinkled ashes on the large snow drift to the southern end of the main hut and round his aerials. Not wishing to use ashes too close to the main hut, I placed tarpaulins on the snow, which had risen too near to the ozone observing hatch. Both techniques worked very well and considerably lowered the snow level.

I rose a couple of hours early on 20th to make a sun shot to determine the azimuth of the 'fixed' mark, and the latitude and longitude of the base. Later on, I continued work on annual reports. Then I took Fred over to the non-magnetic hut to see what he could do about the way the hut was sinking with reference to the piles beneath it. The immediate problem was to prevent the frame round the head of the group of piles from fouling the floor joists. He studied the problem and proposed a solution which should last until the end of the IGY. Because a large sun spot had just been observed, I decided to postpone the work with its consequent interruption to the magnetic records.

After another early rise, I did an azimuth shot and spent most of the day writing reports. In the evening it was my bath and dhoby night. It was my first experience of the Tribble draining system for the bath water. No longer did we have to carry the waste bath-water out of the hut in buckets. After doing that for eleven months, the new arrangement struck me as a great and welcome touch of luxury. There is now a ten-foot long, vertical pipe underneath the bath through which the water safely drains away into the firn below without affecting the foundations of the hut.

On Sunday afternoon, December 22, I went to Halley Bay and skied on the sea-ice. Whilst on the ice, it subsided twice with a loud thump, falling about half an inch. I believe this can be due to the effect of solar radiation melting layers below the surface. It most certainly gives you quite a fright, even though it presages no great danger. A similar thing happens in summer on top of the ice-shelf. Most noticeable since last year was the way the southern headland to Halley Bay had become tilted upwards. One explanation proposed for this phenomenon was the gentle south-western flow of water against this face of the headland. As the water washed against the ice, some of it froze, building up layers of ice deep below the surface, which in turn increased the flotation of the headland, forcing it up.

On 23rd I was up again at 6:30 a.m. to change the blower motor on the fluxplate radiometer. For the rest of the day I typed away at the annual reports. By the end of the day I felt that I had broken the back of the job and was looking forward to celebrating Christmas with the reports largely behind me.

Preparations for Christmas

In preparation for the festivities, Malcolm and Len decorated the lounge wonderfully well, with streamers hanging from the ceiling and a home-made Christmas tree at the end of the room, decorated with lights and cotton wool. Whilst admiring their efforts in the kitchen afterwards, I looked through the kitchen window at the cavern in the snow which had been melted by the heat of the kitchen. The roof of the cavern had recently subsided by about three feet.

On Christmas Eve the rattle of typewriter keys continued with the preparation of reports. In the evening we all gathered together for a Christmas drink and were handed a copy of the *Halley Comet*. It was the third issue of those stalwart editors, Jim Burton and David Cansfield. Their editorial recognised that we were all thinking of the relief ship, *Tottan*, fighting its way through the ice towards us with mail from loved ones and the first proper letters for a year. None of us dissented from the editors dubbing *Tottan* and Captain Jakobsen the 'uncrowned Queen and King of the Weddell Sea'. Well-deserved tributes were paid to the five persons departing on *Tottan*, Ken Amy, Ron Evans, Peter Jeffries, Fred Morris, and Robin Smart. Robin's 'good fellowship, almost incredibly tolerant good nature and wise counsel' were noted. As the new Leader, I was assured by the editors of the determination of the party to 'keep cracking in 1958'.

Looking back, the editors were dead right. No one could have been more proud than I of the expedition members. Their good fellowship

David Harrison & never failed to strengthen me and they continued to keep cracking
Robin Smart take a throughout with outstanding performances in every regard, not only
break from skiing at at Halley Bay but also during the period of data analysis which followed
Halley Bay. back in the UK. In the *Halley Comet,* Robin thanked the members
for their support. He expressed his appreciation for the amount of
sheer hard work done by the party. He said that already there were
clear indications that the results of our work were considered important
by some of the world's top experts. I contributed to the issue a short
article on the Halley Bay Ice-shelf. That evening, in the BBC programme 'Calling Antarctica', we heard the voices of Sir David Brunt
and HRH Prince Philip.

Christmas Day was celebrated in a very traditional style. The day
started with a well-attended Service at which the hymn singing went
with a real swing. Malcolm and Len then produced a splendid lunch
as you can see from the following menu:

Crayfish Mayonnaise
Green Pea Soup
Roast Turkey Belgravia
Roast and Boiled Potatoes
Broccoli in Butter
Runner Beans
The Christmas Pudding and Brandy Sauce
Mince Pies
Fruit Salad and Cream

Cheese
Crystallized Fruit and Nuts
Coffee
Toast: THE QUEEN
Bristol Cream Sherry
Port and Cigars.

After the dinner there was a bottle of 1869 Green Chartreuse on the table, a gift from the Royal Society. We heard that the *Tottan* was at Maudheim. We then sang the following song:

Dedicated to Santa Leif and his Tottan Class Reindeer.
Tune: 'We're going to hang out the washing on the Siegfried Line:

> We're going to have a good Christmas down at Halley Bay,
> For we've heard that the *Tottan*'s drawing near,
> And we know Captain Leif will not let ice delay,
> The bringing us of Good Cheer,
> Whether the weather it be dark or fine,
> We'll just drink our Toasts so merrily,
> Yes, we will have a good Christmas down at
> Halley Bay standing around the Christmas Tree.

After the lunch, Robin, Bill, Jim, David Harrison and I skied down to Halley Bay and spent several very happy hours speeding down the drift slopes underneath the ice cliffs.

On Boxing Day we had another excellent lunch and later on there was a showing of two particularly good movies, 'Quartet' and 'To Paris with Love'. The menu for Boxing Day was:

Cream of Mushroom Soup
Salmon Mayonnaise
Spring Chicken Maryland
French Fried Potatoes
Green Peas
Runner Beans
Tomatoes
Vanilla Cream Trifle
Cheese
Crystallised Fruit and Nuts
Coffee
Cigars
Bristol Cream Sherry
Port.

After lunch on 27th, Fred started work on the piles in the normal variometer room of the non-magnetic hut. He gave an extra five inches (13 cm) of freedom for the piles to rise through the floor. It took Fred until 8:00 p.m. to finish the job. When he finished, I re-installed the variometer and finished that at 1:30 a.m. the next morning. We were back at the non-magnetic hut on the 28th. The job took from 11:00 a.m. until 11:00 p.m. Whilst he was there, Fred also repaired the porch we had put up whilst he was away working for the TAE at Shackleton and South Ice. We had not built it as well as he could, so the roof had begun to sag seriously.

On 29th we heard that *Tottan* was due to arrive on New Year's Eve. This news spurred great activity in the camp, which continued on the 30th. Letters and reports were finished off and parcels packed up. The excitement of her imminent arrival was palpable.

At 6:00 a.m. on New Year's Eve, Robin and Alf went down to the bay to welcome *Tottan*. She docked at 8:00 a.m. We spent a very Happy New Year with *Tottan*'s captain and crew.

References

The Political Legacy of the International Geophysical Year, by the Committee on Foreign Affairs, US House of Representatives, November 1973.

Dr Hugh Odishaw, NSF-NAS Hearings: *IGY Report.*

S Chapman, 1956; The IGY, *Nature* 175 (Jan 8), p. 56.

Annals of the IGY, Vol. V, Part IV, *Radiation Instruments*; Pergamon Press.

RSIAE; 1964, vol. IV, pp. 74–84, 330; The Royal Society.

MacDowall, J; 1955; Total-Radiation Fluxmeter; *Met. Mag.* 84, 65.

Dobson, G M B, 1968; *Applied Optics,* Vol. 7 No. 3.

IGY Ozone Instruction Manual Vol. 5 Part 1, *Annals of the IGY*, Pergamon Press.

Chapter 5

1958 The Second Year in Antarctica

Tottan Returns

By arriving on the last day of December 1957, the 540-ton *Tottan*'s Norwegian crew demonstrated again their consummate skill in threading through the ice of the Weddell Sea. For the third year in succession they were the first to penetrate it, beating by nine days the 6500-ton USA ice-breaker, USCGC *Westwind* and the supply ship, USS *Wyandot*. They also beat the 4500-ton Argentine icebreaker, *San Martin*.

Tottan moored at the sea-ice edge at Halley Bay, which was about 3 km from the ice-shelf at the head of the bay and 2.5 miles (4 km) from the base. On the day before she arrived, Robin and I skied down to Halley Bay to see what the 'harbour' was like. The sea-ice extended right out beyond the headlands of the bay and over half a mile (800 m) further than in the previous year. We found it to be sound, with a surface about 2 ft. (60 cm) above sea level and about 6 ft. (1.82 m) thick. There was one large crack in the bay-ice but it did not extend across the whole bay and was still not large enough to require the bridging we had prepared. There was a 15-knot (28 kph) wind blowing at the time and this caused the crack to open and close about a quarter of an inch (0.6 cm). This movement of the ice made a distinct squeaking noise. Later on, to welcome *Tottan*, we placed a Tilley lamp at the highest point of the headland we called Penguin Leap, and which formed the southern cape of Halley Bay.

The visitors walked up to the base on New Year's Eve in good time for lunch. The remainder of the personal mail was then brought up from the ship. For most of the afternoon we were immersed in the news from our families. It was the first real mail we had received for a year.

Unloading *Tottan* of 110 tons of stores commenced on January 1 and continued until the 6th. Our last task was to load up the *Tottan* with the TAE Auster aircraft. We were favoured with good weather. It was cloudy for most of the time, with a south-westerly breeze of about 10 knots (19 kph), which moderated and moved to the east at the end of the period. The air temperature was about −7°C when we started and warmed up a few degrees after several days, but did not exceed −2°C.

For the tractors, however, the going was poor, with soft snow surfaces causing them frequently to bog down. For the first two days, only two of the tractors were fully serviceable so we were only able to move about 15 tons a day. On one occasion a tractor got a flat tire, which was repaired by Alf and Ivor there on the sea-ice. At the end of the day's unloading, Alf and Ivor were usually still working, servicing the tractors for the next day.

On the sea-ice near the ship, the weight of snow on top of the ice depressed it to below the water level. After a few days of unloading, this compacted snow lost its strength as it saturated. It became mushy and pot-holes developed in the upper layers of the surface. Problems were avoided by lengthening the tow line between the tractor and sledge, so the tractor was able to pull the sledge from a sound snow surface well away from the mushy snow. This avoided tractors bogging down in the crucial area alongside the ship.

The two new meteorologists who were still living on the ship, Ben Ellis and John Smith, were given the task of checking the stores off the ship. They were the 'tally men' on the ship, noting down the numbers marked on the sides of each case which identified its contents. They also made hourly measurements of the sea current off Halley Bay. Up at the base, Les Barclay checked and directed the stores to one of four dumps. We worked each day from 8:00 a.m. to 8:00 p.m. during the unloading period, but also executed the full range of scientific observations at the same time. The reduction and organization of observations was, of course, put on one side until later.

On the morning of January 3, I was sworn in as the Magistrate at Halley Bay and at 5:00 p.m. local time the leadership of The Royal Society Base was handed over to me by Robin Smart. Robin gave me the formal document of my appointment as Leader; it was signed by Sir David Brunt, the Secretary of the Royal Society. I was also given a very friendly letter from my day-to-day contact in London, Dr (later Sir) David C. Martin, Assistant Secretary of the Royal Society. Extracts from the letter of appointment follow:

'The Royal Society
London

'15 November 1957

'To Mr Joseph MacDowall,

'1.   On behalf of the Royal Society I appoint you as Leader from January 1958 of the Royal Society Antarctic Expedition participating in the International Geophysical Year activities ...

'2.   As leader of the Expedition you will be responsible for the good conduct and discipline of Expedition personnel at Royal Society Base, Halley Bay, for the general organization and administration of the station, and for the operation of the scientific equipment provided.

'4.   Your principle task as Leader is to maintain the base with particular reference to its occupation and use for scientific studies, and it should be your aim to assist each scientist in the performance of his particular duties. In Annex I are notes of guidance on the scientific programme and the operation of the equipment. Observations are highly desirable on all these subjects.

'5.   Royal Society Base, Halley Bay is situated on British Crown land and as Leader you will be required to undertake the duties of Magistrate and Postmaster of the territory. You will be responsible directly to His Excellency the Governor of the Falkland Islands and its Dependencies for the satisfactory discharge of the duties attached to these appointments ...

'11.   A ship will be sent to take you and your party away from Halley Bay in January 1959. If the ice should be such in January 1959 that you cannot be relieved, you should continue the scientific programme as far as is possible with the consumable stores that remain ...

'I shall be glad if you will acknowledge the receipt of these instructions and signify the acceptance of them.

'Signed by (Sir) David Brunt
Secretary, Royal Society
15 November 1957'

The annexes which were appended to Sir David's letter ran to 35 pages, giving the salient details of the nine cardinal elements of the Halley Bay scientific programme. It covered meteorological, geomagnetic, auroral, ionospheric, radio astronomy, glaciological, seismological and physiological measurements, plus nuclear emulsion plate experiments.

After reading it all, I sent the following reply to Sir David:

'Royal Society Base, Halley Bay
Coats Land, Antarctica

'3 January 1958

'Dear Sir,

'Thank you for your letter dated 15 November 1957 appointing me Leader at Halley Bay. This is indeed a great honour and I

Curious Emperor Penguins watching the activity around the Norwegian sealer MV Tottan, nestling at its moorings to the sea-ice below the ice-shelf at Halley Bay.

am proud to serve you.

'I have read your instructions and I will do my best to follow them to deserve the great trust you have given me.

'Yours sincerely,
Joseph MacDowall'

After swearing me in as Magistrate, Robin handed over the key to a tin trunk containing the base secret code books, ammunition for a .303 in. (7.7 mm) rifle, etc. I also found in the trunk a set of 'Protest Forms' left over from the pre-IGY Days, when various nationalities had been known to land and make territorial claims.

Shortly after taking over the leadership of the expedition, I considered what should happen in the event I became 'incapacitated for any reason from carrying out my duties as leader', as I put it in the letter I gave to Philip Brenan on the subject. During the 14 months we had been together, I had been very impressed at the way all the young men of the expedition had developed. It was difficult to choose a deputy from amongst them but, in his quiet, friendly but decisive way, Philip had won the respect of all, so I was confident that the expedition would do well under his leadership if I became *hors de combat*. Robin Smart had given me a similar letter dated 23 November 1956 whilst we were on the *Tottan*. In neither year was there any call for an active deputy leader, so I followed Robin's lead in the matter and did not make any formal announcement on the subject.

New Expedition Members

With my appointment as Leader and the imminent departure of Peter
Jeffries, two more persons were needed for the meteorological team. I
up-dated and clarified the appointment of Andrew Blackie as my
deputy in the leadership of the meteorological team, and Ben Ellis
and John Smith joined us from *Tottan*, bringing the team back to full
strength. Sergeant John Gane, RAF came to replace Chief Technician
Ron Evans, RAF, one of the radio operators. The new medical officer,
Flight Lieutenant Bert Brooker, RAF took over the medical duties of
Colonel Robin Smart, RAMC. Our two carpenters, Ken Amy and
Fred Morris, were not replaced because the construction phase of the
base had been completed months before and they had understandably
been itching to go home ever since.

The *Tottan* also brought with her Dr Alan Moore, an administrative
assistant at the Royal Society in London. When he returned to London,
Dr Moore provided the following comment in his visit report to
Members of the Royal Society:

> 'Royal Society Base, Halley Bay is a magnificent organization
> operated by a hard-working, contented group of men, and all
> members of the advanced and main parties of the expedition can
> be justly proud of their achievements, and all those who have in
> any way tendered advice can rest assured that their efforts have
> been well-rewarded.'

During the brief period of the relief, there was very little time for
rest. There was a great deal of mail to be handled and I spent some
time replying to members of the public who had been good enough
to write to us in such friendly terms and in some cases send gifts. In
addition, as postmaster, I had to sell stamps and frank the letters
posted from the base.

Several persons contributed gramophone records, which provided a
most welcome change from the old favourite tunes which had been
played innumerable times during the past year. A thoughtful member
of the staff of the Royal Society in London also sent us about 50 copies
of daily newspapers. For a period of about two months they had
collected all their daily papers and sent them off to us. When I opened
the parcel, I was just about to put them all in the lounge library when
the idea came to me to keep them on one side for dishing out one
at a time each week, on Sunday mornings. So I wrote a letter of thanks
and locked the papers away in my tin trunk along with the code books
and ammunition. The small stock of papers thereby lasted the whole
year, and were read avidly on Sundays after our short religious service.

After surviving for over 12 months with less than 100 words a month from loved ones, the letters we received from home had a tremendous impact. Oonagh's letters were marvellously expressive and gave me a wonderful picture of just those things I was longing for of their life. When I left home, Simon was just four months old and I had missed so much of his development. No one could have done a better job of bringing me up to date with it. She had prepared a scrap book including photographs of home and family, together with pressed flowers cut from our garden.

When *Tottan* sailed away at 5:13 p.m. on Tuesday January 7, she left behind a strong and contented team, refreshed by new blood whilst saddened by the departure of some of last year's companions. Those departing were ready to go and those arriving brought with them welcome new talents and qualities. The fabric of our small community was thereby strengthened.

Visitors

On January 9 we greatly enjoyed a surprise 4-hour visit to the base by 20 persons from the US ships *Westwind* and *Wyandot*. They arrived at 9:00 p.m., two at a time in two Bell helicopters and by launch via Emperor Bay. The party was led by Captain A. Edwin McDonald, US Navy. In the party were observers from Argentina, Belgium, Chile, and France. The scientists in the group included the ionosphericists Drs Morgan and Dale Reed plus a glaciologist. There were also present some representatives of local newspapers in the USA. Captain McDonald took me for a flight to Emperor Bay and back, my first in a helicopter. They were an enthusiastic and colourful group, dressed in yellow (scientists), blue (navy) and red (airmen) jump suits according to their professions.

They delivered to us 22 ozone sondes in a large net hanging below a helicopter. These sondes had been constructed for our use by Professor Brewer of Oxford University and had missed the *Tottan* when she sailed from London in November. They were designed to be attached to a balloon and used to measure the amount of ozone throughout the atmosphere. At the time they may well have provided the means for the first such observations made in the southern hemisphere.

In our conversations, Captain McDonald told me that during their navigation through sea-ice, a helicopter provided continuous reconnaissance ahead of their ice-breaker, *Westwind*. I found it quite an effort not to make too much of the fact to Captain McDonald that, notwithstanding the impressive efficiency and horsepower of their helicopter/icebreaker combination, the little old *Tottan* still arrived here first, despite being the smallest ice-strengthened ship servicing Antarctic bases during the IGY.

The helicopter I flew in had excellent visibility for the passengers.

It was fitted with floats which enabled it to land on almost any combination of ice, snow or water.

In spite of the formidable power of the US equipage, I gather that in 1960 neither the Americans nor the Argentines were able to relieve their bases at Ellsworth and General Belgrano some 220 miles (354 km) to our south.

On January 18 an American helicopter from *Westwind* returned as promised to pick up our mail, a courtesy we greatly appreciated.

Early in the day on January 25, radio operator Henry Dyer came into my tiny office with a cable in his hand. It originated on the previous day from the Argentine icebreaker, *San Martin* and gave notice that she would be passing Halley Bay soon on the way home and would pick up our mail. I alerted everyone and most of us then penned the last real letter we could get delivered home until January 1959.

Half an hour after midnight on January 26, a Sikorsky helicopter arrived for a three-hour visit with ten persons from *San Martin*. The party was led by Capitan Decorbeta Carlos Mayer, Groupo Naval Antarctico, Argentino. Amongst those present was Dr Otto Schneider, Chief of the Scientific Department of the Instituto Antarctico Argentino. The visitors presented us with a crate of Argentine Champagne; we presented them with a bottle of Bristol sherry. I immediately put the champagne away so we could have it for our Midwinter's Day celebrations and other appropriate occasions throughout the year. The party included two members of the Argentine Army Geographic Department, who made relative gravity measurements at two locations at the base and John Sieburth, from the Virginia Polytechnic Institute, USA, who asked Dr Bert Brooker to obtain some bacteriological samples from Emperor Penguins. I conducted Dr Schneider round our base and found it delightful talking to someone so well-informed about Antarctic research. Whilst at the Argentine base, he had installed an all-sky camera.

On their route to the Antarctic continent, Schneider said they came via the South Orkney and South Sandwich islands, then they passed south through the Weddell Sea at about 15°W latitude.

The Wider World Intrudes

Our welcome visitors and the accompanying mail brought with them many things – good bad and indifferent. Of course, on balance, the relief did us all a power of good. The news of my family was tremendously reassuring, delightful and strengthening. The winning for the third year in succession by *Tottan* of the unofficial blue riband for transit of the Weddell Sea reinforced our confidence that relief in January 1959 was assured.

However, not all the news one receives at these times raises the spirits. In any case it is always an emotionally disturbing time. Indeed, one of my colleagues confided to me that he would have preferred to spend the whole two years away without any mail, with its charge of emotion. Another received unwelcome news about family arrangements made on his behalf, which were premature and gravely disturbing because they were out of step with his changed feelings, a situation not perceived by those 10,000 miles away. Once made, there was little he could do about matters until he arrived home. For those of us who were married and with family responsibilities, the year's end financial summaries were rarely uplifting, as has been noted before as follows:

> *And why does England thus persecute the votaries of her science? Why does she depress them to the level of her hewers of wood and her drawers of water? It is because science flatters no courtier, mingles in no political strife ... Can we behold unmoved the science of England, the vital principle of her arts, struggling for existence, the meek and unarmed victim of political strife.*

Sir David Brewster 1781–1868.

The recent visitors to Halley Bay brought home to me the fact that we were accomplishing a full scientific programme without indulging in enormous expenditures on support services. Our efforts were demonstrably second to none in substance, as I had perceived in Paris when hearing what some of the other major powers in the world were doing in Antarctica.

Some Housekeeping

The great end of life is not Knowledge but Action.
Thomas Henry Huxley 1825–1895.

As soon as *Tottan* left, I set up working parties to complete the organization of our stores. All our radio sondes were unpacked and stored in the loft. For safety, a major fraction of our food and fuel was stored outside, but after unloading, much remained to be done to consolidate and organize the dumps. One year ago we had built Dexion platforms for the food boxes, which were four feet (1.22 m) above the snow surface. By doing so, for many months it was easy to find the required box without digging it out. However, now the whole platform lay covered by up to four feet (1.22 m) of snow, we still had to dig out the boxes. Not only that, but the year of consumption had left gaps in the dump which needed to be consolidated. Accordingly, we systematically dug out and raised all last year's food boxes and put them in neat, carefully marked rows with the cases in numerical order across the prevailing wind. This particular job took eight of us seven hours of solid work to complete the reorganization of the food dump.

When our food dump had been first laid out over a year before, the two-year stock had been an impressive sight. Clearly there was not nearly enough room to keep it all inside the main hut. In the loft of the hut, therefore, Malcolm organized a ready-to-use supply of every sort of food. It looked like a grocery supermarket, with row upon row of tins and packages of all shapes, colours and sizes. There was everything there from dried vegetables to the delicacies needed for birthday parties. Whenever any item began to get a bit low, Malcolm or Len had to go out to the dump to retrieve a new box from anything up to six feet beneath the snow surface. They always took a shovel and ice-axe with them for this job, for fierce cold winds can compact the snow until it is the consistency of sandstone. The time taken to retrieve boxes from this giant freezer was totally out of proportion to the size of the item required.

In the west dump, a special store was set up for 'third year' food and canteen supplies. This was the stock required should a 1959 relief ship find it impossible to relieve the base. Since it was likely to be buried deeply, we made it into a compact dump with the cases piled up to a height of four feet (1.22 m).

Much of the stock of Avtur (aviation turbine fuel) for the generators was stacked alongside the generator shed, where it could be used *in situ* with the aid of a long rubber hose. The local store lasted until November 1958, when work started bringing the remainder to the generator shed from the north stores dump. By that time the bases of the 44-gallon drums were ten feet (3 m) below the snow surface.

All our cooking and much of the heating was done with anthracite stoves. Every now and again we all set to for a coal haul. First we dug down to the coal dump and opened it up. On each occasion about 100–200 bags would be carried one by one into the main hut. You needed a windless day for the job because, for all of the first year, the sacks had to be carried through the southern door of the hut and all the way down the corridor to the coal store at the northern end. As the hut became more and more deeply buried, the job became more arduous. We had to dig out the door and scramble up and down the steep slope outside. Furthermore, our boots made a mess in the corridor as we tramped up and down, to say nothing of the coal dust which inevitably spread round. However, after February 4, we no longer had to carry the coal sacks through the length of the hut. Len had constructed a coal chute from the roof directly into the hut. He used the shells of three oil drums connected end to end to line the chute. The chute led directly from the roof to the northwest entrance adjacent to the coal store.

Additional Ozone Observations

The new equipment brought by John Smith for measuring the amount of ozone in the surface layers of air was eventually set up at the south-east corner of the hut, to be upwind in the prevailing wind. The equipment was fitted with an air pump which continuously drew in air from a height of 180 cm above the surface and measured the amount of ozone in it. As the snow accumulated round the hut, the level of the inlet changed so that at the end of 1958 it lay only 30 cm above the surface. Professor Brewer gave the name electrochemical 'transmogrifier' to the device he invented that actually measured the proportion of ozone in the air by converting this into electrical signals. It was a temperamental beast, requiring frequent attention. Barely a day passed without some small adjustment being necessary.

John had set up the surface ozone measuring equipment whilst sailing south on *Tottan* but it did not work very well. When it arrived at Halley Bay, the electronic amplifier was found to be unserviceable. David Tribble dismantled it and completely re-built the amplifier, reconfiguring it into a more compact and better shielded form, which would be less subject to the effects of electrical interference that plagued us.

The delivery of 22 ozone sondes provided a welcome opportunity to expand our programme of upper air soundings to include ozone measurement up to a height greater than 20 km above the surface. The equipment was just as temperamental as that used for surface ozone. For the first three soundings, the ozone sonde was added below a standard temperature and humidity sonde. With the additional dead weight, an unwelcome and sometime unsatisfactory second operation of the hydrogen generator was required to provide sufficient hydrogen to ensure a satisfactory rate of ascent. We therefore decided to launch special ozone flights at 4:30 p.m., in between the routine flights at 10:00 a.m. and 10:00 p.m. local time.

John Smith and his colleagues were meticulous in their preparations for ozone flights. In particular, great pains were taken to ensure the correct operation of the electrochemical transmogrifier. Because of its poor reputation, no flight was attempted until satisfactory operation was assured from two ozone sondes. When one failed at the last minute, the other was selected for launching. During the year, 16 successful ozone soundings were made.

Several other aspects of the scientific programme were expanded for 1958. In addition, improvements were made to the radio communications set-up. Philip Brenan's observation of the scintillations of a radio star in Centaurus at 60 Mc/s were extended to include observations when the radio star was to the east and the west of Halley Bay. He

also set up a galactic noise observing programme, using a spare meteorological recorder I gave him. Philip already had a huge set of aerials
in three locations to make his observations when the radio star was
to our north and south. At each location he had erected ten large
television-type aerials. To these he added a new set for the east-west
observations.

When I looked in at our small workshop in the main hut on January
15, when a fresh easterly breeze and snow drift made work outside
inconvenient, I noted that it was a 'hive of activity' with preparations
for programme expansions, improvements and maintenance. Alf was
working on the lathe, turning valves, and Philip, Gwynne, and John
Gane, the new wireless mechanic, were beavering away. Philip was
cutting and shaping wood for his new aerials, Gwynne was fabricating
bits and pieces for the new 20-foot (6 m) tall mounting for his all-sky
auroral camera and John Gane was making fitments to improve the
communications aerials and their feeders.

On 23rd John started to dig out the radio communications feeders
which ran alongside the southwest side of the hut. These were a set
of wires which connected our radio transmitter to their aerials. As the
snow subsided round the hut, they were forced lower and lower so
that now they were one and a half feet (46 cm) below the top of the
door and interfered with our access. John continued to dig out these
feeders until by February 10 he had cleared a tunnel along the hut for
20 feet (6 m) and was then able to raise the electrical feeder wires to
above the level of the door. Whilst doing this job, he cut the compacted
and clean snow into neat blocks and placed them by the back door
so the gash man could use them to replenish our water supply. Then
John erected a new 12 Mc/s dipole aerial so that we could both transmit
to and receive from Port Stanley at the same time. Outside work on
the feeders was required throughout the year. Their burial had caused
them to fall into an unsatisfactory state and was suspected of causing
undue interference. Eventually, in the spring, they were completely
dug out, raised and laid along a more direct route to the aerials. When
the feeders were moved away from the wall of the hut, we were able
to use the cavern excavated alongside the hut for additional and very
convenient storage. In addition, I was able to build a 15-foot (4.57 m)
high shaft round the back door, equipped with a hatch entry which
could be used in all weathers without letting snow drift into the hut.

Stumpy Our Dog

By January 14 the husky dog presented to us by Norway Base had
settled down. For some reason we never understood, her full name
was Sister Bjoerlund, which was too long even if we could have learnt
how to pronounce it. The Norwegian expedition presented her to us

Stumpy watches me make a measurement of the total amount of ozone in the 1958 spring atmosphere. I had dug down to a hatch in the roof of the main hut and cleared snow away, so that I could look at the sun via the periscope shown poking through the roof. I am now working inside the hut using a spectroscope to find out how much atmospheric ozone there is in the atmosphere. This is done by observing the quality of the ultra-violet light after it has been partly absorbed by atmospheric ozone.

because her legs were too short to run with the other dogs. Since arrival, she had lived just outside the hatch entry to the main hut, which she showed no inclination to enter. She was a very welcome addition to the base and took a great interest in all we did. She particularly enjoyed watching us launch the meteorological balloons. Ivor immediately took Stumpy under his wing and built her a smart, electrically heated and fibreglass-insulated kennel.

On February 16 Philip and Len started training Stumpy to accompany them on a trip to the Dawson Lambton Glacier they took on March 5 to 16 . It was a man-hauling trip, although Stumpy was also harnessed to the sledge, the idea was to have the dog for company but when they got back they reported that Stumpy certainly pulled her weight to a position 33 miles (53 km) from the base on a bearing of 160°.

Stumpy's favourite food was fresh seal, which we shot for her from time to time. A seal Len shot on February 9 was cooked on 11th and 13th and about 50% of us enjoyed the seal steaks and liver which Malcolm and Len had learnt to prepare so well. On February 23, after supper, Bert, Len, Malcolm and I took a tractor and sledge and we went down to Halley Bay with the gun. Bert shot four Crabeater seals and we all helped with the butchering. Three of them were young and in excellent condition, so Malcolm selected a few prime steaks and the livers for us but most of the meat was destined for Stumpy. The flesh of the older seals was unsuitable for consumption.

Incidentally, Bill and I had already learnt to exercise some care in approaching young, active Crabeater seals. We had gone down to the bay on February 3 and seen one youngster in splendid condition with his silver belly shining and an attractive brown coat on his back. It was quite normal to see them there, lying quietly in the sun, but few were in such good condition as this one. Whilst passing nearby, we would often tickle them with our foot. Up until then they had lain quietly snoozing and seemed to enjoy being tickled. This time, however, when Bill and I approached this particular seal, he immediately reared up vigorously and opened his mouth wide, showing off a beautiful set of sharp teeth, which looked quite as effective as those of a large dog. He immediately made for us in a very threatening way, moving rapidly. I can tell you that we both had to run very fast to get out of his way.

Stumpy was the gift of Norway Base, our nearest neighbours some 800 km to our north and a very welcome addition to our party. I was out collecting snow for our drinking water supply and Stumpy decided to accompany me. The saw I used to cut out the blocks of snow is in Stumpy's shadow, on the left of the picture.

Sea Water Movements

In the mail I received from London was a letter dated 6 November 1957 from H. W. L. Absalom of the Meteorological Office. It included the result of a decision made by the British National Committee for the IGY to add some oceanographic observations to our programme. The proposal was that recordings should be made of sea water tides off Halley Bay, on the grounds of oceanographic interest and also to obtain clues as to any magnetic effect of tides on geomagnetic recordings. To help implement this, before he left UK, John Smith had spent time at the National Institute of Oceanography to become familiar with the equipment.

Suitable equipment for this job had recently been developed by Kelvin and Hughes Ltd., who were kind enough to lend the expedition a prototype model for the voyage of *Tottan*. This allowed us to measure sea currents from the side of the ship when she was moored to the ice edge. Ben Ellis and John Smith made these observations from January 1 to 7. They found that the direction of the current reversed rapidly every six hours due to a semi-diurnal tide. The direction of flow was either to the west or the east, following the general line of the ice-shelf. The flow to the west was greater than to the east by 0.1 kt (0.2 kph) to the west on average, under the influence of the prevailing wind which also blew from east to west. Typically the flow changed from 0.5 kt (1 kph) to the west to 0.4 kt (0.8 kph) to the east over a tidal cycle.

The new current meter had to be returned to the UK on *Tottan* so we were then left with a rather cumbersome Ekman meter. We managed to use it from the side of the ship but it proved unmanageable from the edge of the sea-ice. To use it would have meant the cutting of a large hole through six feet (1.83 m) of hard sea-ice and we did not have the equipment or the time to do that.

Further observations of sea currents were made using the potential gradient method, employing two well-spaced electrodes placed in the sea at the sea-ice edge in Halley Bay. The material for the electrodes had to be selected to avoid the polarizing effect of sea-water, and we had obtained suitable non-polarizing silver – silver chloride electrodes from the UK National Institute of Oceanography in Wormley. As the sea-water flowed between these two electrodes in the earth's magnetic field, electricity was generated, which we recorded. These recordings were then related to the mean flow of water between the electrodes. A similar system is used to measure the flow of water through the Straits of Dover. Although the method did not provide the direction of flow, measurements from the ship showed the flow was either to the west or the east according to the state of the tide, and reversing every six hours.

John Smith and I started to lay a cable to the ice edge in Halley Bay on February 5. John and Derek finished the last half mile (800 m) of the installation on the 7th and connected up the electrodes. The electrodes were spaced 600 ft. (183 m) apart, one above the other. We anchored the lower electrode 20 ft. (6.10 m) above the sea bed and placed the upper one 10 ft. (3.05 m) below the bottom of the sea-ice. We obtained satisfactory observations during the period from February 13 to the 21st, when about 120 ft. (37 m) of ice broke off and we lost the set of electrodes. For this period it was calculated by Deacon that

the mean current was 0.18 kt (9 cm/s) with a tidal oscillation of
0.025 kt. (1 cm/s) (Deacon, 1964, *RSIAE* Vol. 4, pp 348–352).

We replaced the electrodes on February 23. The water was deeper
than 700 ft. (213 m) at the new location of the sea-ice edge and we
did not have sufficient cable to reach the bottom. The lower electrode
was weighted down with 56 lb. (25 kg) but not anchored. The upper
electrode was 580 ft. (177 m) higher and 30 ft. (9 m) below the surface.
On March 15 the ice edge broke back yet again and we lost our last
set of electrodes. The average sea current measured on February 24
was 0.71 kt (36 cm/s) dropping to 0.35 kt (18 cm/s) on March 6 and
0.27 kt (14 cm/s) on 12th.

Some Improvements to our Living Conditions

I never ceased to admire the way individuals on the expedition not
only came up with ideas to improve the conditions for all of us, but
also put in most of the hard work involved in its implementation.
Not only that, but they were also sensitive to the need to discuss ideas
first before they barrelled ahead with them.

One of the best examples of this was the innovation to our toilets.
Although it started to be actively promoted by Len on February 11,
the germ of the idea had been around ever since David Tribble had
installed drains into the firn below the kitchen sink, the bath and the
hydrogen generator. At his request, Len and I sat down with our
medical officer, Bert Brooker, to discuss his ideas for the toilet. The
drainage system for the bathroom had worked so well that Len believed
it could be applied to the latrine. Bert had no objection on health
grounds so I gave the go-ahead for Len to proceed with the considerable
amount of effort required.

Until then our latrines had consisted of two 44-gallon fuel drums
located in an unheated part at the southern end of the hut. Wooden
seats were fitted over these drums, at the top of a set of steps, where
you sat on high as if you were sitting on a two-seated throne. This
cold room was not at all inviting and did nothing to improve the state
of the haemorrhoids which occasionally plagued us during the unloading periods. The only thing attractive about the room was the life-sized
picture of a fetchingly adorned Brigitte Bardot, which decorated the
wall directly in front of the throne.

Every now and again, as they filled up, these drums had to be
hauled out using the tractor winch and taken away to a dump. As
part of their service to our little community, Alf and Ivor volunteered
to do this unpleasant job. As the hut steadily became more and more
buried in the snow, the job became more arduous.

Len started immediately by cutting through the hut foundations,
exposing the snow pack or firn below the hut. He lined the first few

feet of the hole with oil drums from which he had first removed the top and bottom. Then several of us assisted, by lighting up the bath water boiler, preparing gallons and gallons of hot water, and pouring it all down the hole, melting the firn to open up a huge cavern beneath the toilet.

Comfortable seating arrangements were fashioned, red spotted lino was laid, and the walls were painted cream with an attractive mural. Finally a new door was fitted and a small kerosene heater installed which maintained the temperature of the room at 70°F (21°C) even in the middle of the winter and about 50°F (28°C) warmer than a year ago.

Len and Ivor appointed themselves custodians and maintainers of this important facility. From time to time they enhanced the capacity of the deep cavern under the hut by pouring more hot water down the hole and they kept the small heater running as necessary. As the snow rose up over the hut, they extended its ventilating chimney and they kept it clear of frost in the middle of the winter.

A Medical and Dental Surgery in the Loft

One of the first things our new medical officer, Bert Brooker, had to do was to build himself an office. The expedition's two previous medical officers had also been the base leaders, so the tiny office for that post had also acted as the surgery. Bert wasted no time in constructing his office in the loft of the main hut. On January 19 I went up there at his invitation to have a look at a tooth that was troubling him.

His surgery was well organized and much more commodious than the facilities available to Robin the previous year. I remarked on the way he had carefully labelled the stores. His idea was to make it easy to find the little things used most frequently, such as Bandaids for minor cuts and salve for haemorrhoids. He decided that, since he could not be in two places at once, it would be useful to organize an open store so people could help themselves, as far as possible, when he was not available. He could also tell people what to get for themselves at times when he was preoccupied.

Later on, when Bert and I were reorganizing the emergency store, we discussed the need for emergency medical stores. So on February 24 Bert cut shelves in the snow wall of the northeast tunnel to accommodate some emergency stores and also scientific records. The location was over 15 feet (5 m) from the structure of the hut, so that we considered it reasonably safe in the case of a fire. In addition, the supplies were accessible from the outside, via the hatch used at one time for taking hot water to the balloon shed and before Alf constructed a heated water tank in that shed.

After admiring Bert's den, I looked at his tooth. It was hurting badly and he had been told by Robin to see me if he needed dental help. The offending tooth looked perfect to me and I immediately realized this was quite outside the modest experience I had acquired ministering to Robin's dental needs. In his case the teeth I had treated were obviously bad. I could easily see the rotten parts and it was a matter of common sense to clean them out with the drill, which easily cut through the bad bits. Filling up the hole I made was not all that different from putting Polyfiller into a hole in a wall, but a bit more delicate.

I asked Bert if he was sure he had isolated the offending tooth, bearing in mind the complex and sometimes confusing way dental nerves were wired up. He replied that he was quite sure and instructed me to drill away into the side of the tooth to see if it was rotten inside. Drilling into what seemed like a perfectly sound tooth was not at all easy, the enamel was very hard indeed and I made heavy weather of the job. At any rate Bert was satisfied with my effort and he was the doctor after all. I eventually made a small hole which he carefully examined. After further heart searching, he announced his conclusion that the tooth must have an abscess at its root and would have to be extracted. Further assistance was needed so Bert also called on David Tribble, who had his den in the loft nearby. A local anaesthetic was administered and then Bert extracted his Right Upper 4 tooth by himself; once it was removed, the alveolar abscess cleared up.

Altogether Bert had a busy year with his dental work. The number of fillings he had to do in a year increased from 11 in 1957 to 25 in 1958, and he had to perform two extractions.

Electricity

To my surprise, I found that already by February 19 we were using up our stock of electric light bulbs too rapidly, particularly in the popular 60- and 100-watt sizes. I was surprised because we had a serious shortage in 1957 and had ordered what we had thought to be a generous supply, which was only delivered in January. As the hut became more buried under snow drift, it seemed as though our appetite for electrical illumination knew no bounds. Clearly the issue of bulbs needed to be rationed again to spread the supply over the year. I instituted a weekly ration in March, which would ensure that in 1959, whether we were relieved or not, we would still have the equivalent of two months' supply at the current rate. Bearing in mind the curtailed activity of such unwelcome circumstances, I judged that to be just adequate.

I had already noticed on January 28 that the consumption of electricity had leapt up since the delivery of the new stock of light bulbs. As a consequence, the Enfield generator had been running for eight to ten hours a day to supplement the power from the big Meadows generator. I sat down to discuss the subject of our consumption of electrical power on February 6 with Bill, the largest consumer, and Alf, the producer. At the peak period of Bill's scientific observations, the ionospheric equipment consumed about one third of the output of one Meadows generator.

At one of our regular gatherings, I urged everyone to be as economical as possible in their use of electricity and I told them about the light bulb situation. The response to this appeal was excellent and no further actions were required to eke out our resources, apart from the rationing of the light bulbs. Each Saturday I put out about 7 bulbs, ranging in power from 100 to 25 Watts, and usually the weekly ration was consumed by the following Thursday or Friday.

The BBC

We were very grateful for the BBC programme called 'Calling Antarctica', which commenced on Tuesday April 15 and went on through the winter. On each Tuesday evening Ines Brown organized a programme specially for Halley Bay and the FIDS bases scattered up along the Antarctic peninsula in Graham Land. In most broadcasts she arranged for family members to record their messages to us. She arranged these for up to three persons on the same evening. During the year Ines tried to bring messages to well over half of our members. This effort and her letter of thanks were much appreciated.

Surviving on less than 100 words per month from our loved ones, we were grateful for this significant addition to their news, even though over half the broadcasts could not be heard because of the normal difficulties of Antarctic radio communications. Oonagh and Simon spoke on the programme sent out on August 19, shortly after my 32nd birthday. Since Simon was only a few months old when I left home, this was the first time I had heard his voice, piping up clearly over the 10,000 miles which separated us. (It was not to be the last time I heard him speak up clearly on radio and TV news broadcasts from faraway places, when, over thirty years later, he served on various peacekeeping missions for the Canadian Army.)

Donald Milner of the BBC was often in touch with us, phoning several times or sending cables requesting I arrange reports and interviews with members. I believe some of the results of our efforts were broadcast in the BBC 'Intrepid' series, featuring 'Men of Antarctica'. He telephoned me on January 19 to ask if we had any news of Fuchs reaching the South Pole, but we only knew what we had heard on Ship Press, which originated from Rugby in England. Although it had never been formalized in any way, Donald seemed to believe that I was the BBC's unpaid Antarctic correspondent. Perhaps it was in return for the good work Ines did for us.

Snowfall

One of the more tricky measurements, and quite timeconsuming, was that of snowfall. It is deceptively easy until you start doing it and travel round the ice shelf studying the results. The problem lies in that it is so easily interfered with and varies from place to place. The slightest change in the elevation or slope of the surface affects it greatly, as does the slightest nearby obstruction. Living on a huge iceberg created by snow accumulation, the importance of getting these measurements right was self-evident.

As soon as the base was built in 1956, a network of nine snow accumulation stakes was laid out by David Limbert for measuring at monthly intervals. On the voyage to Halley Bay, I had discussed the subject with Hal Lister, who had had practical experience in Greenland. Hal liked the pattern of nine set up by David. When we enlarged the base in 1957, the consequent drift effects led me to set up a new pattern of nine stakes to the same design but further away from the base, and also measured at monthly intervals. However, as time went by, we wondered whether or not that pattern was too localized, particularly if we were to undertake the observations every day, as we were considering.

During his sledging journeys round about the ice-shelf, Jim Burton had made a number of important contributions to our glaciological knowledge of the local environment. As a result of his keen observations, backed up by painstaking aneroid barometer measurements made whilst travelling, he was arguably the first person to observe the long wave, undulating nature of the surface of the ice-shelf. This all led up to us designing a new set of accumulation stakes for measuring every day, whilst we continued to measure every month the two historic sets of nine stakes.

Jim laid out the new set of six stakes in a wide arc well away from the buildings on February 2 and 3. The series started from the southern pattern of nine and ended at the declination fixed mark to the north of the non-magnetic hut. Each stake was marked with a distinctive piece of canvas. The route from one stake to the next was marked by a separate series of stakes which were joined together by cord so that the observer could navigate round the network in all weathers without getting lost in the swirling drift of the storms which beset us every few days for nine months of the year. The guidance cords were not attached to the accumulation stakes themselves, so as to avoid any possible interference with the observations by passing traffic, for example.

Jim went round this 1200 yd (1097 m) route in the second gale of the season on March 18 and 19th, when the wind was blowing at about 50 kt (93 kph), a full Force 10 gale. He left the hut at 1:45 p.m. and returned at 3:20 p.m. His observations showed that in the two-day gale, 1.1 cm of snow fell on the 18th and 2.9 cm on 19th, whereas a storm from March 13th to 15th had deposited 10.7 cm of snow. With these two gales we were reminded that the brief summer respite from stormy conditions was probably over for the next eight or nine months.

The result of Jim's initiative allowed us to construct a daily glaciological record in Volume 4 of our scientific publication, which ran to eight large pages of small print packed with information. (Ref: MacDowall *RSIAE* Vol. 4 pp. 269–313. MacDowall, Barclay & Burton *RSIAE* Vol. 4, pp 314–325)

Digging Out of Autumn Storms

The two big storms in March were a challenge. They tested our preparations and reminded us to review arrangements for the winter. Although the total amount of precipitation had resulted in a modest 14.7 cm of snow accumulation or 49 mm of water equivalent, the effect of snow drifting for over six days magnified its impact enormously. Even when it was not snowing on 14th, the wind picked up quantities of snow from the surface, so that heavy drift continued unabated between the days of snowfall. In addition, boxes had been blown off platforms and had to be extracted from where they fell, sometimes from under feet of drifted snow.

On March 22, when Andrew discovered the wind had blown some of the meteorological stores off the top of the dump, he spent much of the afternoon digging them out and replacing them where they were secure. Before the storm, at the northern end of the generator shed, Ivor had constructed a porch to shelter the double doors. Unfortunately, it collapsed in the storm because there had not been enough wood to make it strong enough to withstand the weight of snow drift deposited.

Now that we could not easily bring our skis into the hut via the hatch entrances, we had taken to parking them and their poles out of the freeway on the downwind side of the hut. Unfortunately the first gale had blown them down into the trench, where drift was accumulating rapidly. On March 16 I dug all the skis out and stacked them more firmly on the top of the drift where they would not get buried so rapidly.

In the gale on March 14, there was a 42 kt (78 kph) wind and a visibility of 20 yd (18 m) at the time of the afternoon balloon ascent. For the first time, we employed, with great success, one of the smaller 500 g balloons that had been provided for just these occasions, as a replacement for the 1250 g balloons normally used. By the next morning, the 4m high door of the balloon shed was buried under deep, wind-packed snow. Andrew and I went down and dug the door out and then Ben and Jim launched the balloon in a 44 kt (81 kph) wind, the most severe conditions yet experienced for balloon launching.

As I walked back from the balloon shed, I noticed that the ionospheric drift aerials were waving around in a dangerous manner. Les Barclay later went out into the teeth of the gale and moved the guy ropes to take the strain of the wind better and reduce the wild gyrations of his equipment.

The radio sonde ascents conducted on March 18 and 19th were all done successfully into the teeth of gales. At the evening ascent on the 18th, drift snow had penetrated the side door, blocking it. The only way David Tribble could get into the hut was to climb on the roof and enter via the heavy roof hatch. Then Alf, Ivor, John Smith, and I set to digging out the garage-type door from under metres of packed drift snow. The whole process of digging out the big door was repeated by a fresh team of willing helpers for the morning and evening ascents on the 19th.

The way expedition members materialized voluntarily to assist with arduous jobs, like digging out up to 12 feet (3.66 m) of snow from in front of the garage-type door of the balloon shed, was one of the most rewarding parts of life at Halley Bay. It was inspired by the idealism engendered by the IGY and the challenge of achievement despite bad weather. I do not believe there was ever an occasion when anyone had actively to recruit these volunteers. All members took an ongoing active interest in the scientific work of the base and became very sensitive to its needs. They were aware, for example, that on March 17 a World Meteorological Interval started and that it became very important not to fail in launching both balloons during the second March storm. As a consequence, in 1958 the number of failures in balloon launching was almost negligible despite an increase in the number of severe weather conditions. For example, two full soundings were successfully accomplished in easterly winds of 47 kt (87 kph) during 1958. (Ref: MacDowall & Burton *Upper Air Meteorology RSIAE* Vol. 3 pp. 161–382).

When the gale subsided on March 20, conditions were pleasant for the next few days and most of us went outside to clear up and maintain our equipment. Bert and I went out to maintain the guide ropes and posts. These provided the only safe way to go from one building to the next during winter darkness or storm conditions, when visibility can be reduced to a few yards and the impact of gale winds was challenging. Andrew cleaned up the mess caused by drift inside the balloon shed. Philip and Alf tried hard to implement their idea to use the tractor's digger to construct a tunnel between the main hut and the radio echo hut, where Philip and David Harrison worked. Although they tried very hard all day, the equipment was not up to the job and they had to abandon the attempt.

The scientific equipment in the radio echo hut ran continually and had to be visited regularly throughout the 24 hours to change charts etc. The radio operator, Henry Dyer, volunteered to assist with this job when he was on night duty. Philip was planning to go on one of his sledging trips and he needed someone to change his charts whilst he was away. A tunnel connecting the two huts would have been a great convenience.

Digging in for the Winter

As time went by, our living conditions became more and more adapted to the environment. When it was first constructed, the hut lay above the surface, of course, with outer doors on each side which opened into a lobby equipped with a second door. During the nine windy months of the year, as soon as the wind got up, snow was driven through the tiny cracks that were unavoidable. Once some snow got through the door, it would not close properly and more snow came in, until you had a major problem on your hands to clear every scrap of snow away. That was well-nigh impossible during a storm. The special doors provided for the non-magnetic hut were effective, but only because they were not used more than twice a day. They weighed well over a hundred kilograms each and were a foot (30 cm) thick and fitted with a stepped jamb lined with felt. The doors would not close if small quantities of snow did penetrate the jamb, and that always happened when there was a strong wind. Then after entry during a storm, you always had to clean out the door jamb meticulously and close it very quickly if you wanted it to seal again. We kept a dedicated hand brush just inside the porch for that very job. Before you left the hut, you got down on your hands and knees, with your face in the swirling snow drift, and you carefully cleaned every scrap out of the hinges and the door jamb to ensure it closed soundly. If you left the tiniest crack in the seal, the next time you got to the hut you could easily find the whole porch packed with snow. You only made that mistake once.

Although we all tried out various ideas, we found there was nothing much we could do to improve the performance of the doors of the main hut until they became completely buried. Fortunately we discovered that the small roof hatch, originally designed for auroral observations, could also be left open and used for regular entry. Snow drift did not enter through this hatch, providing it was kept a few feet above the top of the roof. From then on, the side doors were only used for the transport of stores or waste. The door facing the prevailing easterly wind was sealed up and rapidly engulfed by snow. The northern door, too, was very soon drifted up, and left that way. As soon as possible, and before the end of 1956, a cavern was excavated from that door leading into a large food store excavated in the large drift which extended away from the door. Later in the year, this cavern was extended by Ivor to link up with the generator shed. To protect the food from the possibility of exposure to diesel fumes, Malcolm installed an extra door between the food store and the generator shed. The western entrance was downwind of the prevailing wind and remained in use for two years, though it often had to be dug out, until I covered it with a porch with a hatch entrance above.

With guidelines strung between our huts, we were reasonably safe navigating between the huts at the base. But as often as he could, Henry Dyer went down to Halley Bay to do an ice reconnaissance for John Heap's researches on the subject. To assist in navigation to the bay, on March 7 Henry adapted a spare cloud searchlight for use as a guidance beacon, which he erected on one of the towers no longer required for meteorological purposes.

Henry's report on the subject (Ref; *RSIAE* 1964, Vol. 4 pp. 339–347) shows how the sea started to freeze up in February although it was generally clear of sea-ice until the end of March. By the end of April the sea was covered with ice and it usually stayed that way until September or October. Because of the prevalence of shore leads in the area, the change over from a sea open to the horizon to one closed by ice was sudden, particularly at the beginning and end of summer. Several of us used to go and help Henry and others drilling through the sea-ice to see how it developed through the year. The fast ice in the bay started to freeze at the beginning of March and grew to be 10 in. (25 cm) thick in about two weeks. By mid-November it was fully grown and about 100 in. (2.54 m) thick.

Easter and the Change of Seasons

It was in March when I noted a change in our daily round of activity appropriate to the autumnal season. For some time, various members had been preparing for short man-hauling trips or long walks. Len set up and tried out the very lightweight tent he had bought to replace the rather heavy ones provided. Travelling conditions had improved as a result of the March storms packing down the soft summer layers, and temperatures had not fallen to the level at which sledge friction increased markedly. We spent less time out of doors and the indomitable editors of the *Halley Comet* had already, by March 15, canvassed us for contributions to their 4th or Easter 1958 issue, which was published on Easter Saturday, April 5. I had just finished an article on the subject of optical phenomena, which were so frequently brightening up the skyscapes.

By observing the sun and stars, Joe MacDowall monitors the steady seaward movement of the floating Brunt ice-shelf. In the background is part of one of three arial arrays used by the expedition to observe a radio star.

I was spending more time on night work now that I was able to use the stars to measure the slow movement of the huge iceberg we sat on, to determine the orientation of the ice-shelf and its position as it slowly and inexorably moved out to sea. At night, I was also able to use the light of the moon to make ozone measurements. Gwynne had already commenced auroral observations and I had just witnessed my first auroral corona of the winter. Soon the Emperor Penguins would be back to breed in Emperor Bay.

It was absolutely essential to keep track of the movement of the ice-shelf to ensure the accuracy of the geomagnetic observations. Altogether I used a theodolite outside to observe the stars or sun on 52 occasions over a period of 18 months. By these astronomical observations I found the ice-shelf moved towards the west by several hundred metres per year whilst rotating by one third of a degree. To do the job it was essential to make a note of the precise time of observation in Universal Time (UT).

When I first made these astronomical observations, I took out the ship's 'half-chronometer' but soon discovered this exposure caused its rate to vary, as a result of the change in temperature. Eventually I found the most accurate method of time keeping was provided by the Rolex Oyster wrist watch each member of the expedition had been presented with by the Rolex company. Nestling snugly on my wrist, the rate of the watch did not vary and provided the most precise observations of Universal Time (UT). From then on we kept the ships's chronometer in the meteorological office and compared it with the radio time signals from Australia. A daily log of the results of this comparison was kept so that we knew precisely how this instrument compared with Universal Time and how much it was gaining or losing on the daily radio signals. Then, before and after my observations, I compared my watch with the ship's chronometer.

For this year, I had improved my observing techniques over 1957 and developed a more convenient set-up for winter astronomical observations. Now I set the Tavistock theodolite directly over the 'fixed' mark which was located 190 metres to the north of the non-magnetic hut. The mark was provided with electrical power, so I used this to supply power for a set of electrically heated clothing. The temperature was about −25°C with a 7 kt (13 kph) wind when I did the job on April 2. Despite the special clothing I wore, it was always a cold job which sometimes left me with superficial frostbite on the cheeks or nose and my hands were always cold because I had to remove the warm gloves several times during the observation. After the job was completed, on this particular Wednesday night, I went back into the warm kitchen and baked 10 lb. (4.5 kg) of bread, which certainly took the chill out of my bones.

General interest in bread baking had commenced a year before and, as soon as my duties allowed, I joined the team of five or six others for 1958. At the time of unloading, each one of us consumed as much as a pound (454 g) of bread a day but consumption dropped off when we did less heavy work. It was fortunate so many of us took interest in bread making, because to meet that demand would have been a very heavy load for Malcolm and Len to handle alone.

In addition to the pleasure one got from a creative activity, the baking of bread after supper also became something of a social activity. People were attracted by the delicious smell of baking plus the anticipation of sampling the first loaves as they came hot from the oven. The first few piping hot loaves were always snatched up eagerly, sliced up rapidly and complemented deliciously with melting butter.

Travelling Around

On March 3, Bill and Jim undertook a 38-mile (61 km), day trip to the ice-front south of the base. At the most southerly point, where the ice cliff was 30 ft. (9 m) high, they had a good view of the Dawson Lambton Glacier meeting the sea. During the trip, Jim took the opportunity to measure the snow accumulation round four accumulation stakes he had previously planted. Jim planted these accumulation stakes over an area of 60 by 40 km on the Brunt Ice Shelf.

Based on at least ten months' of observations, Jim deduced that, over this large area of the Brunt Ice-shelf, the mean value of annual snow accumulation was 99 cm, which may be compared with the value of 98 cm observed near the base for both 1957 and 1958 (Ref. MacDowall, Barclay & Burton 1964 *Glaciology 2, RSIAE* Vol. 4, pp. 314–325).

Philip and Len had been training Stumpy for a sledging trip since February 16, when they had her harnessed to a sled for a trip to Emperor Bay. Then from March 5 to 16, Philip and Len with Stumpy took the longest trip to date reaching a point 33 miles (53 km) away on a bearing of 160°. This trip was the closest approach we made to the Caird Coast, where they found a badly disturbed area which prevented further progress. The area was extensively crevassed and contained an 80 ft. (24 m) hill. It was probably just as well they turned back when they did because, by doing so, they returned to base just one day ahead of a gale. The following day Philip showed us all the coloured slides he had taken on the trip. The ice features there looked very impressive and you could easily understand why they could go no further to the Caird Coast from this direction. (Ref Barclay 1964 *RSIAE* Vol. 4 pp. 329–338).

They actually first departed the base on March 3, pulling a 6-ft. (1.83 m) sledge with Tufnol runners, whose drag over snow increases rapidly at low temperatures. They found this sledge required an excessive effort to keep it in motion and was so hard to pull through the snow, that they only travelled 4 miles (6.4 km) on the first day. So they left that sledge behind and returned to base with the dog pulling a small ski sledge with a 20 lb. (9 kg) load. Then they returned with a tractor to recover the sledge.

Before starting off again, they did some trials of various runners which resulted in stripping off the Tufnol runners and lacquering the exposed wooden surface. They set out again, this time with the 11-ft. (3 m) long sledge Bill had made and equipped with lacquered wooden runners. Before departure, Bill helped Philip to strip off the compass frame fitted to the rear of his sledge and intended for a larger travelling party, when one man pushed from the rear with the compass mounted in front of him.

The *Halley Comet* Heralds Easter

The Easter issue of the *Halley Comet* was 12 pages long, the largest to date and one with a most attractive cover. The individually hand-painted cover was produced by David Tribble and the contents were edited and typed by Jim Burton and David Cansfield. The attractive cover was most evocative of the time and place. It showed Stumpy looking at a crimson, setting sun under a brilliantly coloured sky, so typical of the season. I was greatly affected by the cover when looking at it again after an interval of 40 years. It triggered off the emotions I felt at the time as I was catapulted by its artistic impact back over the years and miles. The contents included poems by Malcolm Edwards and Bert Brooker, an article by Ben Ellis on Deception Island, and the one I wrote on optical phenomena. In the editorial we gave our congratulations to Bunny Fuchs for his knighthood and for the honours awarded to the advance party members David Dalgleish and George Lush.

The article by Ben Ellis in the *Halley Comet* was based on the year he had spent at the Deception Island, a FIDS base located on a 12-mile (19 km) wide, volcanic island in the South Sandwich group at 63°S 60°W. At Port Foster and Whalers Bay the island had the finest natural harbour in the world, which one entered through a gap in the rocky skirt of the island called Neptune's Bellows. The coastal waters of the tiny island were sometimes heated up to 140°F (60°C) by volcanic action. The island was also the home to innumerable birds. The tall rock formation called the Cathedral, guarding the entrance to the harbour, provided the nesting sites for Cape Pigeons and Blue-eyed Shags, and the nearby Chinstrap Penguin rookery contained half a million birds.

The six men at Deception Island seemed to be an enterprising lot. They had to kill seals and penguins to feed their ten huskies at the base, plus an assorted collection of dogs and cats. For their own table, they kept three ducks and a pig to supplement the diet of tinned goods and they also dined on many of the other local livestock. Ben clearly enjoyed his time there and I appreciated the effort he made with his article to share something of it with us.

Our celebrations of Easter commenced with a short service held at 11:15 a.m. In the afternoon this was followed by a playing of the Messiah organized by Les. At dinner time, Malcolm and Len baked a special Easter cake. Table conversation amongst us was animated and enjoyable. They also produced cheese straws and popcorn for the Easter Saturday film show. Instead of the usual cold cuts, on the next day, Malcolm and Len gave us roast pork for lunch and a special pie followed by a huge iced cake.

Emperor Penguins Return and the Sun Starts to Set

On April 6 Andrew went to Emperor Bay and took ciné shots of hundreds of returning birds. I was down there myself on March 30 and walked on the recently-formed sea-ice that was already 10 to 14 inches (25 to 36 cm) thick. At first sight the bay seemed deserted. But I could hear penguins so I walked out towards the the sea and saw just 15 of them, the first of the returning birds.

On the afternoon of Easter Monday April 7, we showed the movie 'Three Little Words', and in the evening Bert gave us a talk on mountaineering. We had held successful scientific discussions before but this was the first one held on a subject of general interest. The idea was first mooted by Les on March 18 and it worked out very well indeed. Len and Malcolm supported it in style with a variety of cakes. The talk was attended by most of us and led to a pleasant evening of discussion and conversation.

April is the 'sunset month' at Halley Bay, or the month in which the sun sets for about 100 days. After Easter the weather conditions of April were quite good until the last few days. On the 9th, many people took the opportunity to walk down to Emperor Bay and welcome back the 600 penguins they found there.

Back at the base, David Harrison was busy replacing the gear box on his rotating aerial and Alf was driving the tractor, moving solid gash which he had cleared out of the hut to the dump.

The number of penguins at the bay had increased to 2000 on the following day. Most people walked down to the bay because the snow surface had taken on its hard winter characteristics and was carved into deep sastrugi, which interfered with the skis, causing you to slip sideways and to trip. As a consequence of these poor ski conditions and the hard surface, Malcolm tripped over and bruised himself on the hardened and compacted snow surface, that had the consistency of sandstone.

I stayed up at the base on April 10 and fitted hinges to the trap entry at the top of the shaft over the south-western door. In the evening I had a game of chess with Henry. The pack ice was heavy and included many small icebergs embedded in it. When Jim tried to walk from Emperor to Halley Bay, he was prevented by a shore lead under Penguin Leap.

The sun was still above the horizon for seven hours on April 11 and we were making the most of it. David Harrison worked away on the aerial and Philip was calibrating the galactic noise line and receiver by feeding a known signal into it. A new antenna had sprouted from the roof of the radio echo hut. It was used to receive TV sound-only signals from British TV some 10,000 miles (16,093 km) away. No one would expect to receive such signals and so the fact that we could was of some scientific interest. The loudspeaker was in the ionospheric room and Les was keeping a log of the times of reception. A characteristic of these signals was their high intelligibility. On April 21 I received a priority signal from the Royal Society on the subject so they could issue a press release.

There was a gentle breeze on Saturday April 12 and several people were active out of doors. David Harrison still toiled away with his rotating aerial whilst David Tribble and John Smith finished off the work they had done to construct a device to sound the depth of water at Halley Bay. They had built a 12-ft. (3.6 m) long sledge from Dexion on which they mounted a drum for the sounding cable, which then led over a pulley fitted over a projecting prow or bowsprit. The idea was to take this down to the ice edge with the prow poking over the open water, and then lower away the weighted cable until it touched the bottom. They found bottom at 630 ft. (253 m).

Adapting to Colder Conditions

Later in the day on April 12, I went up into David Tribble's den and looked at the thermopile psychrometer he constructed to improve the measurement of relative humidity. In temperate climates, the measurement of relative humidity is easily done by measuring both the air temperature with a thermometer, called the dry bulb, and also the temperature taken up by a thermometer covered with a dampened muslin cover and called the wet bulb or ice bulb in our case. The dry bulb measures the air temperature and the ice bulb is cooler, depending on the relative humidity. The drier the air, the more the ice bulb temperature is depressed below the air temperature. When the air is saturated with water vapour, the two take up the same temperature. However, the depression of the ice bulb at Antarctic winter temperatures below about −15°C is so small it is very difficult to measure humidity with any accuracy. That is why we were searching for better methods.

We had been provided with a number of alternative methods to measure humidity by the British Meteorological Office. A hair hygrograph worked fine down to −10°C. An automatic frost point hygrometer proved to be unreliable and too subjective for consistent results. We also used a device adapted by the US Blue Hill Observatory and called a Dewcel. This was affected by wind, radiation and hoar frost so that it required the use of complicated calibration charts. An aspirated Assmann psychrometer proved the most reliable down to −15°C. The range of operation of the latter method was extended by David Tribble by using a 40-junction iron-constantan thermopile to increase the accuracy of measuring the ice bulb depression. The device was aspirated and provided with shields to protect it from solar radiation reflected from the snow surface.

An Antarctic Winter Diary

SUNDAY APRIL 13. At 4 a.m., local time, the temperature was −22°C. There was a fresh breeze with some snow and drift when I went out to have a look at the three ventilators which stuck up from the roof of the hut, exhausting stale air. They were almost fully blocked with ice so I found an ice chisel and cleared a basinful of ice from each one of the pipes. We had noticed no marked deterioration in the quality of air and ascribed this to the fact that there were now several tunnels alongside the hut, and elsewhere an air gap had been melted between the hut and the packed snow. However, we took no chances over this and continued to clear the pipes when needed.

APRIL 14. At 4 a.m. the air temperature was −18°C. The moderate breeze continued today. Bill and Henry were both working outside. Henry was repairing the searchlight he had fitted to guide him in his walks to the headland to observe sea ice and Bill was erecting an additional aerial to monitor a broadcasting station. Bert was down with the penguins again and when he came back he told me that he had seen a Snow Petrel flying along the cliffs at Penguin Leap.

APRIL 15. At 4 a.m. the air temperature was −32°C. It was a fine day with a moderate breeze blowing.

We composed a birthday greeting message from members of the expedition to Her Majesty the Queen and then beamed it to London via the Royal Society.

To date the Meadows No. 1 generator has run for 7740 hours and No. 2 has operated for 2363 hours. The Enfield generator is now always run during working hours and supplies the darkroom heater and tanks, the surgery heater, a heater in the ionospheric laboratory, and the heater in Malcolm's and David Tribble's part of the loft. Each one of these heaters consumes 1000 watts.

APRIL 16. At 4 a.m. the air temperature was −29°C. There were six people working outside when I went to clear out some empty boxes so that Alf could add them to the pile he had on a sledge behind the tractor to haul off to the dump. Then I opened some new boxes of canteen stores.

Bill continued his work erecting an aerial and David Tribble was taking photographs of sastrugi which had been carved by the recent winds.

Later on in the day, Ivor asked if he could have the temporary use of bridging timbers to roof over the double door entrance to the generator shed. Alf and I were not convinced the work was required because it would take less than a day for one man to dig out the double doors at the end of the winter when we required their use again. In addition, we never knew when we would need the bridging during unloading next summer and it could be tempting fate to embody them in a structure.

During the course of our discussion, Alf said that he had started to devote some of his free time to the punching of meteorological data on Holerith cards. This was very good news and welcome assistance to the meteorological group, who always had more than enough on their hands. Ivor too had a project. He was devoting time to driving a tunnel from the main hut to the generator shed via the food store at the northeast door.

APRIL 17. At 4 a.m. the air temperature was −34°C. It was another fine day with a gentle or moderate breeze.

The first sonde launched today failed. The second one launched was a great success in that it went up to a record height of nearly 28 km, where the air pressure was 12 mb, so the balloon had risen through over seven-eighths of the atmosphere.

When I went over to the non-magnetic hut to make some observations, I noticed that the floor of the absolute room was being pushed up by the piles. We had had the same problem the previous year in the recording room but fixed it. We will probably have to do the same in the absolute rooms.

APRIL 18. At 4 a.m. the air temperature was −32°C. The weather was partly cloudy with a moderate breeze.

David Harrison was outside again today, servicing his rotating aerial. Bill was out there too working on his aerials. I noticed that four of the communications aerials had cracks in the base. The most northerly one had a crack one and a half inches (4 cm) wide.

Then I went up on the roof and found the ventilating pipes were nearly fully blocked again so I cleaned them out, only five days after the previous cleaning.

I then went over to the non-magnetic hut and I removed the stuffing box from round the piers of the magnetic vertical force room.

Alf informed me that the over-loading of the two electrical generators was now occurring regularly.

Fire Breaks Out – We Overload our Electrical Generators

APRIL 19. At 4 a.m. the air temperature was –25°C. The day was partly cloudy with fog and 150-yard (137 m) visibility in the afternoon; there was very little wind.

In the morning I removed the stuffing boxes in the absolute horizontal force room of the non-magnetic hut.

At 10:30 a.m. that morning, a tin of fat caught fire which had been accidentally left in the oven. It was very rapidly and efficiently extinguished with an asbestos blanket normally kept nearby for just that purpose.

After lunch John Smith and I took the Ekman current meter to Halley Bay. We cut through four inches (10 cm) of sea-ice at a recently refrozen crack and lowered the instrument down to a depth of 15 ft. (4.6 m) The sea current there was negligible. A second sounding was attempted but the instrument froze up too quickly and we could not get it defrosted.

At supper I made an announcement about the regular overloading of the electrical generators and how I believed this could be avoided if people thought before switching on the electricity. I told them that overloading had occurred on one or more phases for every day of the week, for the first time. This was a serious situation and could become more so before the end of the winter. Already Philip was asking for an additional 500 watts to combat a serious temperature sensitivity in his galactic noise equipment. Alf felt confident he would be able to provide this for Philip somehow.

SUNDAY APRIL 20. At 4 a.m. the air temperature was –24°C. It was a cloudy day with a light or gentle breeze blowing.

We held our usual Sunday service at 11.15 a.m. and then I spent the rest of the day organizing the scientific discussion evening we planned for Monday.

Malcolm and Len were particularly busy today preparing the Queen's Birthday Dinner laid on for tomorrow.

APRIL 21. At 4 a.m. the air temperature was –23°C. It was a fine day for working outside and Alf took the opportunity to start up a tractor and clear away the solid gash that piled up so quickly inside the hut. At the north side of the generator shed Ivor persisted in his valiant efforts to put a verandah over the double doors. Philip was out at the his remote aerials, fitting a thermostatic control system to the remote hut housing his galactic noise receiver.

At 5:30 p.m. we sat down for the Queen's Birthday Dinner of chicken washed down with Argentine Champagne, and then we toasted her health with a glass of port.

A scientific discussion commenced at 7:30 p.m. and included talks on their work by Philip, Dave Tribble, Bill, David Harrison, Gwynne and Andrew. It was clear from the animated discussions which followed that the occasion was a success.

Emperor Penguins Pair Off

APRIL 22. At 4 a.m. the air temperature was −34°C. It was another fine day for several of us to go down to Emperor Bay, where the number of penguins had risen to between ten and twelve thousand. Bert told me that he reckoned the birds were now in the process of pairing off.

David still toiled away outside in his efforts to make his big rotating radar antenna rotate more rapidly. Apparently it worked quite well at the regular speed but he also wanted the ability to run it at high speeds. This is proving to be a much more difficult task than anticipated due to the inertia of its large mass.

Inside the hut, making use of the long corridor through its centre, John Gane was busy making a new set of communications feeders.

During one of his schedules, Henry brought me a cable confirming that the loyal birthday greetings we had sent off to the Queen on April 15 had been delivered on her birthday.

We also received a signal from Bugaev, the Chief Meteorologist at the Soviet base at Mirny, thanking us for sending him a copy of this year's climatological summaries. He also requested some additional meteorological data, which I prepared for him and sent off.

I sent off a cable today to the Royal Society letting them know that BBC London television sound was being received daily from 13:00 to 18:00 GMT on 41.5 Mc/s. Occasionally, we also received the video signals on 45 Mc/s.

APRIL 23. At 4 a.m. the air temperature was −27°C. It was a mainly fine day with a moderate breeze in the early morning and a light breeze for the rest of the day.

We finally found out why John Smith had not been receiving any mail via Port Stanley. His family had been sending their air letters to the post master there, who was expected to open them and read them to us over the radio. Unfortunately the formal notification of John's inclusion in our party had never been received so the mail had been left sitting unopened in Port Stanley. I took the opportunity to make sure the list in Port Stanley of our expedition members was now complete.

At 3:35 p.m. as the sun was setting, there was a red loom of the sun as it sat there on the horizon. It took on an almost rectangular shape due to anomalous refraction through the lowest layers of the atmosphere.

APRIL 24. At 4 a.m. the air temperature was −23°C. The weather was cloudy with a light or gentle breeze.

Alf and Malcolm were busy today digging out a number of food boxes from the food store we used just outside the buried north-east door of the hut.

Ivor too was digging away to enlarge the entrance to the double door of the generator shed, so it could be used as a shelter for the tractor.

Henry received a signal from the IGY Weather Central located at the USA base, Little America, telling us that they had never received our weather data, which should reach them via Port Stanley in their FICOL broadcasts. Henry said the reason was that Little America did not have the correct time for FICOL broadcasts and he had advised them accordingly.

Stimulated by the recent discussion, I looked over the last two years' records to consider a reasonable division of the year amongst the seasons. It seemed to me that the summer season extended for the four months November, December, January and February. Autumn would be March and April and winter certainly extended for the five months May to September, possibly longer. For spring I felt that only the month of October qualified for this transition month. This division of the year would certainly correspond to the view of the *Meteorological Glossary*, which was that 'spring and autumn tend to disappear in polar regions.'

APRIL 25. There was a moderate breeze and a temperature of about −25°C when I went outside in the afternoon to make the first of a series of observations on the change in wind speed over the lowest two metres of the atmosphere, or wind profiles. Altogether I made eleven of these observations over the period April 25 to May 15. I used four sensitive cup anemometers mounted at 25, 50 100, and 200 cm over the snow surface. To obviate differences between the anemometers, each instrument was exposed for 10 minutes at each of the four levels.

At the generator shed, Ivor was finishing off the work he had done at the north end of the generator shed to construct a verandah above the double doors for parking a tractor.

APRIL 26. At 4 a.m. the air temperature was −31°C. There was a gentle breeze blowing all day. Slight snow fell in the morning and the rest of the day was cloudy.

During the day Alf was out with a tractor clearing up solid gash.

The Saturday evening get-together and film show was particularly jolly, as befitted a celebration of St George's Day. As a special treat for us all, Ivor made ice lollies from orange juice but he presented a very special 15 lb (7 kg) monster one to Jim, which was moulded in a fire bucket.

A Particularly Cold Day

APRIL 27–28. On Sunday the weather was fine at first but by 9 p.m. there was some snow drift and the temperature had fallen to –46°C, particularly low for the time of year. On Monday there was a fresh gale. In the early hours of the morning, at 4:00 a.m., there was a 19 kt (35 kph) wind with an air temperature of –44.5°C, producing a wind chill factor of 2460, not too far off the coldest conditions we had experienced on 29 July 1957 of 30 kt (56 kph) and –45.0°C (wind chill factor of 2670).

The cold wind blew down the shaft we had built to replenish the bathroom water tank, freezing up the plumbing system and the washing machine. I was the gash man at the time and discovered the problem early enough to apply some extra heating so as to ensure there was no permanent damage.

APRIL 29. At 4 a.m. the air temperature was –30°C. The gale continued most of the day, so we needed to dig out the large door of the balloon hut before the radio sounding could be made.

A cable was received today with a message from the Queen's Private Secretary saying that Her Majesty was very pleased to receive our kind and loyal message, which she much appreciated.

In the evening reception of the BBC programme 'Calling Antarctica' was fair and we heard most of the talk given by Alan Moore of the Royal Society.

The Sun Sets for 100 Days

APRIL 30. At 4 a.m. the air temperature was –15°C. There was another gale in the morning, heralding the winter and sending the sun off for 100 days.

During the last few weeks, Alf and Ivor have been busy digging a tunnel to join up the main and generator huts through the north-east door of the hut and via the food store. Today they were only 12 feet (3.66 m) away from success.

Alf had also just completed a de-carbonization of the No 2 Meadows diesel engine. Today he was completing the job after fabricating a new part it required.

The fresh water tank was cleaned out today by David Tribble during the course of his gash duties. Although we had not noticed the taste of any contamination, the tank proved to be rather dirty and contained a lump of coal and an aerial insulator. It was last cleaned out on 11 December 1957, when diesel fuel contamination could be tasted.

Derek Ward cleaned out the chimney and fitted new fire bars to the anthracite stove in Number 2 bunkroom.

May to July 1958 from the Diary of the Second Winter

The Winter Routine

MAY 1, 1958. The air temperature at 4 a.m. local time was −25°C. Snow fell most of the day in a gentle breeze which increased to a 20-knot (37 kph) wind at 10 p.m.

Henry marked the fact that we were moving into the second third of the year by displaying in the lounge a new and more pleasing P&O poster, by courtesy of his employer, the P&O Orient Lines.

MAY 2. Snow fell all day and it was drifting in a fresh breeze, so we could not confirm the sun had actually set for the winter. In actual fact, the sun was already below the horizon but its rays are normally bent round the earth by about half a degree (36°), which would have allowed us to see it, had the day been less cloudy. The minimum temperature for the day was −16°C.

Bill asked for general assistance in digging out his noise aerial, which had been placed by the advance party in 1956 and now lay under at least 8 ft. (2.44 m) of drifted snow; a work party was set up for the following week.

MAY 3. In the morning there was a fresh breeze with low drift. In the afternoon it was fine with a moderate breeze. The minimum temperature was −32°C.

The air temperatures in the upper atmosphere had fallen sharply in April and had dropped to −80°C at a height of about 20 km. Last year this caused many of the twice-daily balloons we sent up to burst at heights as low as 10 km. This year we were soaking them in oil before launching and they usually got twice as high. Today however, the balloon burst at a height of 11 km. We launched three balloons, the one launched just after lunch was carrying an ozone sonde.

SUNDAY MAY 4. A fine day with some low-level snow drift in the afternoon driven by a moderate breeze. The minimum air temperature was −35°C.

After the service, which I led at 11:15 a.m., I put out the weekly ration of year-old newspapers. As usual, there were quite a few of us who were very pleased to see them. The donor could not have anticipated the great pleasure they gave.

Ivor was busy today tidying up the coal house in preparation for a coal heave to be held on Monday.

MAY 5. It was a fine day when Ivor and I went out to start the coal haul. I opened up the coal dump whilst Ivor started the tractor. The air temperature was –34ºC and there was a fresh easterly breeze blowing at 17 kt (31 kph). When I got to the bamboo stakes which marked the location of our anthracite dump, there was no sign of it above the snow surface. This large dump, which was placed on the surface in January, was now completely drifted up and had become indistinguishable from the general snow surface. I dug down and found that the highest point of the dump lay just one foot below the surface.

Whilst I was opening up the dump, Ivor started the tractor, no mean feat in those temperatures. His first step in the starting process was to light a small oil fire in an old tin can and place this under the engine, heating it up most effectively. The process looks somewhat dangerous as the flames lick round the engine. And it is dangerous unless done with skill and care. But it is highly effective. The trick is to ensure that the flames only lick round the relatively non-inflammable side of the tractor. I believe the technique was originated by soldiers starting tractors in Russian winters. It took eleven of us about one hour to fill the coal store in the main hut with 195 sacks. Whilst the tractor was running, Ivor loaded up 150 cu. ft. (4 cu. m) of solid garbage from the main hut and hauled it off to the dump. We had accumulated this amount of solid garbage in six days.

Whilst we were working outside, we were treated by nature to one of her more remarkable optical displays, the Novaya Zemlya effect, named after the Russian island to the north of Archangel in 75ºN latitude and where the phenomenon was first sighted. From 13:25 to 13:45 UT the whole of the sun was observed above the horizon in a greatly flattened form. To be seen at this time of the year, the rays must have been bent round the earth by nearly three-quarters of a degree.

MAY 6. There was surface drift most of the day in a 18-knot (33 kph) wind. The minimum temperature during the day was –33ºC.

Much of the day I was inside working in my tiny office. There was some geomagnetic work to be done and the regular weekly signal to be composed and sent off to the Royal Society in London. In the cable to London I again reported the details of the loss of parcels sent to David Harrison, Henry Dyer, Les Barclay, and Jim Burton, which should have arrived on *Tottan* in January. Then there was a great deal to report of our scientific observations. This included some brief details of the April weather, together with the measurements I had made of atmospheric ozone using both the sun and moon. I also reported the observation of the Novaya Zemlya effect for the world data centre that existed for this interesting phenomenon. Radio astronomy observations from Philip and David were sent to Professor Lovell in Cheshire. Then there was a great deal from Bill reporting to Professors Smith-Rose and Piggott on the ionospheric physics observations.

I baked a batch of bread this evening. We had developed the habit of placing new loaves left over at the end of the day directly into the cold store at a temperature of about –18°C. When thawed out, even after several weeks, their freshness was maintained.

MAY 7. It was a fine day for our work party to dig out Bill's ionospheric noise aerial. The air temperature at 4 a.m. was –29°C and the daily minimum was –34°C.

Bill, David Harrison, Jim, Ben and I were out there in the morning and for the first time this winter we needed to light a Tilley kerosene lamp. After lunch, Bert and I continued working outside with Bill until we had excavated to the base of the mast, which was 9 ft. 6 in. (2.90 m) below the surface. Then we took the mast down.

In the afternoon I made a wind profile observation.

MAY 8. A fine day with a gentle breeze and a minimum temperature of –41°C.

Bill continued his outside work measuring for the feeders needed for the installation of a new noise aerial. Outside, near noon, there was just sufficient light to read instruments, but only for two and a half hours each side of noon.

I worked up the star shots I took last night for the azimuth of the fixed mark and used this to allocate the corrections needed for recording the direction of the magnetic meridian. Then I used some of the special silicone grease on the levelling screws of the theodolite, which had become particularly stiff. When I started the astronomical work last night, the air temperature was –20°C but whilst I was out there it cooled down to –30°C.

In the afternoon I went outside to do a wind profile observation.

MAY 9. It was misty for most of the day with much rime deposition. The sky was partly cloudy and there was a light breeze. The minimum temperature was –40°C.

During his night duty, David Tribble fitted an automatic system to turn on the ventilation motor of the thermopile psychrometer, just before the hourly observations.

At the evening radio sonde ascent, a rubber balloon was used which had been soaked for three hours in a mixture of Avtur and lubricating oil. The balloon was heavy and about 8 ft. (2.44 m) in diameter, so it was cumbersome to launch. However, it went up to 30 mb, an excellent performance for a winter ascent.

After several days of hard outside work, Bill today erected a new, 40 ft. (12 m) high, noise aerial on top of the snow drift thrown up by the main hut.

After many weeks of solid effort, Alf and Ivor completed the long tunnel linking together the main hut and generator shed. To prevent the possibility of diesel fumes contaminating the food store, Malcolm later fitted a door in the tunnel between the store and the generator shed.

I spent much of the day inside working on the analysis of geomagnetic data. I also responded to a request from the Russian base at Mirny for information on any 1958 weather anomalies which they thought might have occurred. I sent them a reply saying that the only thing I could see in our weather records which could be considered a little unusual was the particularly low minimum and mean temperatures during April. However, since our records only commenced in 1956, it was too early to say anything more.

An Explosion in the Hydrogen Generator

MAY 10. It snowed all day in a gentle breeze in the morning and a fresh breeze for the rest of the day. The minimum temperature was −27°C.

The hydrogen generator exploded in Jim's face this morning, incapacitating him for two days. The balloon was very heavy after being soaked in oil all last night and therefore required a second charge of the Gill hydrogen generator to obtain sufficient hydrogen for an ascent. Apparently, the waste from the first charge had not drained out of the Gill, which had then become blocked, so liquid remained. When Jim put in a new charge of aluminium and caustic soda, there was an immediate explosive reaction and the caustic chemicals shot out of the filling tube and at Jim's face.

A vinegar-and-water mixture was used by Bert to treat the burns, which were somewhat aggravated by his beard, which had trapped and retained some of the caustic soda. Notwithstanding these very difficult and dangerous circumstances, Jim and the team carried on until they completed the launch of the balloon, which rewarded their persistence by rising to a height of 20 km.

Andrew, John Smith and I worked all morning to try and solve the problem and repair the Gill. After lunch, Ivor, David Tribble and Derek came over to help and we worked away there until the job was done at about 8:00 p.m. Our immediate reaction was to ascribe the trouble to freezing of the valve, but we ultimately found it was due to a gradual build-up of a hard deposit above the valve. Finally we used a blow-lamp to heat the deposit, causing it to crack into small pieces which could be removed. Before the week was out, we were to discover that we had not yet solved this problem. We had not seen the end of minor explosions inside the hydrogen generator.

SUNDAY MAY 11. At 4 a.m. the air temperature was −37°C. A slight amount of snow fell at times, whilst a gentle breeze blew all day.

The hydrogen generator worked well this morning although the drain valve was frozen open and had to be thawed out.

I led the service this morning at 11:15 a.m. and then worked on the analysis of geomagnetic records for the remainder of the day.

MAY 12. It snowed today. There was a fresh breeze blowing and it was rather cold outside with a minimum temperature of −39°C.

I spent much of the day inside continuing with the analysis of our magnetic records.

Then Malcolm and I conducted a review of our food stocks. The fresh potatoes were in poor condition and were rarely used as a consequence. In fact they arrived in a poor, soft condition. John Smith said that he thought the deterioration had already set in when they were on *Tottan*. We had a very large stock of dried potatoes, which would be more than sufficient for a third year without relief. Malcolm therefore proposed that we allocate only 120 tins of the more popular tinned potatoes into the third year emergency reserve. This would release a larger supply of tinned potatoes to replace the now rotten 'fresh' ones. Apart from the bacon, all of our stock of fresh meat in the storage tunnel was still in good condition. We had a surplus of tinned fruit, which had therefore been added to the breakfast menus.

Today we heard that members of the TAE had arrived back at Southampton and we heard many references to them on the BBC broadcasts.

MAY 13. It was a cold, calm day with a minimum temperature of −46.8°C. These rather unusual conditions caused the heat from the radio echo hut to affect the temperatures registered in the meteoro-logical enclosure 180 ft. (55 m) away. It also resulted in large clouds of steam rising from huts and the generator shed, making it difficult for Gwynne to do his night-time auroral observations. Even at noon, a large cloud of water vapour from the generator shed enshrouded the whole of the balloon shed and could be seen drifting as far as Halley Bay.

I reviewed with Alf our fuel stocks. They were more than adequate until January 1959, but what would the situation be if that relief ship did not arrive? I later reviewed with Philip the situation in the event of an unrelieved third year. Based on Alf's careful fuel custodianship, we came to the conclusion we could still get by without a relief but there would not then be sufficient fuel to run the Meadows generator 24 hours a day. However, there would be sufficient fuel to run the smaller Enfield generator. We would have a very meagre ration of electrical light bulbs left if not relieved. Our current Avtur consumption was about one and a quarter 44-gallon drums per day and it was probably increasing slightly. This could be reduced if an anthracite stove was fitted into the ionospheric room, but that would not be suitable for the scientific equipment Bill operated there.

Reception for the BBC programme 'Calling Antarctica' was excellent. There were messages for Jim and Len, and we heard more about TAE's return home.

I prepared a signal for the Royal Society, sending off to London scientific data in the fields of meteorology, geomagnetism, seismology, ozone, and radio astronomy.

MAY 14. It was a partly cloudy day with a gentle or moderate breeze and snowfall at times. The minimum temperature was −31°C.

I was delighted and relieved to see Jim out and about again in the afternoon, on his long walk round the snow accumulation stakes. His face was healing rapidly.

We had given a great deal of thought to the process of hydrogen generation as a result of the accident. We came to the conclusion it would be best to avoid using the Gill generator twice in order to lift balloons soaked for too long in the mixture of Avtur and lubricating oil. Instead of leaving them in the oil for many hours, we commenced soaking them for only two or three minutes. During this short time they absorbed much less oil and did not require two charges of the Gill. On the other hand, they did not rise quite so high through the atmosphere.

Gwynne instructed me in the operation of a photometer for measuring the intensity of twilight during the day whilst he was in bed resting from his night of auroral observations.

Ivor's birthday was celebrated today. His birthday cake was decorated with the contents of a birthday telegram. He was also presented with a new mid-section for the full size 'pin-up' photo of Brigitte Bardot he had put up on the wall of the toilet.

Apropos of pin-ups, Jim and David Cansfield were organizing a competition to select favourite pin-up girls. They were offering prizes of 'spiritous liquor' for those persons correctly guessing the winners of an election on the subject.

MAY 15. Snow fell all day. The wind was a gentle breeze in the morning but became a fresh breeze for the rest of the day. The minimum air temperature was −25°C.

Malcolm and I went to the food dump in a freshening breeze with snowfall which went on all day. The tops of the boxes were just level with the snow surface. He carried with him a detailed plan of the dump with box numbers and was able to go directly to the particular one required.

Alf and Ivor had a tractor running. They hitched it up to the sledge mounting for the radar and moved it up on to the new snow surface, about one foot higher. Unfortunately, the sledge was frozen in harder than usual and so the tow bar got torn off in the process.

In the afternoon we heard of the launching by the USSR of an artificial earth-orbiting satellite weighing over one ton and 12 ft. (3.66 m) long. I sent a signal of congratulations to their Antarctic base and asked for the radio frequency and orbit details so we could receive its transmissions.

A radio sonde was launched at 9 p.m. into a fresh south-westerly breeze. The wind was blowing directly into the door of the balloon shed and so we had to fight against the wind, hoping the balloon did not burst in the process.

I finished off the monthly analysis of geomagnetic records and then commenced the analysis of seismological records. With the nearby sea frozen, seismological records were much less noisy and records of earthquakes were of better quality, allowing me to identify many more earthquakes.

In the evening I played chess with Henry for a while and then read from the *Oxford Book of English Verse* for a short time just before retiring.

We Receive Information
from the Third Sputnik

MAY 16. It was a cloudy day with a 4 a.m. temperature of −25°C. A gentle breeze was blowing in the early hours which later became calm at times.

I continued with the analysis of seismograms and also worked on the meteorological part of the daily glaciological data record sheet.

At 5:10 a.m. Bill was logging the radio signals from the Third Sputnik launched yesterday. The transmission frequency was 20 Mc/s and it could be heard until 10:13 a.m., for up to 25 minutes on every orbit as it circled round the earth. Again in the evening at 8:56 p.m. it was heard again.

We received a signal from Gaston de Gerlache, the Leader at the King Baudouin base of the Belgian IGY expedition at Breid Bay. Belgium was the 12th county to mount an IGY Antarctic expedition. I was informed of its location in the Norwegian area of Queen Maud Land on the Princess Ragnhild Coast, to the east of our Norwegian neighbours at 70°25'S latitude, 24°19'E longitude and 10 miles (16 km) inland from the ice-front and west of the site of the former Japanese base. The expedition was equipped for an extensive travel programme and had already visited the mountains 100 miles (161 km) to the south of their base. Gaston, who had served in the RAF in the Second World War, is the son of Adrien de Gerlache, leader of the *Belgica* expedition of 1898, which was the first to winter in Antarctica. The warm-water form of fossils found by Stokes, the artist of that expedition, provided the first clue to the fact that the Antarctic continent once experienced tropical conditions.

Keeping Track of the Penguins' Love Life

MAY 17. The day was partly cloudy with a gentle or moderate breeze. The minimum temperature was −32°C.

We continued to receive radio signals from the Third Sputnik.

Bert returned from a trip to Emperor Bay, where he had been observing the penguins' copulation in preparation for fixing the age of embryos he would later collect. Keeping track of a penguin's love life was by no means a simple task. In one case he was trying to keep track of, he observed two males copulate with the same female, one immediately after the other.

I was pleased to hear from Alf that there had been no further overloading of the electrical generators since I had appealed to everyone to be more frugal in their use of electricity. Fuel consumption, however, had increased from 1.2 to 1.3 drums per day, partly as a result of the longer period of time we ran the small Enfield generators and partly due to the heavy loading on the larger Meadows equipment.

In the evening we joined together to celebrate David Cansfield's birthday.

SUNDAY MAY 18. A fine, cold day with light winds and a temperature below −40°C.

The service was led by Les.

There was another slight explosion inside the hydrogen generator, whilst David Tribble and Derek were operating it for the evening ascent. Fortunately, having learnt to keep well clear of the filling tube, they were not injured physically. It was the same old problem of the formation of aluminium hydroxide just above the drain valve, which was quickly cleared with the heat of a blow-lamp. We still did not understand why this new problem should occur this year but not in 1957.

MAY 19. A fine day with a gentle breeze. The temperature at 4 a.m. was −33°C.

Another blockage in the drain of the hydrogen generator occurred this morning. Samples were later collected to see if we could discover the cause of the problem.

MAY 20. A fine day with a gentle south-westerly breeze blowing. The minimum air temperature during the day was −44°C.

Mail started to arrive more regularly. We were supposed to receive one air letter per month but for some reason these had been held up recently, so that it seemed a very long time since we had received anything.

In a signal from the Russian base we learnt that their new satellite was orbiting 1880 km above the earth and had a 65° orbit. Bill was monitoring the reception of radio signals and had constructed a chart illustrating his results.

I sent a signal off to the Royal Society asking for advice on the recent problem that had developed with deposits forming in the drain of the Gill hydrogen generator.

At 8 p.m. we had a gathering to celebrate Andrew's birthday. Later in the evening I played a game of chess with Henry and then read some of my favourite parts from Shakespeare.

MAY 21. The weather was fine in the morning and cloudy for the rest of the day. A gentle easterly breeze was blowing. The air temperature was below −40°C all day.

The low air temperatures of the day created a problem in the morning with the operation of the wind-finding radar motor generator.

I was busy much of the day working on the analysis of geomagnetic records.

MAY 22. It was a fine day with a light or gentle breeze blowing and air temperatures below −40°C.

This morning Derek had some difficulty with the hydrogen generator. It started to react prematurely. David Cansfield, who was a chemist, had looked at the problem and made some helpful suggestions. As a result, we added some extra insulation round the lower part of the Gill.

At 10- to 15-minute intervals throughout the day, I made zenith twilight observations for Gwynne.

MAY 23. The day was partly cloudy with a moderate breeze and temperatures above −37°C.

The work of insulating the hydrogen generator was completed and a more efficient handle was fitted to the door of the balloon shed.

I completed the analysis of the April geomagnetic records. In the evening I baked eight loaves of bread.

MAY 24. It was a fine day with a light breeze, The air temperature was −30°C at 4 a.m.

In the early hours of the morning Les made radio contact with the

USA base at Ellsworth, 220 miles (354 km) to our south. They were interested in our progress with ozone observations.

SUNDAY MAY 25. At 4 a.m. the air temperature was −30°C. It was a fine morning and cloudy for the rest of the day.

This morning, after the service, I put out the daily newspapers for 13 October 1957. This weekly distribution remained universally popular. The sequence, so thoughtfully collected by some of the Royal Society staff, will last us until January 1959.

In the afternoon we played a 4-hour duration recording of Hamlet.

MAY 26. The weather was fine at first with the air temperature of about −34°C. The wind then rose rapidly to become a moderate gale in the afternoon.

Ivor hoisted a brand new Union Jack this morning, replacing the previous flag which the winter winds had torn down to half size.

In the afternoon I went out and made a wind profile observation.

Alf, Bill and I sat down to discuss the need to ensure a sufficient Avtur reserve in the event of a relief not being possible this summer. Fuel consumption of the electrical generators had risen still higher since I last looked at it. This was due to the longer and longer periods we have needed to run the Enfield generator this winter. There were two possibilities: we could replace the electrical heating for the iono-spheric laboratory by an anthracite stove, or we could disconnect the 2-kW immersion heater which was used in the generator shed to humidify the air drawn into the generators. The humidifier was installed to combat an unacceptably high rate of slip-ring wear expe-rienced by the Advance Party in 1956. Anthracite heating for the ionospheric laboratory would have been incompatible with the re-quirements of somewhat delicate equipment. Alf therefore agreed to disconnect the immersion heater whilst carefully monitoring slip ring wear. This turned out to be a very satisfactory solution and allowed us to reduce the daily running period of the Enfield generator to four hours per day, thereby reducing fuel consumption to an acceptable level.

Malcolm and Len prepared a very tasty chicken for our Whit Monday dinner. Then we had a special film show at 8:30 p.m. of the movies *Jungle Air Lift* and *Three Musketeers*.

During the night the tunnel to the generator shed became blocked at the far end. At the same time there was a faulty catch on the workshop door which trapped Alf for a while in the coldest part of the hut. Fortunately, shortly afterwards I went to the nearby coal store, accidentally discovered his predicament, and released him.

Auroral Displays Light up the Winter Sky

MAY 27. The air temperature at 4 a.m. was −32°C. There was a strong breeze in the early hours of the morning but the rest of the day was partly cloudy with a moderate breeze.

We may have discovered why we have had so much trouble with the hydrogen generator after a relatively trouble-free 1957. We found that on the occasion of the last four malfunctions, the tins of caustic soda were damaged and punctured. The dampness penetrating had therefore changed the character of the chemical, triggering off the problem. The tins are now scrutinised carefully before use. The evening ascent reached the good height of 25 km, passing through 98% of the atmosphere.

At night there was an active auroral display with a corona and at one time the whole sky was filled with flaming rays.

MAY 28. The air temperature at 4 a.m. was −33°C. It was a fine day with a light or gentle breeze blowing.

Every 10 minutes during the day I made an observation of the twilight in the zenith. Then I covered the auroral watch until 7 p.m., when Gwynne was able to resume his normal duties. There was another brilliant auroral display during the night.

MAY 29. At 4 a.m. the air temperature was −31°C. It was a fine day with a light or gentle breeze blowing.

I made twilight observations all day again today and then cleaned the optical parts of the ozone spectrophotometer.

For the first time for many weeks, we lost track of the balloon with the radar. At this time of the year, the wind direction changes very rapidly in the lowest layers of the atmosphere. A year ago, when we were less experienced, these wind changes caused us quite often to lose track of the balloon.

The Vigour of the Antarctic Atmosphere in Winter

MAY 30. The air temperature at 4 a.m. was −33°C. The weather was cloudy with a gentle or moderate breeze blowing.

Bill and I had a further talk about the problem of noise measurements, which have to be done at some distance from the base. Since a wire already runs down to Halley Bay, he might use this to make remote measurements.

Despite the greater heights we were now achieving with our balloons, the switches on the radio sondes were working much better than last year. This was due to the greater amount of hydrogen used to raise the oil-soaked balloons, which also caused them to rise more rapidly through the atmosphere and reduce the likelihood of switch stoppages.

Today was the last of a four-day series of voice transmission tests to the Ship Press transmitter in Rugby, England, and held at 22:55 UT on 5.8 Mc/s. All the tests were satisfactory.

Since January the quantity of ozone in the surface air has risen steadily from 0.5 to 1.5 parts in one hundred million. This ozone originated in the sunlit stratosphere and its increase is clear evidence that the general circulation is mixing most vigorously in this winter period, bringing the ozone down from great heights and from more northerly, sunlit latitudes.

Derek was down at Emperor Bay today taking flashlight photographs of the penguins.

MAY 31. It was a fine morning but the wind rose after lunch to become a fresh breeze with drift at 10 p.m. The air temperature was −32°C.

Derek developed his photographs taken yesterday, and showed them to us in the evening. They were the first colour photos we had seen of the winter activities of the penguins and they were of an excellent quality. He used Kodak Ektachrome with his own electronic flash equipment. We all appreciated his show. I was very pleased to see his initiative, which is the best way to ensure the winter does not become a drag.

There were two films shown at 8:30 p.m. and one of them called *Geordie* was declared first-class by one and all. Ivor served his frozen orange juice again. It has become everyone's favourite and is rivalling beer in its popularity.

SUNDAY JUNE 1. The temperature at 4 a.m. was −25°C. A strong breeze in the early morning soon died away to leave a fine day with a gentle breeze.

To mark Trinity Sunday, the service was slightly longer than usual and the hymns were rendered in a lusty fashion.

A full moon at maximum declination shone brilliantly, which I used for measuring the total amount of ozone in the atmosphere.

Though there was a strong breeze in the early hours, this soon died away, leaving a fine day of which Jim and Malcolm took advantage for a walk to Emperor Bay and then round the headland on the sea-ice and back via Halley Bay. The air temperatures during the day were mainly over −36°C. There were three lone penguins on the sea-ice about a mile (1.6 km) away from the many thousands at the rookery.

JUNE 2. The air temperature at 4 a.m. was −33°C. It was a fine day with a moderate breeze. In the early hours of the morning, the wind from the SSW took warm air from the main hut into the meteorological enclosure and occasionally affected the measurements of air temperature.

In the morning I commenced work on the analysis of last month's geomagnetic records and later I worked with John Smith to prepare an ozone sonde for its flight. When we analysed the results of the ozone sounding, we found that about 7% of the atmospheric ozone was below the tropopause, the largest proportion we had yet observed. This is another indication of the great vigour of the Antarctic winter circulation and its ability to bring down quantities of ozone from the sunlit stratosphere many miles to our north.

As another gratuitous and welcome contribution to our comfort, Ivor fitted a small kerosene heater in the toilet.

JUNE 3. The air temperature at 4 a.m. was −28°C. The morning was cloudy with a gentle breeze. It snowed in the afternoon and from then on the wind increased steadily, becoming a 34 kt (93 kph), gale-force wind at 10:30 p.m.

Jim and Bill brought two 12 ft. (3.66 m) sledges into the hut to remove the Tufnol runners and replace them with lacquered wood. This was the best we could do with the materials available to reduce sliding friction to a minimum.

I sent a long signal off to the Royal Society containing meteorological, geomagnetic, ozone and radio astronomical observations.

In response to a request from the BBC, we sent some comments on the frequencies used for the transmission of 'Calling Antarctica'. We recommended a lower frequency be used. In the evening, reception of the 'Calling Antarctica' programme was poor. There was a message for Henry this week, so he exercised his prerogative by rigging up the radio to ensure he could receive it in absolute privacy.

JUNE 4. The moderate gale ended in the early hours of the morning when the air temperature was −17°C. The rest of the day was cloudy with a light breeze.

I was on gash duty. With the various improvements implemented this year, the task had become noticeably easier. For example, the installation of snow chutes made it much easier to fill up the water tanks and one no longer had to empty the urinal cans at regular intervals. I said that I felt it was a pleasant relaxation from the usual work routine, providing the opportunity for a change in social interactions. However, those who joined us in 1958, not having experienced the rigours of gash duty in the previous year, told me that they did not share this view.

Henry and Jim went to Halley Bay to make sea-ice observations.

The fast sea-ice there was now 4 ft. 4 in. (1.32 m) thick with 2 in. (5 cm) of snow on top. Last year at the same time it was 3 ft. 2 in. (96 cm) thick with 14 in. (36 cm) of snow on top.

Bill was working outside freeing the guy ropes on an ionospheric aerial, which were now stressed by the snow drift from the recent gale. Andrew too was outside checking the stocks of hydrogen chemicals and taking into the balloon shed a new supply of small reflectors.

Ivor re-hung the door to the latrine; with the little heater in there the temperature was now 70°F (21°C).

Bad Winter Weather Conditions

JUNE 5. The air temperature was −28°C at 4 a.m. The wind rose during the early hours of the morning to become a strong gale before lunch. When the balloon was launched at 9 a.m., the average wind speed was 46 kt (85 kph) and it was gusting to 60 kt (111 kph).

The visibility was so poor in the thick snow drift at noon that Andrew was not able to locate the daily accumulation stakes. A guide line of cords was strung between bamboo poles and led one to within a few feet of each of the accumulation stakes to be measured. After lunch I accompanied Andrew. We used as guides the cloud searchlight and the light on the geomagnetic fixed mark. The wind was gusting to 60 kt (111 kph). This time we managed to find the guide line and successfully measured the snow accumulation stakes.

JUNE 6. The air temperature at 4 a. m was −19°C. The morning was cloudy with a gentle breeze. The wind then increased to become a strong gale by the end of the day.

Ivor painted the latrine door he re-hung yesterday.

I discussed with others our plans to celebrate Midwinter's Day, which was by tradition the most significant Antarctic celebration of the year.

David Harrison joined the night watch so that he could make some parallel visual observations of radio echoes of aurora normally recorded photographically.

JUNE 7. The air temperature at 4 a.m. was −14°C. Yesterday's gale died away and then another one sprang up in the evening.

We had to dig out the balloon shed door before launching this morning's balloon.

In the evening, before the film show, Derek projected an 8-mm movie made by David Tribble. It was John Smith's birthday so our Saturday night celebration was more pertinent than usual. I contributed to the festivities the bottle of whisky Robin had given to me before he left.

The series of gales we are experiencing must have been due to a nearby deep depression, because the air pressure of 956.7 mb, recorded at 4 a.m., was the lowest we have seen since January 1957.

SUNDAY JUNE 8. At 4 a. m the air temperature was −28°C. There was a moderate gale at first which eased during the day to become a moderate breeze at 10 p.m. There was snow drift all day with a partly cloudy sky.

At the Sunday morning service there were nine of us present and we made a fair noise with our singing.

JUNE 9. The temperature at 4 a.m. was −25°C. It was a fine day with a moderate breeze.

Bert took advantage of the fine weather to take some good colour photographs of Emperor Penguins, using an electronic flash and Ektachrome film.

As a special effort for a Regular World Day, the ionospheric team maintained continuous operation of their equipment throughout the day.

At night, David Harrison maintained simultaneous visual and radar observations. I continued with a regular calibration of the ozone spectrophotometer.

In the kitchen, Malcolm was busy with his monthly chore of cleaning out the kitchen stove. David Harrison was in the workshop wrestling with the stove used to heat the bath water. Before it is lit each evening, a current of cold air normally flows down the flue. When he lit the stove this evening, the hot air from the fire did not manage to overcome this cold draft so the fumes of the fire were driven out and filled the workshop with pungent wood smoke. Finally he cured the problem by placing a lighted paper in the top of the flue to start the convection process going.

We received a message for Dr Martin to say that Ben and Malcolm will tomorrow receive family messages on the BBC programme 'Calling Antarctica'. The programme is listened to much more keenly than it was last year. This may be partly due to the fact that Henry has rigged a loudspeaker in the lounge.

JUNE 10. It was a fine day with a perfectly clear sky and air temperatures above −43°C.

Philip was down at Emperor Bay taking photographs in a perfectly fine clear day.

I made observation of twilight every 10 minutes for much of the day.

The 30 ft. (9 m) -long geomagnetic fixed mark sighting tube had become blocked and was dug out and cleared. This is the tube we use to sight through the snow drift at the fixed mark to the north of the non-magnetic hut.

To prevent the latrine hole becoming blocked, Len enlarged it by pouring down large quantities of hot water.

John Gane, Ben and Malcolm only heard some of the messages sent to them via 'Calling Antarctica'. Conditions were not good enough for them to hear the whole broadcast.

The Exchange of Midwinter's Day Greetings

JUNE 11. The air temperature at 4 a.m. was −41°C. The weather was fine and a moderate breeze was blowing.

Malcolm was busy today preparing for our Midwinter's Day feast. A customary part of the celebrations of that day was the exchange of greetings amongst the various bases maintained by the 12 nations operating in Antarctica. We were already in regular radio contact with the Russian station at Mirny, Norway Station, the French at Adelie Land, the Australians at Davis base, the FIDS bases of Port Lockroy and Argentine Islands, the Belgians at King Baudouin base, and the USA bases at Little America and Ellsworth. For those we were not able to contact directly, I requested London to send them midwinter's day greetings. We also sent our midwinter greetings to the British National Antarctic Committee and former members of the expedition who had served with both the advance and main parties.

JUNE 12. At 4 a.m. the air temperature was −31°C. The wind speed increased during the day to become a strong gale of 45 kt (82 kph) at 9 p.m. The wind then dropped slowly to fresh-gale strength at midnight.

I had a very busy day. In addition to the usual round of scientific work, I responded to a request from London for details of our plans for the Midwinter's Day festivities. I wrote the following account for the Royal Society:

Midwinter's day will start with a special breakfast of bacon and eggs. At breakfast the midwinter edition of the *Halley Comet* will be issued. A five-course lunch is planned, based on the generous hamper presented by the Royal Society and food kept fresh in the deep freeze. It includes many items presented by kind friends. Items on the menu for lunch include lobster, fresh turkey, Argentine champagne, raspberries, crystallized fruits, fresh oranges, Norwegian cheese, cigars and port. Some of us have tantalizing boxes marked 'not to be opened until Midwinter's Day', but when distributed, these are confidently expected to provide presents and entertainment for all. One year ago we brewed ginger-flavoured mead which should be ripe now and assist our rendering of the Advance Party song traditional on Midwinter's Day. In the afternoon we will show the film 'Dam Busters' and eat ice lollipops. If the day is fine, we will visit the Emperor rookery. As we leave the hut, we will be greeted by the husky dog, content outside and replete with two pounds of seal meat frozen to the consistency of a yule log.

Then I had to fix a problem with the seismographs, which were not working correctly. I opened up the snow cave where they were kept and descended the glaciological pit and examined the seismographs there, lying snugly 30 feet (9 m) below the surface. I discovered that the ice-shelf had tilted upwards on the northern side, causing the problem. It was not the first time we had observed that the whole ice-shelf on which we sat was tilting up to the north as it moved forward and rotated.

In the five months since January 1958 we have used 238 electric light bulbs. The consumption was less rapid during the last three months, when they were rationed to some extent. We obtained 384 in January plus a gift of 200 from TAE. I was a little alarmed to discover from the records that the total consumption in 1957 was 460 bulbs. This would imply that the rationing regime for the future must be a little stricter if we are to have any chance of leaving any for 1959, in the event of no relief this summer.

We had to fill three balloons in the strong gale which was blowing this evening. The first one burst in the shed, the second was launched with a sonde only and the third carried the radar reflector. The gale blew down the ventilated fluxplate radiometer but it came to no harm and was replaced.

Before the gale started, John Gane was erecting yet another aerial. He strung the antenna between scaffold poles fixed to the shaft over the south-west door of the main hut and the old meteorological tower.

Bert did one of his routine tests for carbon monoxide in the air of the main hut; he found no trace of this dangerous gas.

After supper I brought out a bottle of port so that we could drink to Robin Smart's health on hearing that he had been awarded the CBE in the Birthday Honours List.

JUNE 13. The air temperature at 4 a.m. was −17°C. In the early hours of the morning, the wind speed dropped rapidly, to leave a cloudy day with slight surface-drift snow, kicked up by a 12 kt (22 kph) moderate breeze.

When we went out to measure the daily snow accumulation stakes, we found that the recent gale had deposited five centimetres of snow and carved pronounced sastrugi. In one place I noticed a sastrugi which was over one foot high (30 cm) with one sheer side.

I spent much of the day measuring our geomagnetic records and subjecting them to a rigorous mathematical analysis to see if there was any evidence of a relationship between geomagnetic and meteorological variations. No significant relation was found between the daily changes of air temperatures at about 18 km and geomagnetic activity.

There was another explosive reaction in the hydrogen generator this evening as Jim was operating it. Apparently, after the morning ascent, not all the water had drained from the chamber. The surface of this water had frozen during the day. We inferred that when the chemicals were added, they sat on the skin of ice for a moment and when they broke through the surface, they reacted violently, shooting the caustic mixture out of the filling tube and all round the balloon shed. Fortunately Jim's face was not in the line of fire this time; once bitten twice shy.

Bert weighed all of us and measured our fat thickness, a weekly chore he undertook on Fridays. The results of the weighings, but not the fat thickness, were now the subject of friendly competition. David Cansfield retained his position as our heaviest member.

I baked bread in the evening but for some reason it would not rise properly.

JUNE 14. At 4 a.m. the temperature was −24°C. Snow fell much of the day and the wind speed varied between calm and 12 kt (22 kph).

The safety valve on the hydrogen generator would not seal this morning so it was replaced. Before this was done, however, three operations of the generator were required, the hydrogen from the first two being wasted via the safety valve. In addition, the 'cold' outlet for hydrogen was partly blocked. This particular outlet was not used, so its state did not interfere with the operation of the equipment.

A new source of interference with the operation of our radio transmitter has emerged. David Harrison and John Gane worked together in an attempt to cure the problem.

David Harrison was at Emperor Bay during the day, where he observed penguins with eggs.

There was a signal today from Robin thanking us for our congratulations. He said that he considered the award a recognition of everyone's first-class performance last year.

Normally on a Saturday evening we do not send up a meteorological balloon, so as to allow everyone to see the film show and to keep within the limited supplies of some meteorological stores. However, on this Saturday, the organizers of the IGY declared a World Meteorological Interval, which requires two ascents. By showing the film at 4:30 p.m., everyone was able to watch it.

SUNDAY JUNE 15. At 4 a.m. the air temperature was −24°C. The morning was fine with a moderate breeze; in the afternoon there was a fresh south-westerly breeze with snow drift and a little cloud.

We removed the canvas cone from under the ceiling of the balloon shed. We did this to provide the space to inflate, at the same time, two of the smaller 500 g balloons for those occasions, like today, with a fresh south-westerly breeze blowing. This wind direction created the most difficult launching conditions because it blew right into the door of the balloon shed. Our new technique of coping with this situation was to use one balloon for the sonde measuring air temperature and humidity and the other for the radar reflector to measure winds.

Preparations for Midwinter's Day were moving ahead. The editors of the *Halley Comet* were receiving the last entries for the pin-up competition to select the six most favoured ladies out of a field of 46 glamour girls. Meanwhile Malcolm stuffed three turkeys for the dinner and Len worked on an attractive menu.

The Miss Butler's Wharf Competition

JUNE 16. The air temperature was −22°C at 4 a.m. There was a fresh breeze in the morning with cloud and surface snow drift. The afternoon was cloudy with a moderate breeze.

Ivor was busy outside in a fresh breeze clearing drift snow in the vent pipe from the latrine. Then he came inside and enlarged the tunnel to the generator shed. A new hole was made for liquid waste alongside the old one in the tunnel from the north-east door.

For some time now we have been concerned because our meteorological observations were not getting through to the IGY Weather Central at Little America, the US Base by the Ross Sea. Finally today, John Gane heard directly from Little America that they were now getting all the data required.

The operation of our transmitter was still causing a new form of interference on David Harrison's radio echo equipment. David and John worked away together again today to try and sort this out.

In the evening, carefully scrutinized by others, Jim was in the lounge counting the votes cast amongst the six candidates for the Miss Butler's Wharf contest. The winner received over 1000 votes, there being no limit set to the numbers of votes cast by each of us. I am not sure the editors realized this loophole when they framed the rules of the competition. Apparently some people are very strongly committed to their favourite pin-up. Jim's Yorkshire character took all this in his stride and was completely unperturbed by the popularity and hot competition engendered by the contest.

Len finished the Midwinter's Day menu. The cover was decorated with an elegant sketch of Halley Bay and the menu was finished off with a silken ribbon in Cambridge blue.

JUNE 17. At 4 a.m. the temperature was −17°C. It was a cloudy day with a gentle westerly breeze at the surface but, in the upper air, the

westerly winds were blowing at speeds of up to 90 knots (167 kph)
near the tropopause. They were so strong and consistent that the
balloon was blown out of the range of the radar before it burst. The
last we saw of the balloon, it was 105 km away and still moving at
70 kt (130 kph) at a height of 13 km.

David Cansfield and Malcolm went down to measure the thickness
of the sea-ice in Halley Bay. It was 4 ft. 3 in. (1.30 m) thick, about
the same as it was a week ago.

Bert and John Smith collected the first Emperor Penguin eggs of
the season. This was five days earlier than last year, although David
Harrison took an egg from a bird three days ago and then gave it
back again. When Bert came back to the hut, the embryos were
extracted and preserved for further study.

David Harrison reported as cured the recent problem with the radio
transmitter, clearing up most of the resulting interference. However
there was still some problem with the aerial feeders.

'Calling Antarctica' could not be heard on either frequency, a relay
of the programme from Port Stanley on 3 Mc/s was heard rather poorly
at 11:15 p.m.

I prepared a signal for the Royal Society providing them with ozone,
meteorological and geomagnetic data, together with a report on the
very poor seasonal reception of the BBC programme 'Calling Antarctica'. I recommended that further messages via the BBC be delayed
until the radio propagation conditions improve. I also passed on from
the USSR base at Mirny greetings on the occasion of the Queen's
birthday to all British parties in Antarctica.

In the evening I made a determination of azimuth using stars.

JUNE 18. At 4 a.m. the air temperature was −31°C. The weather was
fine with a moderate breeze in the morning and a light breeze for the
rest of the day.

I was on gash duty today and also made for Gwynne measurements
of twilight from the zenith sky. We estimated that twilight started
about an hour and a half earlier than usual. From 9:20 to 10:30 a.m.,
the northern sky was exceptionally red. The level of twilight illumination at 9:45 a.m. was remarkably high and 18 times the level observed
ten days ago. Shortly before noon, the intensity of red in the north
became less and cloud came over the zenith, terminating twilight
observations.

The balloon was blown out of range for the second day in succession
by strong west winds throughout the atmosphere.

I sent out many midwinter greetings and some were received.

JUNE 19. The temperature was −31°C at 4 a.m. It snowed all day with
a moderate or fresh breeze driving low-level snow drift.

Malcolm, assisted by David Tribble, who was on gash duty, have decorated the lounge and dining room, spreading a festive air throughout the hut. I think that more balloons were burst than finally hung due to their fascination with the balloon pump provided.

John Gane and David Harrison continued to work on interference problems. Some progress has been made as David now gets whole days free from trouble.

The exchange of midwinter's greetings from home and other bases continued apace.

JUNE 20. At 4 a.m. the temperature was −24°C. Snow fell all day whilst the wind speed increased slowly from 17 kt (31 kph) at 11 p.m. on the 19th to 33 kt (61 kph) at 11 p.m. today.

The radar was unserviceable at the time of the morning ascent. A sonde was therefore sent up at the normal time and the wind-finding ascent made a little later, as soon as David had fixed the problem.

In the evening Len gave several of us special Midwinter's Day haircuts. He gave Andrew a monk's cut, Ben was cropped like a convict with a dyed beard, whilst David Tribble sported a Huron Indian haircut.

Midwinter greetings continued to roll in and Jim was hard at work typing them into the midwinter edition of the *Halley Comet*.

The Celebration of Midwinter's Day Whilst Gales Rage

JUNE 21 – Midwinter's Day. At 4 a.m. the temperature was −17°C. Snow fell all day for the third full day in succession. It was driven by a moderate gale, which became a strong gale in the evening.

The day opened with a breakfast of fruit followed by bacon and eggs. The morning was greatly enlivened by the night shift in fancy dress. A bearded Gwynne tried to masquerade as Eve, John Smith wore a coal sack and David Cansfield was dressed in a sheep's skin.

Sherry was served before lunch at 12:45 p.m. when we all wore our best suits and the *Halley Comet* was issued. The cover displayed an artistic rendering of an auroral display by David Tribble. Inside there was the usual entertaining potpourri of material, including Jim's editorial, a poem attributed incorrectly to Les, an amusing cartoon by Ben which encapsulated each day of the week by a simple and descriptive, line-drawn, vignette cartoon. The results were announced as follows of the 'Miss Butler's Wharf 1959' completion to select the most 'charming young ladies'. The idea for the contest came from Les. The challenge was to place six photographs in their order of popularity. It was won by Ivor with Ben second and Les third. The three most popular ladies were: Jackie Curtis 1420 votes, Anna Maria Alberghetti 893 votes and Shirley Ann Field 686 votes.

A fine lunch was served at 13:30 p.m. of lobster, turkey, raspberries and fruits accompanied by some of the Argentine champagne, beer, and the port in which we toasted HM the Queen and the Royal Society. We sang some songs, pulled many crackers, blew hooters and then retired to the lounge wearing hats and smoking Dr Martin's gift of cigars.

In the afternoon the film *Dam Busters* was shown, followed by a bar-buffet in the lounge. Prizes for the *Halley Comet's* competition were distributed and Malcolm organized a lucky dip for gifts donated by his sister, with the gifts embedded in flour.

Since the day also happened to coincide with a Special World Interval and a World Meteorological Interval, there was quite a bit of scientific work to be done. Accordingly, the festivities were carefully timed to fit everything in, both work and play.

Outside in the winter darkness, snow fell all day and a moderate gale raged for much of the time. The air temperatures outside were mainly over −18°c.

SUNDAY JUNE 22. The temperature at 4 a.m. was −17°C. There was a fresh breeze all day and some snowfall.

Les conducted the religious service this morning, which was well attended.

In the course of launching the evening balloon, Ben strained a muscle in his abdomen. Bert examined him and said that he should recover after two or three days of bed rest.

JUNE 23. The temperature at 4 a.m. was −12°C. It snowed all day and a gale blew in the morning, but the wind moderated later.

In the afternoon Ivor went down to see the penguins at Emperor Bay. There was a well-marked water sky off the bay, indicating the presence of a shore lead there.

The general overseas programme of the BBC broadcast included several members of the TAE talking about their crossing of Antarctica. Unfortunately reception was rather poor.

JUNE 24. The temperature was −15°C at 4 a.m. and there was hardly any wind.

John Gane and David Harrison continued searching for the cause of occasional interference. The intermittent nature of the interference made it very difficult to trace and was thought cured on several occasions. John said that he had almost come to the point where a new communication schedule would have to be designed.

One of the hydrogen outlets of the Gill was cleaned with a strong solution of hot caustic soda. We received information from the Canadian operator to say they had not observed the type of sudden blockage we have experienced.

In the forenoon, the northern sky was a beautiful deep red for about three to four hours. Under this splendid show, Alf was outside starting up a tractor to remove solid gash to the dump, whilst Ivor was out there repairing the outside light on the radio echo hut.

Malcolm went to the food dump to dig out some boxes of beans. While he was outside, at 3:40 p.m., he saw a very bright meteor which gave out a bright green light and had a flaming red tail. The meteor was in the east but apparently moving down to the north. Henry and Jim also saw the meteor whilst they were at Halley Bay, where they went to measure the thickness of sea-ice; it was 4 ft. 9 in. (1.45 m) thick. At the time Jim was facing west but it lit up the snowscape so he turned to see it. The weather was deteriorating at the time but the illumination was so strong, his immediate thought was that it could have been a rocket I had fired to provide them with guidance home.

I sent off a long signal to the Royal Society in London with some seismological and ionospheric data. We also thanked Dr Martin for the gift of cigars and the Royal Society for the Midwinter's Day hamper. In the cable Bill suggested we use the ionosonde on the voyage home to conduct an ionospheric traverse of the South Atlantic.

JUNE 25. The temperature at 4 a.m. was −26°C. There was a fresh breeze blowing for most of the day which became stronger at night.

The morning balloon ascent went up to a height of 20 mb where the air temperature was −92°C, the lowest we have recorded so far.

John and David continued to wrestle with the chronic but intermittent interference problem.

JUNE 26. The air temperature was −21°C at 4 a.m. The wind rose during the day developing into a whole gale just after noon with a 52 kt (96 kph) wind which was gusting up to 65 kt (120 kph). Launching the balloon in these conditions was difficult, but successful.

Alf found that the air inlet to the Meadows generator was nearly blocked by an accumulation of ice. This has not been previously observed. The problem was not noticed until the size of the inlet was reduced to half an inch (1.3 cm) and the diesel began to labour.

The evening radio sonde ascent was delayed slightly due to a radar fault which had to be fixed.

David Cansfield and David Tribble were working together to concoct a better black ink, which we could use for stamping on the geomagnetic charts. The ink we were using was the Post Office standard stamping ink, which we found had not dried four months after use and therefore became prone to smudging.

We received a request from Tolstikov at the USSR Mirny base for some details of our work for publication by their newspaper, *Izvestia*. I prepared a 1000-word article, which was published on 2 and 3 July 1958 in special sections of the paper called 'Antarctica Speaks'.

JUNE 27. The temperature at 4 a.m. was −15°C. The end of the gale at 7 a.m. brought snow with it. So we were out in the morning digging away the six to eight feet (2.44 m) depth of snow packed round the garage-type door of the balloon shed. Two balloons were filled to prepare for the strong winds but these fell uncharacteristically rapidly, so there was only a strong breeze by launching time.

Bert and Derek were at Emperor Bay during the day to take photographs of penguins in the process of laying their eggs.

Alf was changing the fuel injectors on the No. 2 Meadows. He gave us a striking demonstration of their action in a test rig by lighting some of the atomized fuel and creating a spectacular ball of fire.

There was a bright moon at night and I stayed up late, using it for ozone measurements, and then I shot the stars for an azimuth determination.

Though Ben was up for part of the day, he still did not feel at all well, not having recovered from the strain to his abdomen whilst balloon launching the other day.

Bill and I talked about the arrangements he was considering for a spring sledging trip planned for October 24 to 30.

JUNE 28. At 4 a.m. the air temperature was −28°C. It was fine for most of the day so I went outside in the evening for some time and made astronomical observations to determine the azimuth of the fixed mark used to control the geomagnetic records.

David Harrison reported that, although not completely eliminated, the mutual interference between the communications transmissions and his radar had been reduced to tolerable levels. He will continue to search for problems but does not now require any changes to the communications schedules.

In the lounge this evening we had a showing of the colour slides taken by several people recently of the Midwinter's Day celebrations and of the Emperor Penguins. Those taken by Philip Brenan were of an excellent quality.

JUNE 29. The temperature at 4 a.m. was −33°C. It was a mainly fine day with a moderate breeze blowing all day.

A black rubber-stamping ink has been concocted by two of the Davids. It was made by adding anti-freeze to Indian ink and then slowly boiling off the water in the Indian ink. This mixture dried in about half an hour and was judged to be fully satisfactory for our purposes of providing a permanent and smudge-fee notation for our chart records.

Philip started work on a snow chute for replenishing the drinking water tank in the kitchen. Then he brought into the hut our remaining stock of tongue-and-groove timber.

Alf was repairing the radiator of No 2 Meadows, which yesterday sprang a leak.

JUNE 30. At 4 a.m. the temperature was −15°C. It was a cloudy day with a fresh breeze blowing.

The morning meteorological ascent reached the height of the 17 mb pressure level located at about 26 km. As the balloon rose through a second tropopause at 45 mb (19 km), the winds reversed direction.

Philip and Les continued to work on the installation of a snow chute for the kitchen tank. First they had to dig down to the roof and, once they got there, they removed a tarpaulin which had been placed on that part of the roof in the previous summer to prevent snow entering into the tunnel alongside the hut. Then a hole was cut through to the kitchen.

I did seismic work for most of the day, and then worked to fix a problem which had arisen with the direct current electrical supply to the illumination of the geomagnetic recorders.

JULY 1. The temperature at 4 a.m. was −30°C. It was a partly cloudy day with a gentle or moderate breeze.

We were delighted on this day, the anniversary of the commencement of the IGY, to be in a position to send off to London a full analysis of the June weather, within a day of the ending of the month. June was a typical winter month. In it we recorded the lowest air pressure to date of 956.7 mb on 7th, the greatest monthly pressure range of 58.9 mb and the highest mean wind since last winter. Snow accumulated through the month at the large rate of 15 cm or 15% of the annual total. In this signal, there was also a report on auroral and radio echo observations undertaken in June.

Bill was making active preparations for his spring journey.

Malcolm and Jim walked on the sea-ice from Emperor Bay to Halley Bay. The ice was undisturbed since their last visit but there was some more snow cover. On the trip they observed 7 Weddell seals.

'Calling Antarctica' could not be received on 12 Mc/s.

I sent off to Port Stanley several 'Air Letters' on learning that this service, the only relatively inexpensive way to communicate home, would not be available again until about September 18.

JULY 2. The temperature at 4 a.m. was −26°C. The day was mainly cloudy or misty with a moderate breeze. The cloud cleared late at night with the onset of an easterly wind.

We heard from our neighbours to the north-east at Norway base, that our advice to soak their balloons in diesel fuel had resulted in them achieving greater heights.

Radio Tokyo announced that Syowa Base, which was abandoned near the end of 1957, would be re-occupied next year for two years.

Philip and Les finished off their installation of a snow chute in the kitchen.

I did seismological work all day and then baked 9 lb. (4 kg) of bread in the evening, which rose nicely for me this time.

Fuel Consumption is Kept Within the Available Supply

JULY 3. The air temperature at 4 a.m. was −31°C. It was a partly cloudy day with a gentle breeze at first, which dropped to become a light and variable wind.

There were three balloon ascents today, the two normal ones plus an ozone sonde in the middle of the day. All the balloons reached a good height and well into the ozone layer.

Several people were at Emperor Bay, where Bert was busy collecting penguin embryos.

It was satisfactory to note that, despite the recent severe weather, 10 drums of fuel were used during the last 10 days. Clearly the measures we had instituted have worked to moderate fuel consumption, so we should have no difficulty in lasting through 1959, in the unlikely event of there being no relief this summer.

The snow chute leading to the kitchen tank was in use and had the advantage of speeding up the disposal of snow from round the ozone loft.

During the morning I continued with the seismic work and then in the afternoon I went into the radio sonde room, to prepare an ozone sonde for its flight.

JULY 4. At 4 a.m. the air temperature was −31°C. There was a light breeze for most of the day. The morning was cloudy but the rest of the day was fine.

Bill started work on the runners of our new man-hauling sledge. The Tufnol runners were removed a few days ago so today he was cleaning and smoothing the wood.

The large roller blind door of the balloon shed was cleared of compacted snow and hoar frost by means of the 'swing fog' heater, which generated a blast of hot dry air over the roller. After this treatment, the door again moved smoothly.

At night I made some star shots to determine the azimuth of the mark. The air temperature was −37°C but there was little or no wind, making it a good and comfortable night for this work.

JULY 5. The temperature was −30ºC at 4 a.m. It was a fine day with a gentle breeze blowing.

I was on gash duty today.

We heard from the USSR base at Mirny that the issues of *Izvestia* published on July 2 and 3 included a special section called 'Antarctica Speaks'. Contained in it were reports from several Antarctic bases, including our own report.

We showed our usual film show at 8:30 p.m.

SUNDAY JULY 6. At 4 a.m. the temperature was −29ºC. The weather was fine with a gentle breeze.

Eight persons sang lustily at the religious service I led at 11:15 a.m.

In the workshop, Bill continued to work on the man-hauling sledge in preparation for his spring sledging journey.

JULY 7. The temperature was −26ºC at 4 a.m. The day started off as a fine one but the wind soon rose to become a strong south-westerly breeze before noon and remained strong for the rest of the day.

A strong south-westerly breeze made balloon launching difficult this evening. Three balloons were filled before one successful flight was achieved.

I worked during the day on the geomagnetic data and the astronomical observations.

In the workshop, Bill was lacquering the wooden runners of the sledge.

An Unusually Long and Bright Display of Aurora

JULY 8. At 4 a.m. the air temperature was −40ºC. A light or gentle breeze blew for the day, with variable cloud, some fog and a little snow.

It was unusual to observe auroral activity from 9 a.m. when there was a brilliant red and green drapery in the sky. The aurora at 1:08 p.m. formed an arch extending in elevation from 14º to 45º and was red. As soon as I saw it, I woke Gwynne, even though he had only just gone to sleep. He said he was very pleased to be wakened to observe such a display. This particular display was probably the most intense we saw and continued on until 9 a.m. on the 9th.

The disturbed ionospheric conditions, associated with the auroral display, closed down all our radio communications. I could not send off to London our regular Tuesday report for the Royal Society. We could not hear either the Ship Press transmissions from Rugby or the 'Calling Antarctica' programme.

At Halley Bay, David Cansfield and Malcolm drilled a hole in the sea-ice and measured it to be 4 ft. 10 in. (1.47 m) thick.

Bert continued working at Emperor Bay on his penguin embryo collection.

JULY 9. The air temperature at 4 a.m. was −41°C. It was a fine or partly cloudy day with a light or gentle breeze.

Communications improved slightly, so we could make a start sending to Port Stanley our backlog of meteorological reports. The backlog took an hour and a half of solid transmitting to clear. Our air letters were still held up and we could not make any contact with London.

I spent much of the day working on the analysis of the seismic records.

JULY 10. The 4 a.m. temperature was −40°C. It was a fine day with a clear sky. At night it became very cold. Conditions were coolest at 10:00 p.m. when the temperature was −46.6°C (−52°F) and there was an 8 kt (15 kph) easterly wind which would give a windchill factor of 2110. (Ref. Siple 1945).

The very clear sky conditions permitted me to make twilight observations at 15-minute intervals throughout the whole day.

Bill completed a major part of the work required on the man-hauling sledge and hung it up out of the way in the corridor. As a side benefit of the recent spate of activity there, the workshop has been cleaned up and looked a deal healthier for it.

Alf reported that the removal of a humidifier from the generator shed had not resulted in any significant extra wear on the generator slip rings or the generation of sources of interference.

At 11:50 a.m. the local television sound receiver was turned on and signals from London were received. This was considered unusual, for these signals were not expected to return until September.

For a week now the temperatures at the top of the balloon sonde ascents had shown no significant change. This compares with the situation through June, when these temperatures fell day by day down to −95°C. Now they have remained steady for several days at −90°C. We are still able to fly the balloons up to satisfactory heights.

Malcolm was busy in the north-eastern tunnel, where the subsidence of the roof had trapped some of the food boxes. This job was still a lot easier than extricating them from the food dumps outside.

Today was Bill's birthday, so we gathered together in the lounge at 8 p.m. to drink to his good health and help him celebrate the occasion.

JULY 11. At 4 a.m. the temperature was −45°C, the minimum temperature was −48°C. It was a very cold day with a partly cloudy sky.

Bert collected penguin eggs at Emperor Bay. He now has about 50 embryos in his collection. In the evening he measured our weights and fat thickness. The thickness of your layer of fat was measured with a pair of graduated calipers which pinched a fold of fat at your waist.

This morning we used a 1000 g silicone rubber balloon for the ascent after dipping it in an Avtur and lubricating oil mixture. It ascended to the 20 mb level.

From 10:40 to 11:30 a.m., London television sound was received surprisingly well for the season, the signal was Strength 1 at times.

I went up to the non-magnetic hut today and adjusted the normal geomagnetic variometer.

JULY 12. The temperature at 4 a.m. was –31°C. The wind rose steadily though the day and developed into a fresh gale at 8 p.m.

In the afternoon I took an extended walk round the base to look at all the store dumps and aerials and, incidentally, to take some exercise. The third-year (1959) hydrogen chemicals and emergency dumps, originally four feet (1.22 m) above the surface on Dexion platforms, remain two feet (60 cm) above the snow surface and show no signs of imminent burial. Two tractors were placed on top of one of last year's larger drifts and were skilfully placed to minimize any drift effects. The top of our food store and the third-year food boxes were now level with the prevailing snow surface. Dump 5 and the other Dexion platform dumps erected last spring were becoming buried. The boat was suspended on davits four feet (1.22 m) above the surface, to keep it free from drifting snow and ready for immediate use in an emergency. There was no sign, apart from their marker stakes, of the oil and coal dumps. All dumps were well marked.

Alf finds that about 10% of fuel oil supplied last year caused heavy deposits of carbon on the fuel injectors. This fuel also smells unpleasant and is thought to have a high water content, due, perhaps, to being drawn from the dregs of a large store.

The day was notable for the large range of the air temperature, from –41.3 °C at 00:00 UT (10 p.m. on the 11th) to –12.9°C 24 hours later.

SUNDAY JULY 13. The temperature at 4 a.m. was –15°C. The rather gusty gale continued, accompanied by heavy snowfall. As a consequence, the balloon shed required a considerable amount of digging out both in the morning and again in the evening. Derek took photographs of Andrew, John Smith and me doing this work in the evening and stimulated our efforts.

Les took the morning service today.

JULY 14. The temperature at 4 a.m. was –13°C. The gale ended in the early hours of the morning and drifting snow ceased by 7 p.m.

I went out in the morning to dig out the balloon shed door, which now lies between walls of snow nine feet high (2.74 m). Thirty feet (9 m) downwind of the hut a ridge of snow-drift has formed midway between the previous snow-drift ridges. During the storm you could see how this new ridge was formed by the confluence of the snow drifts emanating from the north and south sides of the hut. Last year, by contrast, each side of the hut formed a separate drift ridge with the larger one being thrown up from the north side.

For much of the day I worked on the analysis of the seismic and geomagnetic records.

JULY 15. The temperature at 4 a.m. was −26°C. There was a moderate breeze blowing for most of the day. Cloud moved over the base during the day.

In the morning I typed up to date the Base Diary and prepared the signal to the Royal Society which went off every Tuesday. We reported on the most intense displays of aurora seen on the 8th and 9th, in addition to the routine load of scientific information on meteorology, ionospheric physics and radio astronomical observations. Our best wishes and the following message were sent to the UK Delegation to the Fifth Antarctic IGY Conference:

> We are confident that your efforts will maintain the atmosphere
> of fruitful cooperation to digest the IGY expedition observations
> and provide a springboard for the future.

During the night, Les was in radio contact with the Belgian base, using the amateur band of frequencies. We also heard from the Australian base at Mawson that they had experienced winds of 120 knots (222 kph), which had blown down some of their aerials. Radio reception on other wave bands continued to be poor, so that we could not receive the regular broadcast of 'Calling Antarctica' with its messages for expedition members.

A Warm Day in Midwinter

JULY 16. At 4 a.m. the air temperature was −15°C but five hours later it was up to −9°C. It was cloudy in the morning and there was snowfall in the afternoon. After a short spell with a fresh breeze, for most of the day the wind was a gentle breeze.

At the launching of the balloon in the morning, there was a 19-knot (35 kph) north-westerly breeze. With this unusual wind direction, handling the balloon was difficult as we dragged it against the force of the wind. The first one burst as it struck the gallery to the roof of the shed. Another balloon was filled and launched successfully.

Les added an extra electronic valve to our overworked record player.

With an additional stage of amplification, the improvement to the quality of the sound was quite marked.

We made radio contact with the New Zealand party at Scott Base on the other side of the continent by the Ross Sea. We have had a regular communications schedule with Scott Base on Tuesdays and Fridays in the 8 Mc/s band. The quality of this particular link was generally excellent. The New Zealanders there were in the middle of a cold spell, with air temperature of −52.2°C being recorded. By contrast, our temperatures had recently shot up from below −40°C a few days ago to reach −9°C today. The relative warmth of the day caused water to drip from our ventilators.

JULY 17. The temperature was −14°C at 4 a.m. It snowed all day in a light or gentle breeze. The condition of the surface was like that prevailing in the summer.

There was a change in the international conventions and nomenclature for reporting geomagnetic phenomena, which meant I had to re-work my geomagnetic analysis. I worked away at this for part of the day; so far I had gone back over the records to January.

The temperatures outside were more like those of spring and the soft snow surfaces reminded you of summer. At the morning flight, the radar set developed a fault due to hoar frost deposits in the waveguide, the sort of thing we normally only experienced in the spring or summer.

I reviewed the consumption of Avtur through the recent cold spell. In the last 20 days, the rate of consumption had dropped to a satisfactory level. Bill expressed his satisfaction with the amount of electricity allocated to the ionospheric programmes. He had not noticed the reduction in the period of running of the Enfield generator, which was a part of the new economy regime. I then went out to look at the coal dump and the amount inside the hut. Outside there was now three feet (91 cm) of snow on top of the coal dump. Inside the hut there was sufficient coal for about three weeks, 60 bags and a full bunker.

The number of electrical light bulbs used in the past month dropped slightly, due to rationing. The level of lighting was satisfactory and there had been no complaints. At this rate there will be a small reserve left for 1959.

The warm spell resulted in considerable melting of snow from round the generator shed. As a consequence, Ivor had to shore up the verandah over the north door of that shed.

We heard the good news that in August there would be a collection of our air letters arriving at Port Stanley.

Signs of the Return of the Sun

JULY 18. The temperature at 4 a.m. was −19°C. It was either cloudy or snowing all day in a light or gentle breeze.

It became clear today that the duration of twilight was increasing every day. This brightening up had been concealed by recent heavy cloud. As it broke, we appreciated that the sun was indeed on its way back to us and this raised everybody's spirits.

A coded confidential signal was received from the Royal Society today. It was incomplete and corrupted by poor radio transmission conditions. As far as I could make out, it concerned our relief ship and the possibilities of taking *Tottan* as far as Capetown. It would be another day before we would know fuller details of something that was in all of our minds – our relief in December.

For the rest of the day I continued on a geomagnetic analysis of magnetically quiet and disturbed days. I also examined the records of 240 bay-like changes to the earth's magnetic field recorded in our first six months.

It was Simon's second birthday and I wondered what he and Oonagh were up to.

We Start to Consider Our Return Voyage

JULY 19. The temperature at 4 a.m. was −26°C. It was a cloudy day with a light breeze.

I received the corrections to yesterday's fascinating cable. Apparently the Royal Society were considering hiring the *Tottan* to relieve the base in December and possibly take us to Capetown for transshipment to regular ocean liners for the rest of the trip home. Nothing was yet firm.

There was no doubt we all approved of *Tottan* and her crew. This ship was actually built in Yorkshire. After the war, the Norwegians bought and refitted her for use as a polar sealer, with a range of action to 10,000 miles (16,093 km). With a displacement of 540 tons, she was the smallest of all the vessels used to service IGY bases in Antarctica but she had a reputation for successful ice navigation, which we recognized as second to none. If *Tottan* was hired for us, most of us believed we had the best possible chance of getting home in 1959. The idea of Capetown sounded great, though those attractive ladies some had left behind in Montevideo would be disappointed.

From yesterday's examination of the bay-like disturbances in the earth's magnetic field, called 'bays', I formed a qualitative picture of the nightly movement of the current systems to produce these distur-bances. This comprised a clockwise current vortex to the north of the auroral zone and on the average, say 600 to 1200 miles (966 to 1931 km) in diameter, and a very much smaller anti-clockwise vortex to the south of the zone. These would be centred near magnetic midnight and ahead in time of the northern vortex. There would be an east to north-east current in the north. This picture fitted the information from Terre Adelie, Argentine Islands and Halley Bay. It was similar to Figure C on page 881 of Chapman and Bartels, but the southern vortex would be weaker and smaller.

In his workshop up in the loft, David Tribble was fashioning a reversible mounting for Moll solarimeters to simplify the measurement of albedo, or the proportion of solar radiation reflected from the snow surface.

SUNDAY JULY 20. At 4 a.m. the temperature was −27°C. There was snow or thick cloud all day with a gentle or moderate breeze. In this rather dull weather, some of us went for short walks.

There were eight of us at the service this morning.

In the workshop, Bert and Philip were busy.

After doing some seismic analysis, I had a long conversation with David Harrison on the observations we had made and the character of the variation we had determined from our measurements of the earth's magnetic field.

JULY 21. The temperature was −29°C at 4 a.m. Snow fell again today and the wind rose to become a strong breeze.

The windows of the lounge, sealed by the advance party to keep out snow drift, were opened, fitted with catches and trimmed by Philip. They now open into the melted cavity beside the hut and provide excellent ventilation in all weathers.

We were requested by the Meteorological Office to punch on to Holerith cards the winds at higher levels than was our practice. During last night the meteorological team had taken this work back to January 1958. Alf now spends much of his spare time punching these Holerith cards, which has speeded up this aspect of our work.

David Tribble continued his work on a reversible solarimeter mounting.

I was on gash duty but also had the time to use the geomagnetic records to examine in detail the current vectors during the course of the recent great magnetic storm. To coincide with David Harrison's interest, I concentrated on July 8 for the period 18:00 to 22:00 UT. David and I continued our discussion until the early hours of the morning on the subject of geomagnetism and radio echoes from aurora.

The Base at Halley Bay May Not
Close Down After All

JULY 22. The temperature was −24°C at 4 a.m. Launching the balloons today was very tricky in the strong south-westerly breeze of 27 kt (50 kph). The meteorological team successfully accomplished these challenging launches in the morning and again in the evening.

The moon shone in a clear sky, accompanied by a faint mock moon and a pillar. The sky was red at 4 p.m., a rare sight at this time of the year.

Malcolm and I talked about the rate of milk consumption, which has increased, and certainly more would be drunk if it was available. We were both under the impression that a greater supply had been ordered last year but that does not seem to have been the case. Bert helped us out by giving Malcolm some of the surplus Complan from the medical stores, which can act as a substitute for milk. I reminded every one that the supply of milk was limited and had to be held to a strict ration.

Reception of 'Calling Antarctica' was moderate.

After analysing the seismic records, I compiled a very long report for the Royal Society. Amongst the usual scientific reports, there was a closely written, foolscap page report from David Harrison based on his analysis of the magnetic storm on July 8. During this storm, his radar was observing echoes from aurora which moved at speeds of up to 2000 m/s, at heights of about 110 km and some 400 km to our south.

In a cable from London we learnt that the future of the base at Halley Bay was being considered. Up till now it had been assumed that we would close the base upon our departure in January 1959. Now it seems there is a possibility of us being replaced by a new team for 1959.

JULY 23. The temperature at 4 a.m. was −29°C. The sky was mostly clear of cloud today, with a strong south-westerly breeze until lunch time and for the rest of the day there was a moderate breeze. The winds blew away, or ablated, six centimetres of snow in the last 24 hours, exactly the same amount of snow which had been deposited in the previous 48 hours.

For the first time since before midwinter, it was possible at midday to read a thermometer without the aid of a torch.

The first balloon burst when we tried to launch it this morning so we filled and successfully launched another one.

Len and Derek measured the fast sea-ice at Halley Bay to be 5ft 4 in (1.63 m) thick.

I completed the latest batch of seismic work and then prepared a short cable to London. I told the Royal Society that we can now notice each day being lighter than the previous one, with the period of winter darkness nearly ended. I also told them how the expedition members had remained in good health.

JULY 24. The air temperature at 4 a.m. was −31°C. The weather was cloudy with a gentle or moderate breeze.

It was fine out in the morning when I walked round some of the stores dumps. In one place, a box at an unmarked section of a dump was becoming buried so I carefully marked it with a new bamboo pole. Alf was outside too, removing solid waste to the gash dump. Bert was at Emperor Bay collecting eggs.

After completing some geomagnetic analysis, I talked with Bill about the close relationships between ionospheric and magnetic data. In particular I had noticed in the ionospheric data from Port Lockroy, that F Layer ionisation was greatly increased in the hours of maximum disturbance of the earth's magnetic field at Halley Bay. Bill had not yet examined this point using the Halley Bay data.

JULY 25. The air temperature at 4 a.m. was −28°C. There was a gentle breeze all day; the morning was fine and the afternoon was cloudy.

After lunch I talked with Joe Farman at the Argentine Islands base of FIDS; it was the first time contact had been possible for many months. We discussed the new conventions for the international exchange of geomagnetic data. We agreed it was an improvement over the former convention. Then I did some more work on the great magnetic storm of July 8 and discussed the results further with David Harrison.

Our weights and fat thicknesses were measured by Bert in the evening.

JULY 26. The temperature at 4 a.m. was −21°C. It was cloudy all day with some snowfall and snow drift kicked up by a fresh breeze.

During the day's seismic work, I examined the waveforms of the microseisms observed. I concluded they had the characteristics of very irregular Rayleigh waves. There were other disturbances, not from earthquakes which I thought local too, but with characteristics usually markedly different from those of microseisms. However, it was sometimes difficult to distinguish between these two classes of local disturbance.

The radar picked up an iceberg in a new position 19 km away on a bearing of 252°. The same berg was 21 km away on 21 July and a month ago it was 22 km away on a bearing of 260°. Keeping track of the places these bergs run aground give an indication of the topography of the sea bottom in the vicinity.

Weekend Hobbies Pursued Whilst
Winter Gales Rage

The hand is the cutting edge of the mind.

Jacob Bronowski

SUNDAY JULY 27. The temperature at 4 a.m. was −27°C. The weather deteriorated during the day, with snowfall and a strong breeze established by lunch time. The wind speed increased further to become a fresh gale at 4:35 p.m. At 10 p.m. snow was falling and the wind speed was up to 46 kt (85 kph).

There were five of us at the morning service.

The weather deteriorated during the day. The wind was gale force at 4:35 p.m. and continued to rise until it developed into a strong gale with Force 9 winds of 46 kt (85 kph) at 10 p.m. Despite the prevailing snow-drift conditions, very little digging was needed at the balloon shed before launching balloons.

With visibility down to 10 yards (9 m), it was not a good day for Sunday walks. Consequently the pursuit of inside hobbies was a feature of the day. Some were busy with their hands in the workshop, others were taking photos or developing films, or in the lounge reading, listening to music, playing chess or darts.

JULY 28. The temperature was −19°C at 4 a.m. A strong gale lasted until 10 a.m. but gale force winds persisted until just after noon. At 12:45 p.m., a cold front passed through the base, lowering temperatures by 6°C and backing the wind from 050°, 31 kt (57 kph) to 300°, 20 kt (37 kph).

Although the gale deposited the relatively large amount of 19 cm of snow on a level surface, there was 12 ft. (3.66 m) of snow to be cleared from in front of the balloon shed door before we could launch a balloon.

Then I needed to get to the seismographs in the glaciological pit. First I removed the 3 ft. (91 cm) of snow the gale had deposited over the entrance and then I climbed down the 30 ft (9 m) pit to adjust the seismographs.

Later on, I went over to do some work in the non-magnetic hut. I noticed that, as a result of the heavy snow accumulation of yesterday's storm, the instrument we used to standardize observations of magnetic declination, or the direction of magnetic north, now lay just below the level of the snow surface. Unless something was done, we would no longer be able to sight on the fixed mark 190 m away and be unable to refer magnetic north to true north.

Building Work Again Needed
in the Non-magnetic Hut

JULY 29. The temperature at 4 a.m. was −39°C. It was partly cloudy in the morning with a light breeze. The afternoon was overcast with poor visibility and snow drift in a freshening breeze. The radio sonde ascent showed how the recent northerly upper winds had led to a warmer upper half of the atmosphere together with a cooler lower half. The net result was to change its character completely.

First thing this morning I prepared to fix the problem in the non-magnetic hut, noted yesterday. I took a 12 ft. (3.66 m) sledge over to the appropriate stores dump and dug down until I found the stock of non-magnetic bricks, sand and cement. I loaded about 85 lb. (39 kg) of building supplies on the sledge and laboriously dragged it through the soft snow to the non-magnetic hut, along with some water to make mortar. Then I removed the marble slab on the top of the declinometer pillar and raised it by four courses of brick set in mortar, or over a foot (30 cm) in height.

Malcolm and David Cansfield set out for Halley Bay to measure the ice thickness. The visibility was so poor in the swirling snow drift that they failed to reach the bay, but returned safely to base.

In the generator shed, Alf and Ivor were busy decarbonizing the No. 2 Meadows.

I received a signal from London telling us the welcome news that the base would continue to operate next year, under the auspices of FIDS.

At 8:15 a.m. we received a 'Geocast' message from the USA base at Little America advising us that a solar flare was active at 1:00 a.m. and so magnetic, auroral and ionospheric disturbances were probable.

Continuation of Base Excites
and Occupies Us All

JULY 30. The temperature at 4 a.m. was −18°C. There was a strong breeze in the morning, a fresh breeze in the afternoon, and drift or snowfall all day.

I spent the day doing some seismic work and considering the requirements of the base for 1959. I prepared a 7-page signal for the Royal Society containing the report requested on the status of the base for continued operation in 1959. In brief, I reported that the major part of the base was capable of operating its programme of scientific observations through 1959. Most of the buildings were in good shape, but the generator shed was showing strains due to melting of the foundations. I said that the 1959 party should be equipped and prepared to lift the generators and repair the shed foundations. The tractors also needed overhauling. I recommended that a small, light sledge-mounted hut be supplied for ozone observations in 1959. The scintillation aerials would not function in 1959 due to burial, and a tunnel would need to be constructed for the geomagnetic fixed mark. As far as possible I sent off a signal which would make those coming aware of the special problems we saw them facing in 1959.

Most of the expedition came and expressed their pleasure at the news of the continuation of the base. Bert told me that he did not want to stay on for another year. John Smith said he did want to stay here and Ben told me he was thinking it over.

JULY 31. The temperature at 4 a.m. was –33°C. The weather was partly cloudy with a gentle breeze.

I finished off the work in the non-magnetic hut and cut a hole through the north wall at a higher level for sighting on the fixed mark. Then I placed the declinometer back on the top of the heightened pillar. When I put my eye to the telescope of the declinometer, the line of sight was well above the snow surface and I could again see the fixed mark, sitting there 190 m away and telling me where true north lay.

Bert collected the last Emperor Penguin embryos and Derek took photographs of the operation.

References

Siple, P. A. and Passel, C. F. 1945 *Proc. Am. Phil. Soc.* Dry Atmospheric Cooling in Subfreezing Temperatures.

Chapman and Bartels, Fig. C, p. 881.

Deacon, 1964, *RSIAE* Vol. 4, pp 348–352.

Dyer, 1964 *RSIAE* Vol. 4 pp 339–347.

MacDowall *Glaciology* 1, 1964 *RSIAE* Vol. 4 pp. 269–313.

MacDowall, Barclay & Burton *Glaciology* 2, 1964 *RSIAE* Vol. 4, pp 314–325.

MacDowall & Burton *Upper Air meteorology RSIAE* Vol. 3 pp. 161–382.

Chapter 6

The Return of the Sun in
1958 – Preparations for 1959

And then my hibernating soul
Will wake and drink again
Of sundeep warmth and joy of life.

L. W. Barclay in the *Halley Comet*

AUGUST I, 1958. The air temperature at 4 a.m. was −34°C. There was a moderate breeze and the day was cloudy at times.

Malcolm was opening food boxes and clearing out the empty crates from the food loft in the hut. Alf was out there taking empty boxes to the gash dump and clearing solid gash from the main hut.

Bill started to free the feeders and the ionospheric mast guy ropes, which were buried during the recent heavy snowfall. He was also constructing a tunnel for the feeders to the aerials.

We wired up a circuit to use the synchronome clock in the meteorological office so as to provide time markers for the ionospheric drift equipment.

At night I baked 6 lb. (2.7 kg) of bread.

AUGUST 2. At 4 a.m. the air temperature was −29°C. It was a cloudy day with a gentle breeze blowing.

I received a very lengthy and detailed coded signal from the stores officer in London about the stores required for 1959. Heaven knows why he should have gone to the trouble of coding and giving us both so many hours of extra effort.

The final form of my report on the probable state of the base for 1959 was sent off to the Royal Society.

I fixed a problem with the vertical variometer in the non-magnetic hut, which had lost its base line.

After lunch an ozone sonde was launched. We noticed an increase in the quantity of ozone in the lower atmosphere compared with one month ago.

Ivor, who always managed to keep himself busy with a wide variety of jobs, was busy sharpening all our kitchen knives.

Inside the hut, I was busy checking long lists of stores for 1959 and then I did a little seismological work.

In the morning we changed an electric motor on the fluxplate radiometer.

AUGUST 3. The air temperature at 4 a.m. was −25°C. The weather was cloudy at first with a gentle breeze. The wind freshened later, blowing up drift snow, which continued for the rest of the day.

At about 9 a.m. the bend at the base of the ionospheric mast became much larger and stayed that way for the rest of the day. Consequently I spent the morning helping Bill and Les to get out from a stores dump the equipment needed to erect a new aerial. By the end of the day, two of the four new aerial masts were erected and the folded dipole was laid out in the corridor ready for erection.

For the rest of the day I spent the time going over lists of stores for the 1959 party.

AUGUST 4. The temperature at 4 a.m. was −24°C. Snow was drifted all day, driven by a fresh easterly breeze.

It was the August Bank Holiday so we worked the Sunday routine. There was chicken for lunch followed at 4:15 p.m. by a showing of one of our better films called *John and Julie*, after which an excellent buffet supper was served.

I took Bill's gash duty because of the problems he faced in providing a replacement for the damaged ionospheric aerial masts, which could collapse completely at any time.

During the day many of us were busy going over the lists of stores required for the operation of the base in 1959.

AUGUST 5. The air temperature was −29°C at 4 a.m. Although a gale did occur in the evening, the wind for most of the day was a strong breeze and there was snow in the afternoon. The old, bent mast was unaffected by the gale.

Bill erected the spare ionosonde aerial.

We were again disappointed in not being able to receive the BBC programme 'Calling Antarctica', either directly from London or via the relay from Port Stanley.

I discussed with Alf some of the additional work we would have to do to ensure the continued operation of the base in 1959. The floor of the generator shed needed securing and the tractors required additional servicing. He would also need to tidy up the wiring system of the hut to make it easier for new people to manage. The new party should be equipped with lifting tackle in case they have to lift up the generators. They would need at least one new engine for the tractors.

AUGUST 6. At 4 a.m. the temperature was −22°C. There was a strong breeze for most of the day, with snow falling in the morning and a gale in the evening.

The bent mast sustained another short gale with no visible change to its state.

Many of us continued on the rather tedious and lengthy, but essential, work of going through the long lists of stores, updating them from the current holdings, listing the new requirements for 1959 and transmitting these to London.

Henry started to receive the radio transmission of our air letters from Port Stanley, which had just arrived there by sea from Montevideo. They were the first air letters we had received since the autumn. Their receipt greatly stimulated conversation as we shared with each other some of our news from home.

AUGUST 7. The air temperature was −8°C at 4 a.m. The moderate gale in the morning kicked up high drift snow. Later on the wind dropped and it snowed for the rest of the day.

We were working away on stores lists or indents for much of the day. Seven long lists of general stores were finished and telegraphed back to London. I also informed the Royal Society that John Smith had definitely decided to stay on for 1959, whereas Ben Ellis had decided to return home. Then I did some seismic work.

Bill and Les continued work on the feeder to the stand-by ionosonde aerial. The shaft and hatch entrance I constructed over the south-western hut door were of assistance to their work, which would have been more difficult in the poor weather without this facility.

Alf and Ivor were also busy outside, digging out and repairing the ladder from the north door of the generator shed.

AUGUST 8. The temperature at 4 a.m. was −13°C. Snow fell all day, moderately at times. There was a fresh breeze for most of the day but at 10 p.m. there was a moderate gale force wind blowing.

We finished three more stores lists and sent them off to London. The specialist lists of scientific stores were coming along well and will be ready in good time.

I went over to the balloon shed in the evening and joined in digging the door clear of snow with Gwynne, David Cansfield, Andrew, and Derek. With a larger than normal component in the wind from the north, the drift from it formed a two- or three-foot (60 or 90 cm) high ridge on the south-west side of the hut which took us about half an hour to clear.

The ionospheric group continued work outside on their stand-by aerial feeder. There was no change to the condition of the bent mast during the day. It still stood up and did its work.

We received a Geocast signal from Little America warning us of moderate solar flare activity.

I received an air letter from Oonagh dated June 7. It was the first one I had received for nine weeks.

It was a very busy day preparing stores lists and digging away drifted snow. I finally got to bed in the early hours of the morning after preparing an important and urgent cable for the Royal Society regarding 1959.

AUGUST 9. At 4 a.m. the air temperature was –16°C. The wind remained at gale force all day, peaking at a speed of 42 kt (78 kph). There was some snowfall during the day.

More stores lists were sent off today, which only left unfinished the lists for tools, generators and scientific stores.

In the afternoon I tidied up a part of the general store in the loft. The two films *Landfall* and *Geordie* were shown.

At about 2 a.m., and in filthy weather, Bill and Les finished the new aerial connection. There was a gale out there with a 42 kt (78 kph) wind.

Ivor used the swingfire heater to clear away the ice deposited in one of the hut ventilators.

SUNDAY AUGUST 10. The temperature at 4 a.m. was –14°C. The weather improved today after a long spell of continuous snow drift or gales. The snowfall and gale-force winds of the morning moderated during the day, so by 7 p.m. there was only a light breeze blowing.

After finishing my job of clearing up the general store, I went for a walk with our dog, Stumpy, who was very lively.

I was disappointed that cloud to the northern horizon prevented us seeing any sign of the sun, which was due back any day now.

The Sun Shines On Us Again

AUGUST 11. The air temperature at 4 a.m. was –29°C. It was a splendid day outside, with just a light breeze blowing and the sun visible over the horizon from 10:50 a.m. to 12:20 p.m.

We took the opportunity of the fine day to bring 7 tons of coal into the hut and also cleared up the solid gash. After breakfast I went over to the coal dump to open it up and was joined by John Smith. Soon there was a party of eight of us working away with a will, with four more persons toiling away inside the hut. There was 3 ft. (91 cm) of snow on top of the dump and dragging the 260 sacks up the extra distance slowed us down by comparison with the last time the job was done. Six persons dragged the sacks out of the dump, two more carted them to the hut and sent them down the chute, for the other four to finish the job by stacking the bags neatly in the store. The job was completed just after 1 p.m. Whilst the coal dump was open, I took the opportunity to obtain an independent check on the coal stock which would be available for the 1959 party.

Bert visited Emperor Bay and could clearly hear that the chicks had been born. What perfect timing to arrive on the day of the sun's return!

Len and Derek drilled a hole in the sea-ice at Halley Bay and found it was 6 ft. (1.83 m) thick.

In the afternoon John Smith was learning how to do some of the geomagnetic work in preparation for his duties in 1959.

David Harrison was extracting his third year scientific stores from the dump to simplify the work of the incoming party.

Ivor fitted an extension to the southern main hut ventilator pipe to prevent it from becoming buried.

The Birth of an Iceberg at Halley Bay

AUGUST 12. The air temperature was −34°C at 4 a.m. It was another fine morning with some cloud in the afternoon. There was a light or gentle breeze blowing.

At 9 a.m. several of us noticed a marked change in Burlington Bluff, our name for the southern cape of Halley Bay, which had risen up by 50 ft. (15 m) in less than 24 hours.

In the morning Andrew and I went out with our spades to extend the tunnel in the snow which allowed us to sight on the fixed mark.

Ivor lifted up the floor boards of the generator shed and I examined carefully the foundations of the hut. Melting below was most marked in the centre of the room, where the No. 2 Meadows, which had been most used during the year, discharged hot air. The maximum extent of melting was three feet (91 cm) below the foundations. However, melting at the edge of the hut was slight and I could see no reason to suspect catastrophic subsidence of the hut or generators.

For the first time since before midwinter, the BBC programme 'Calling Antarctica' could be heard in moderate strength on both 9.7 and 12 Mc/s.

Ivor deepened the passage to the generator shed.

I sent the weekly signal off to the Royal Society containing more information on stores requirements for 1959 and scientific information in meteorology, geomagnetism, seismology, and radio astronomy.

AUGUST 13. At 4 a.m. the air temperature was −40°C. The early morning was fine but there was slight drift in a moderate or fresh breeze for the rest of the day.

Alf and Ivor have been very busy in the generator shed, improving it for 1959. They have reinforced the foundations of the hut and reduced the rate of under-floor melting by increasing the ventilation inside the hut. Then they started additional work on the tractors to extend their life in 1959.

During their spell of night duty, David Harrison and Gwynne made arrangements to conduct simultaneous visual and radar auroral observations.

The Geocast received at 2:15 a.m. from Little America said that solar flare conditions were quiet.

AUGUST 14. At 4 a.m. the air temperature was –39°C. It was another fine day with a gentle breeze, with the air temperature going down to –45°C in the early afternoon.

I went on to the sea-ice at Halley Bay to see Burlington Bluff, that broke off from the western cape of Halley Bay two days ago. It was a remarkable demonstration of the forces of nature at play under the ice shelf. A depth of 100 yards (91 m) of the bluff had broken off on a front of about 400 yards (366 m). On breaking, the northern edge closest to the bay had tilted upwards so that it ended up 60 ft. (18 m) above the general level of the remaining cape. The inland edge was sunk below the general level. The whole block was tilted with its upper edge resting against the shelf. Observations of the area were somewhat hampered by the fog produced by our generators, that had drifted down with the wind to shroud the whole area, giving it a ghostly appearance in the half light conditions which still prevailed in this season.

Alf and Ivor continued their work on the tractors to ensure they will be fully capable of unloading and will be in the best possible shape for the 1959 party.

Les erected a dipole aerial to use for his work communicating via the amateur, or 'ham' radio waveband.

In the evening we gathered together to celebrate the birthday of Derek Ward and myself, after which I was finally in a position to announce to everyone that *Tottan* had now been booked to relieve us in December. There was general satisfaction with the news.

I received a telegram from Oonagh and I sent off replies. Both Derek and I received telegrams with birthday greetings from the Royal Society.

AUGUST 15. The air temperature was –33°C at 4 a.m. Most of the day was cloudy but the sky cleared during the evening; there was a light or gentle breeze blowing.

Ben fitted a pane of glass at one end of a packing case which was open at the other end. Then he placed this at the top of a shaft he had dug down to one of the bunkroom windows. His initiative provided the only natural light entering the main hut at present.

Alf and Ivor continued working on the tractors.

Bill started to dig out from the stores dump the supplies of chemicals and photographic recording paper required for ionospheric operations in 1959.

There were two very good radio sonde ascents today. One rose to the 25 mb pressure level and the other to 22 mb.

During the night Gwynne and David Harrison were making joint observations of the aurora.

For part of the day I analysed seismological records and in the evening I took observations of the stars to determine the azimuth of the fixed mark. Then I baked 4 lb. (1.8 kg) of bread and enjoyed eating some of it, hot from the oven and dripping in butter, in the company of Gwynne and David Harrison, who were also up that night.

AUGUST 16. I spent a very pleasant day outside in a partly cloudy day with a moderate breeze and an air temperature near −40°C. Bill and I were digging out 27 crates of ionospheric stores and carting them into the hut. This cleared all scientific stores from that particular dump, which now only contains food and canteen supplies.

The morning balloon reached the 15 mb pressure level at a height of 24.85 km. We considered this to be an exceptionally high level in any season.

The meteorological screen was raised by 16 inches (41 cm) to allow for snow accumulation.

SUNDAY AUGUST 17. At 4 a.m. the air temperature was −41°C. The day was mainly fine with a moderate breeze.

I took the religious service at 11:15 a.m. this morning.

Bill was sorting out his third year stores; some were put into the general store and the rest were stacked in the corridor.

One balloon burst this morning whilst we were attempting to launch it in a tricky SW wind. A second one was filled and launched successfully.

Derek collected plankton from the sea-ice at Halley Bay. Many diatoms could be seen under the microscope.

There was a display of aurora at night with a corona at times. I went outside to look at it, by lying on my back in the snow and observing in great comfort a splendid corona which lit up the sky from 9:15 to 9:30 p.m.

Some of the ionospheric equipment was blacked out by the resulting ionospheric disturbances, but they could be observed on the ionospheric drift equipment.

AUGUST 18. The day was mainly fine with a light breeze and the temperature below −40°C for most of the day.

A new battery bank was fitted up for the geomagnetic recorders. This supply was separate from that used to supply the fluxplate radiometer motors and not subject to continuous trickle charge.

Alf and Ivor finished work on the tractor.

David Harrison was playing back his tape-recorded comments on the aurora and correlating them with radio echo observations.

Bert flushed out the latrine hole with quantities of hot water.

I was busy with geomagnetic work, looking at the relation between radio blackouts and geomagnetic K indexes, and I also checked the FIDS Base F list of phenomena. Then I worked on the analysis of some of my astronomical work. Afterwards I enjoyed the luxury of my bath night.

AUGUST 19. A mainly fine day with a gentle breeze and an air temperature which fell to −46°C in the morning.

We heard from the Royal Society that the message we sent was read out at the 5th Antarctic Conference of the Special Committee for the IGY (SCAR), who in turn replied to us. In the signal I sent off to London, I thanked Dr Martin for his birthday greetings to Derek and myself. The signal also contained scientific data in the fields of meteorology, geomagnetism, ionospheric physics, seismology and radio astronomy.

Bill showed me radio echoes from meteors recorded by his absorption equipment. Watching from 4:15 to 5 p. m, we saw seven of them at a range of about 120 km.

I did stores work all day, working on more of the official requisitions, or indents of the stores for 1959.

Philip was working in the kitchen giving a coat of paint to the snow chute he made for the water tank.

Reception of 'Calling Antarctica' was good so I was fortunate to be able hear the personal message it contained for me.

AUGUST 20. At 4 a.m. the air temperature was −46°C. The weather was cloudy with a gentle or moderate breeze kicking up light snow drift at times. Although the air temperature was no colder than it was during the last two days, it seemed very cold outside due to the stronger winds.

Alf and Ivor were outside much of the day. One tractor was running and they were in the process of starting the other by towing it.

David Tribble was attempting to make an induction motor drive the ventilating fan for an Assmann psychrometer. If this were possible, it would reduce both the amount of maintenance required and the interference caused by the brushes of the present electric motors.

I continued to work on the stores requisitions for 1959 and sent off to London the indents for general tools, building materials and specialized tools.

AUGUST 21. The air temperature was −33°C at 4 a.m. There was slight low drift and snow for part of the day and it was cloudy for the remainder.

The last of the requisitions for general stores were sent to London, covering bedding, recreational equipment, camping equipment, post office stores, medical supplies and supplies for our voyage home. The inventory of meteorological stores was complete and all items consolidated into one list.

Philip was working at the remote huts beside his aerials.

Electric light bulbs are in short supply, with the weekly ration being exhausted in five days. The rationing does ensure that no place is short of light for more than two or three days per week. Of course, the total number of lights used has been reduced and those parts of the hut not used for close work are now dimly lit by 15 Watt bulbs and look a little dreary.

AUGUST 22. At 4 a.m. the air temperature was −38°C. It was cloudy most of the day with a gentle breeze.

Derek collected diatoms, stones, and part of a penguin egg shell from a section of Burlington Bluff recently heaved up from below water level.

At the balloon shed this morning, a filler cap, stowed on top of the generator, fell on Andrew's face and cut his lip. We brought him back to the hut and Bert put a stitch in his upper lip. Bert was noticeably full of beans after being able to practice his craft for a change. His display of good humour no doubt helped Andrew too.

In the morning I went out to the food dump and dug down to the third-year store of beer to check the quantity against our records; it would not do to get the amount of this commodity wrong. There were 21 cases there, which did in fact agree with our calculations. I also did some glaciological work and then sent a report of our geomagnetic phenomena to Joe Farman at FIDS Base F.

David's induction motor Assmann psychrometer was in use.

AUGUST 23. At 4 a.m. the air temperature was −33°C. It was not a very good day outside, with snow drift and a fresh breeze for much of the time. Despite the weather, Bill, Jim, and Malcolm went for a walk from Emperor Bay to Halley Bay on the sea-ice.

I spent some time working inside on the glaciological data forms which provide the daily record of snow accumulation and other glaciological information.

SUNDAY AUGUST 24. At 4 a.m. the air temperature was −29°C. Most of the day was fine with a gentle breeze.

I was on gash duty and took the morning service; there were six of us present.

Many of us were out taking a walk to the bays and Len was out trying to find a seal for Stumpy's dinner.

Philip was putting a second coat of paint on the snow chute to the kitchen water tank.

AUGUST 25. At 4 a.m. the air temperature was −28°C. It was a cloudy day with a gentle breeze.

I spent much of the day typing up various reports.

During last night John Gane made modifications to the radio cabin, improving its facilities and appearance.

The boxes of ionospheric stores remaining in the corridor were cleared away to the general store.

The runners of the second man-haul sledge were lacquered.

For the evening radio sonde ascent, two balloons had to be filled.

AUGUST 26. At 4 a.m. the air temperature was −20°C. It was a mainly cloudy day with a gentle or moderate breeze.

During the morning I did some seismic work.

Because he plans to stay at Halley Bay next year, I took John Smith with me to the non-magnetic hut, to show him the ropes when I went there to adjust the three normal sensitivity variometers for the gradual rotation of the ice-shelf.

In the 'Calling Antarctica' programme, the Director-General of the Meteorological Office, Sir Graham Sutton, gave a talk to us which was greatly appreciated. He told us about the poor August weather experienced by the UK, the plans for our base in 1959, and his recent visit to Moscow for the meeting of the Special Committee for the IGY. Reception was good.

John Gane continued with his good work to improve the radio cabin. He had laid new lino on the floor, improved the facilities for stowing spares, and he had fitted a home-made version of an anglepoise lamp.

AUGUST 27. At 4 a.m. the air temperature was −27°C. It was a cloudy day with a light or gentle breeze blowing.

I sent a signal to Vinje at Norway Base giving the details requested of our ozone sonde.

Len deepened the tunnel leading to the generator shed and then he went off to the bay with the rifle to see if he could get any seals for Stumpy. Although he found many seal tracks, together with some bloody tracks and blow holes, he was not able to find any seals.

After cooking all day, Malcolm was still working away in the kitchen in the evening cleaning the paintwork and the windows.

AUGUST 28. The air temperature was −35°C at 4 a.m. The wind rose during the morning and remained a fresh or strong breeze for much of the day. An extensive and dark water sky to the northwest of base gave a clear indication of the open water lying below those clouds. It was the largest water sky I had seen since before midwinter.

Philip was at the south remote aerial hut. Drift snow trapped him whilst he was working away inside the hut. This occurred because the hut was partly buried below the snow level, so he had to dig the door out before entering. Whilst he worked away inside the hut, snow drift silently started, built up and compacted against the door, holding it firmly closed. He escaped by knocking a hole in the door above the snow level. To prevent this from happening again, he fitted a canvas bag entrance to the hut similar to those fitted to tents.

Drift snow also gave us a problem in the generator shed, where it had entered via the improved ventilation.

Before launching a balloon this evening, David Cansfield, Andrew and I dug out the balloon shed door whilst John Smith worked away inside the hut generating hydrogen and filling the balloon.

David Tribble has fitted some new red lino inside the Decca radar.

I spent the day working on the glaciological data forms and added the pressure values back to February.

AUGUST 29. At 4 a.m. the air temperature was −28°C. The day was cloudy at first with a gentle breeze but after lunch it deteriorated. It started to snow and the wind rose to gale force by 5 p.m. and then increased further to a strong gale with 41 kt (76 kph) winds and a visibility of 15 yards (14 m) at 10 p.m.

In the morning Len was out sealing but again had no luck.

Notwithstanding these challenging conditions, balloons were successfully launched in the morning and again in the evening when the Force 9 gale was blowing at its strongest.

I baked 6 lb. (2.7 kg) of bread in the evening.

AUGUST 30. At 4 a.m. the air temperature was −22°C. It was a stormy Saturday. One gale ended at 5:20 a.m. with 48 kt (89 kph) gusts, but, after a brief respite, another one commenced 12 hours later.

David Tribble showed some of the photographs he has been taking of sastrugi, the ever-changing shapes carved by the wind into the snow surface.

After the evening film, several people showed the coloured slides they had taken during the winter. Philip's were up to his usual high artistic standard.

SUNDAY AUGUST 31. At 4 a.m. the air temperature was −14°C. There was a strong gale at first but the wind dropped during the day to 19 kt (35 kph) at 4 p.m. The air temperature went up to −5°C and freezing rain fell at 7 p.m. together with granular snow which was 4 mm in diameter.

A considerable amount of digging effort was required in front of the balloon shed door in the morning but it remained reasonably clear for the evening ascent.

In response to an article in *Communications and Electronic Journal* for Nov. 1956, I spent some time writing a short note on the subject of the operation here of electronic equipment.

SEPTEMBER 1. At 4 a.m. the air temperature was −11°C. There was snow and drift all day in a fresh or strong breeze. Glazed frost 2 mm thick was observed.

We had to dig our way to the balloon shed door again.

Len and Derek were clearing the passage from the main hut to the generator shed.

I was occupied with the seismic work for much of the day. I also talked with Bill about the close relationships between geomagnetic and ionospheric data.

SEPTEMBER 2. At 4 a.m. the air temperature was −15°C. It was cloudy most of the day with a moderate breeze. At night there was snow and drift in a fresh breeze.

I finished off my seismic work and then did some of the regular monthly summaries of the scientific work. This included a survey of August weather to send off in the Tuesday signal to the Royal Society. The cold winter temperatures had continued through last month combined with frequent gales. The month was notable for the heavy snow accumulation, the large range in air temperature and the lack of calm conditions. The extremes of air temperature ranged from −47°C on the 18th to −5°C on 31st.

I completed an inventory of food stocks and an estimate of the stocks which would be left on 1 January 1959 to hand over to the new team.

In the evening the 'Calling Antarctica' programme was received fairly well. There was a personal message for John Smith.

In our regular daily radio contact with Norway Base, we learnt that their relief ship would be arriving in December and staying until February to assist with the conduct of aerial survey of the area.

SEPTEMBER 3. At 4 a.m. the air temperature was −18°C. There was some slight drift at first but the day was mainly cloudy with a gentle breeze.

An ozone sonde was launched at 2:35 p.m. It reached the 24 mb level and was followed by radar out to a distance of 16 km, even though there was no radar reflector attached to the balloon. It was not our normal practice to use a reflector on ozone ascents or to measure winds, but David was working on the radar at the time of the ascent and was curious to know how far you could follow the rig without a reflector.

Andrew was out clearing snow from the tunnel installed to protect the line of sight to the fixed mark just to the north of the non-magnetic hut.

I spent much of the day analysing our geomagnetic observations and then had a further discussion with Bill over our scientific findings.

Ivor constructed a shaft leading down from the surface to the generator shed tunnel. It was equipped with a Dexion ladder and a hatch entry at the top.

Len went out sealing again but had no success.

As usual, at about 8 p.m. on Wednesday, the bottle of rum was available for those who liked a tot after dinner. An enterprising rum fancier discovered that the day was the tercentenary of Cromwell's death and proposed we recognise this anniversary in an appropriate manner. I agreed that was a good enough excuse to increase the ration of rum from one to two bottles amongst the 20 of us. A jolly evening did result and we all hoped the dour Protector did turn in his grave with his predictable disapproval.

SEPTEMBER 4. At 4 a.m. the air temperature was −31°C. The morning was cloudy with a gentle breeze; for the rest of the day there was snow with a fresh breeze and drift.

There was poor visibility due to snow and wind-driven drift when Jim took the ice drill to Halley Bay to measure the thickness of fast sea-ice there. It was 6 ft. 3 in. (1.9 m) thick.

I analysed yesterday's ozone ascent, which was one of the most successful, and appeared to penetrate right through the ozone layer. At first sight I questioned the degree of agreement between this ascent using Brewer's transmogrifier and the spectroscopic measurement made with the Dobson apparatus. I later found the two methods to be in very good agreement (Ref. MacDowall, J. in *RSIAE* Vol 3, p. 65 and 105).

It was very reassuring to find this measure of agreement between two methods based on such different physical principles. Dobson's depended on the spectroscopic character of ozone and Brewer's on the electrochemical effects of ozone. The former measurements were made from ground level and used a spectroscope to observe the degree ozone changed the quality of sunlight or moonlight. In the latter technique, we sent a detector into the ozone layer, sucked ozone-laden air through a liquid, and then measured the amount of electricity produced by the ozone.

Anthracite consumption in August was 4000 lb. (1814 kg).

Aurora was detected all night through cloud cover.

We received a cable asking about the re-establishment of the direct telephone link to London, as was done last year. The only problem was the possible effect of our powerful radio transmissions on the conduct of our ionospheric and radio echo observations, which I discussed with Bill, Philip, and David Harrison. It was agreed that we should use a schedule similar to the one of last year, which avoided some of the times of their observations. In addition, Bill said that he would prefer it if we delayed the commencement of the link until after the next World Meteorological Interval in the IGY Calendar, when he made extensive ionospheric drift measurements.

We were only able to hear part of the daily 'Ship Press' broadcast from Rugby, due to disturbed ionospheric conditions.

I sent off a cable to make the arrangements for Christmas presents to be delivered to Oonagh, Simon, and other members of my family.

SEPTEMBER 5. At 4 a.m. the air temperature was −26°C. Snow and snow drift driven by a strong breeze prevailed for most of the day.

The balloon shed door was dug out before we could launch a balloon, which rose up to the 20 mb pressure level in the atmosphere. This was a good performance considering the poor conditions prevailing at the launch, which often resulted in an early burst.

Using the most recent consumption figures, I recalculated the requirement for expendable meteorological stores in 1959.

John Smith came to express his concern that he had not yet had any response to his offer to remain at Halley Bay in 1959. I tried to reassure him and sent off an urgent request for London to speed up their bureaucratic staffing procedures for the 1959 party.

SEPTEMBER 6. At 4 a.m. the air temperature was −26°C. There was a moderate gale at first with snow, but for most of the day the wind was a moderate or fresh breeze with some drift and a little snow.

The Secretary of FIDS, the organization taking over Halley Bay in 1959 from the Royal Society, sent me a signal to say that he was happy with the stores arrangements we made for the hand-over of the base.

The USSR base at Mirny provided us with the heights above sea level of their three inland bases as follows: Komsomolskaya (74°5′S 97°29′E) and Vostock (78°27′S 106°52′E) 3420 metres, and Pionerskaya 2700 metres respectively.

Just before screening the Saturday night movie called *Turn the Key Softly*, David Harrison showed a time-lapse film, taken in August at one second intervals, of radio echoes from aurora. It was most effective and featured some very large echoes.

Signs of the Approach of Spring

SEPTEMBER 7. At 4 a.m. the air temperature was –25°C. It was cloudy most of the day with a gentle breeze.

Once again Len was out looking for seals but without any success. Fortunately we have not yet run out of food for Stumpy.

I went skiing on the slopes down from the ice-shelf to Halley Bay, for the first time since before the winter. Although no open water could be seen, there was frost smoke rising, indicating open water near a pressure ridge about a mile off Penguin Leap. Near the Leap, there was a group of about 20 penguins. Many more could be seen to the north and north-east and all of them were moving steadily southwards on their bellies. Bert said this return of penguins to Emperor Bay had been going on for the past week and that, as a result, the population had risen 50% to about 15,000 adults. They had been off to the sea to gorge so that they could return with full stomachs to feed their chicks.

Jim and I were looking over the year's observations of the winds at the 30 mb pressure level. We noticed that there was a change-over in about March from light north-easterlies in summer to strong south-westerlies or westerlies in winter. The 30 mb wind at present is normally from the west, as expected for the winter regime.

SEPTEMBER 8. At 4 a.m. the air temperature was –32°C. It was a fine day with a moderate or gentle breeze blowing.

As another sign of approaching spring, BBC London television sound broadcasts on 40 Mc/s were being received for three hours a day near noon.

Ben was constructing another of his skylights; this time he was bringing daylight down to the kitchen window.

Ivor spent most of the day constructing a small ventilating tower up from the generator shed to increase the degree of ventilation within this hut, which is often overheated.

A new mounting for a sunshine recorder was erected by David Tribble. At the same time, the Feuss solar radiation recorder was brought into use.

I spent the day measuring seismograms to determine the times of arrival of earth tremors from distant earthquakes.

Once again we had to remove snow from the tunnel built to allow us to observe the fixed mark from the non-magnetic hut.

Jim made up a new mixture of Avtur and lubricating oil used in the balloon shed for the pre-flight treatment of rubber balloons, a conditioning which permitted them to rise to much greater heights. As soon as we discovered that the mixture was most effective when fresh, we started to mix up a fresh dip every few days.

SEPTEMBER 9. At 4 a.m. the air temperature was −41°C. The sky was mainly clear but the wind rose during the day. Snow drift started just before lunch and, by the end of the day, there was a strong breeze with snow drift.

I sent off the regular weekly signal to the Royal Society with scientific data in several fields. Then I continued with the analysis of geomagnetic records. Later on John Gane and I talked about the close relations he observed between radio communications and magnetic storms.

We were told by the Royal Society that the *Tottan* was expected to arrive to relieve us at Halley Bay on 31 December 1958.

Apparently the scientists of the world planned to designate the year 1959 as a year of International Geophysical Cooperation. It sounded as though it was to be a mini-IGY for those who joined the IGY late or wanted to continue on for a few more years with their new or expanded scientific programmes.

Ben continued on with his good work to bring daylight to the kitchen.

Malcolm and David Cansfield went down to Halley Bay and measured the sea-ice to be 6 ft. 5 in. (1.83 m) thick.

The radio sonde ascent told us today that upper air temperatures were colder than usual. It was already below −90°C at the 65 mb level and −93°C at 44 mb.

Malcolm went out to the stores dump and dug out some boxes of food.

The 'Calling Antarctica' programme came through well this evening and David Tribble received his personal message.

The water storage tank in the balloon shed developed a leak and was replaced.

SEPTEMBER 10. At 4 a.m. the air temperature was −28°C. There was snow drift all day in a moderate gale or strong breeze, which blew the snow well above the surface.

Ben continued his work to fit a skylight over the kitchen window.

John Smith and I talked about the present difficulties of making total ozone observations due to the burial of the hut. The problem arose because the floor of the main hut loft, on which the Dobson instrument sat, was so far below the present level of the surface. This burial, combined with the low elevation of the sun, meant that we had to dig a long sighting trench in the snow every time we wanted to look directly at the sun. Even when observing the moon at higher elevations or the zenith sky, the slightest wind kicked up snow drift which interfered with the observations. Another solution would be to enlarge the hatch to the ozone loft and physically raise the whole spectrometer. Fortunately, the 1959 party should be bringing with them a separate small ozone hut to my design, which will be sledge-mounted and therefore able to remain on the surface.

Bill was busy making his regular Wednesday observations of the drift of ionospheric features.

I was on gash duty but also managed to type up all of the meteorological group's stores requirements for 1959 and sent them off to London in a signal 800 words long.

Alf and Ivor were decarbonizing the No 2 Meadows diesel.

SEPTEMBER 11. At 4 a.m. the air temperature was −28°C. The day was mainly a fine one with a moderate breeze.

A geophysical alert was in operation and the Geocast from Little America reported moderate solar flare activity.

Alf had a tractor running to clear solid waste away to the gash dump.

Ben completed his job of digging out the kitchen window and mounting a skylight on the top of the shaft flush with the snow surface. I copied Ben's idea by digging down to a window in the No. One Bunkroom and installed a skylight there.

Ivor extended by 3 ft. (91 cm) the ventilator to the toilet.

Malcolm brought some boxes of food over from the dump.

Following up on the discussion with John Smith, we started work to improve the facilities for ozone measurements.

We received a signal from Ostrekin at Mirny requesting the exchange of ionospheric data. He said that, at the Mirny Base, the ionospheric equipment receives reflections from a layer at an altitude of 45 km, which we do not observe.

I prepared and sent off more requisitions for scientific stores for 1959.

SEPTEMBER 12. At 4 a.m. the air temperature was −24°C. It was a rather cloudy day with a gentle breeze and some sunshine.

More scientific indents were prepared and sent off. Bill was checking his stores, too.

Although the alert continued, the Geocast was 'quiet'.

Our modifications to the ozone loft continued.

Bill and I went down to Emperor Bay and took ciné shots of the parents feeding their chicks. The adult birds were continuing to return to the rookery from their foraging expeditions. Then we spent a little time enjoying the pleasure of skiing down some of the steep slopes, which gave us an exciting ride down from the top of the ice-shelf to the sea-ice over 100 ft. (30 m) below.

In the evening I spent a little time teaching Len to make astronomical position fixes.

SEPTEMBER 13. At 4 a.m. the air temperature was −31°C. A dull day with slight snow and a light breeze.

Alert geophysical conditions continued with a Geocast forecast of moderate solar flare activity.

Bill and I both continued our work on the stores lists for 1959.

Because it was a World Meteorological Interval, we showed the movie from 4:15 to 7:45 p.m. so that the meteorological team could both see the films and launch their evening balloon afterwards. This practice did, of course, rather dampen the social period after the film show as we lost the pleasure of the company of several met. men. Fortunately this did not happen every Saturday.

SUNDAY SEPTEMBER 14. At 4 a.m. the air temperature was −28°C. The day was mainly cloudy with some snow and a gentle breeze.

At the morning service there were eight of us present and the singing was good and lusty.

I tidied up the general store and I went over, with John Smith, the meteorological requirements for 1959. John added to the list a few items he would need.

SEPTEMBER 15. At 4 a.m. the air temperature was −39°C. A beautiful day with blue sky, gentle breeze and a well-miraged landscape, a rare pleasure for us all.

A small hatch in the upper part of the ozone hatch was completed.

Henry measured a thickness of 6 ft 9 in. (2.06 m) for the fast sea-ice at Halley Bay.

The Alert conditions continued and the Geocast forecast of solar flare activity was quiet. The improved receipt of Geocast messages was mainly due to them being sent out regularly at the beginning and ending of the 2:15 a.m. broadcast from Little America base. Previously the time of dispatch varied. The seasonal improvement in ionospheric conditions has also improved the quality of radio communications with Little America.

The last of the long series of official requisitions for the stores needed in 1959 was completed and transmitted to London. Then I returned to finish off the glaciological data sheet for August, which I had put on one side for this important and welcome task so as to ensure success with the continuation of this base for at least one year.

SEPTEMBER 16. At 4 a.m. the air temperature was −30°C. It snowed for most of the day with snow drift from 5 a.m. The wind increased to gale force from just after noon and lasted until 6:15 p.m. Because of the weather, I went down to the balloon shed before the evening ascent, but rather little digging was in fact required.

In a signal from Dr Martin, we heard that the radio scintillation observations would not continue in 1959. In the same signal, he said that the Rolex company intended to present us with the watches we were all wearing. This particular item of news was very well received and appreciated. I found the accuracy and convenience of the Rolex watch quite invaluable for astronomical work, particularly during the winter.

I spent much of the day doing geomagnetic work or sending various signals off.

'Calling Antarctica' was heard very well this evening and Henry received his message.

SEPTEMBER 17. At 4 a.m. the air temperature was −19°C. Snow fell in the morning, then there was a strong breeze or moderate gale blowing for most of the day.

After helping to dig out the balloon shed in the morning, I did some geomagnetic work, including the consideration of a long signal on the subject from Joe Farman at FIDS Base F, Argentine Islands.

We studied the records of slip-ring wear on the Meadows alternator. We were relieved to find that the wear continued to be normal since the abandonment of the humidifier in the generator shed, which had consumed 2 kW of electricity. Prior to this, there had been excessive wear, and we now attribute this to more frequent overloading conditions rather than low humidity.

It was my bath night and afterwards I baked 6 lb. (2.7 kg) of bread.

More Signs of Spring and a Reminder of Summer

SEPTEMBER 18. At 4 a.m. the air temperature was −20°C. The weather cleared up rapidly in the early hours to leave a partly cloudy day with a gentle breeze. It almost seemed like a summer's day, with drops of melt water observed on the cloud searchlight.

There was a shore lead about a mile (1.6 km) off the ice-front and about six miles (10 km) wide. In the forenoon, a small berg drifted past Halley Bay moving south.

Ivor cut a hole through the roof of the generator shed to improve ventilation.

The modifications to the ozone loft were completed. The floor was raised so that the Dobson instrument was only three feet (91 cm) below the snow surface. In addition, the 2 ft 6 in. (76 cm) sun director could be poked through a small trapdoor in the upper half of the hatch. I discussed the programme with John Smith and we agreed that, with these changes, we were in a better position to institute an enhanced spring programme of ozone observations.

I did geomagnetic work for much of the day and then skied to Halley Bay to observe the sea-ice conditions.

SEPTEMBER 19. At 4 a.m. the air temperature was −21°C. It was a partly cloudy day with a light or gentle breeze.

The generator shed was cooled with the roof open. However, in starting up the generator, it was now necessary to place sacks over the radiator immediately after starting to shorten its warm-up period.

At 1:15 p.m. I spoke to Gaston de Gerlache from the Belgian base at Breid bay. He told me that he had recently spoken to Bunny Fuchs, who sent his regards to us all. Gaston was to continue his travel programme on October 10, when two men with two dog teams were to leave base, followed on October 20 by two Snocats, and then on October 30 by their helicopter. They were to pick up a depot laid in March and explore the mountain ranges to their south and south-east.

SEPTEMBER 20. At 4 a.m. the air temperature was −34°C. The morning was fine and the afternoon cloudy. There was a light or gentle breeze blowing all day.

The wide shore lead of yesterday was closed off by the south-westerly wind.

I continued with my geomagnetic analysis and then took some photographs of the new ozone-observing arrangements.

With the auroral observing season ending, Gwynne started working a part of the day on the analysis of his observations.

The film show was held in the afternoon because there was a World Meteorological Interval. The movies shown were *This Man is Mine* and *For Better or Worse*. The latter was being shown for the second time at the request of Les.

SUNDAY SEPTEMBER 21. At 4 a.m. the air temperature was −26°C. A gale started at 6:15 a.m. and lasted for most of the day. Snow fell from midday, reducing visibility to 15 to 20 yd. (14 to 18 m) in the swirling drift.

Les took the morning service at 11:15 a.m.

Some snow came in through the windows of the generator shed, so at 3 a.m. Alf was busy clearing up and sealing the windows.

Bill showed us some of the results of his ionosonde recordings made at one- and five-minute intervals.

Just before launching a radio sonde ascent, I went down to the balloon shed to help dig out the big door.

SEPTEMBER 22. At 4 a.m. the air temperature was −17°C. The gale continued all day with the easterly wind blowing at up to 40 kt (74 kph) at times. Snow continued to fall and the visibility for most of the time was between 40 and 80 yd. (37 and 73 m). It took four of us about 45 minutes to dig out the big door of the balloon shed, both in the morning and again in the evening.

At 1:30 p.m. the sun shone in a clear sky whilst the gale still raged. It was not often we had lighting conditions which allowed us to take photographs in bad weather. Usually, when a gale blew, you could photograph nothing but the whiteness everywhere. So David Tribble took the opportunity to carry the 16 mm ciné camera to the top of the anemometer tower and photographed the base.

I was typing for most of the day, when I was not digging away snow drifts.

During radio contact with the FIDS base at Deception Island, Les heard that the meteorologists there were not coming to Halley Bay next year. They were due for relief on November 15.

SEPTEMBER 23. At 4 a.m. the air temperature was –15°C. The gale ended in the early hours of the morning; for the rest of the day there was a strong breeze with cloud and drifting snow.

I went out in the morning and again in the evening, to join the party helping to dig the big balloon shed door clear of snow. For the rest of the day I was typing up signals, reports, and the base diary.

The snow drift from a recent northerly wind covered up the hatch at the northern end of the non-magnetic hut.

David Tribble was working to fix a problem with the radar.

The reception conditions were good for the receipt of 'Calling Antarctica' this evening. Alan Moore spoke well on the programme about his recent trip to Moscow and the interesting return journey he took through Scandinavia, where he saw the *Fram*.

We heard that the ionospheric equipment will have to be loaded up on *Tottan*, when she arrives in January, because it is required back in the UK.

The 1000th Balloon is Launched in a Strong Gale

SEPTEMBER 24. At 4 a.m. the air temperature was –17°C. Yet another gale started at 4:40 a.m. and created a filthy day. The east wind was blowing at 45 to 50 kt (83 to 93 kph) in a Force 10 gale for most of the time, reducing the visibility in the swirling snow drift to between 8 and 10 yards (7 and 9 m).

In the morning we launched what we called a split rig, by first launching a radio sonde on the smaller 500-gram balloon and following this with a second balloon carrying only a radar reflector. This was much easier to accomplish in the strong gale conditions of the day. Both balloons were launched successfully. It was the one thousandth balloon we had launched at Halley Bay.

The successful launch of the 1000th balloon was celebrated in the evening by showing the film *Dam Busters* and the special issue of a crate of beer.

A small amount of drift snow was entering the hut via the auroral hatch and water was dripping into the corridor below.

David Harrison was correlating radar and visual observations of aurora using the tape recorder.

SEPTEMBER 25. At 4 a.m. the air temperature was −9°C. The gale ended during the morning and the rest of the day was cloudy with snow drifting in a moderate breeze.

The balloon shed door was completely buried for the first time this morning. John Smith, John Gane, Andrew, Derek, and I were digging to clear it from 7:45 to 9 a.m.

Bill and I did more digging to salvage some of his empty boxes, which will now be required to take home the ionospheric equipment. The pile of boxes had been well-staked out but they were buried under at least three feet (91 cm) of snow.

Bill, Jim, and Henry were down at Halley Bay to make sea-ice observations. The fast sea-ice was 7 ft. 1 in. (2.11 m) thick. Snow drift prevented them seeing the state of sea-ice off the bay.

There was a great deal of discussion about the options for travel home. Several persons are thinking about leaving *Tottan* at her first port of call to make their own way home from wherever that may be.

Return of the Petrels

SEPTEMBER 26. At 4 a.m. the air temperature was −16°C. It was a cloudy morning with a little snow and a gentle breeze. In the afternoon there was snow drift with a fresh or strong breeze.

Bill and I returned to the tasks of digging out ionospheric crates and managed to extract about one-third of the pile.

There was a solitary Emperor Penguin chick at Halley Bay who had found his way round the headland from the rookery. A Snow Petrel and an Antarctic Petrel were seen there, the first we have observed since before the winter.

Les's birthday was celebrated with a sponge cake and then we toasted his health in sherry.

For the remainder of the day I did geomagnetic work. The recent snowfall had almost buried the fixed mark so we made a start with improving the arrangements. As a first step, the tunnel used to sight the fixed mark was dug out.

Alf had a tractor running and cleared away to the dump ten days' accumulation of solid gash.

Many people were now talking about the options for making their own way home from the first port of call of *Tottan.*

SEPTEMBER 27. At 4 a.m. the air temperature was −13°C. There was a strong breeze, cloud, drift, and some snow in the morning. The weather improved later and at 10 p.m. it became fine with a moderate breeze.

David Tribble was repairing the balloon shed roller-blind door, which was damaged during the recent poor weather.

John Gane started replacing the poles supporting the feeder poles where they had become buried under snowdrift.

Les fitted an extra circuit to the lounge record player so that it could act as a loudspeaker for broadcasts received in either the radio cabin or the ionospheric laboratory.

I was busy for part of the day with the geomagnetic analysis of quiet days, the so-called Q analysis.

SUNDAY SEPTEMBER 28. At 4 a.m. the air temperature was −27°C. It was a fine Sunday with a light or gentle breeze

I was on gash duty and also took the morning religious service at 11:15 a.m.

In the afternoon, whilst skiing at Halley Bay, I saw my first Snow Petrel of the season swooping along the edge of the ice shelf.

Alf saw a Leopard Seal when walking round the headland near Penguin Leap,

Les and Philip shot a Weddell Seal, so we had some of its liver for supper. Most of the party ate some and declared it to be good.

Due to its imminent burial, the fixed mark for controlling geomagnetic observations has been extended upwards.

SEPTEMBER 29. At 4 a.m. the air temperature was −31°C. There was light snowfall most of the day with a light breeze.

Repairs to the balloon shed roller-blind door were complete. The lower edge of the door was strengthened with Dexion fitted with replaceable wooden pegs at the edge to fit into the runners fixed to the door jamb.

Bill dug out nine more empty ionospheric equipment cases.

Len and Philip, aided by the dog in a harness, brought back part of the seal they shot near the ice edge off Halley Bay.

I worked on geomagnetic analysis for much of the day. Later on, I received from the US Geological Survey one of the many regular messages they sent to me giving the times of occurrence, location, and depths of earthquakes round the world. Using a small globe, from this information, I was able to estimate the approximate times of arrival at Halley Bay for the various tremors. Then I scanned the records and measured the exact times for several phases and reported this data back to London, who in turn sent it on the IGY seismological data centres. It was these precise times of receipt which were later used by the US scientist Frank Press to define the extent of the Antarctic continent.

Capetown Here We Come

SEPTEMBER 30. At 4 a.m. the air temperature was −26°C. There was slight snow or drift most of the day with a moderate breeze.

David Cansfield and Malcolm measured the thickness of sea-ice at Halley Bay.

Air Letters from our families started to arrive once again.

Ben was digging a tunnel to the south-east door of the main hut from a point midway between the main and radio echo huts.

The last of the present series of the 'Calling Antarctica' programme was heard; it included a message for Gwynne. We were able to enjoy the programme in the comfort of the lounge, thanks to the electronics Les has added to the record player. We appreciated the BBC lengthening the programme by 15 minutes.

Philip was curing the skin of a small seal found dead near the edge of the sea-ice near Halley Bay.

Alf was in the workshop during the day turning valves on the lathe.

We were all very excited to hear that our route home would probably be direct to Capetown and then by an ordinary ocean liner to the UK. Those who believed that the *Tottan* was a bit small felt that, for such a short trip, any ship was suitable. I composed a suitable reply to the Royal Society, saying how very pleased we were with the news of our routing home.

Preparing to Pack Up the Harvest
of Scientific Data

OCTOBER 1. At 4 a.m. the air temperature was −24°C. There was a fresh breeze with snow drift in the morning but the remainder of the day was cloudy with a gentle breeze and air temperatures above −28°C.

John Gane continued to work outside, digging out and placing above the snow surface the wires which connected our radio equipment to their aerials.

In the afternoon, I dug out half of the remaining canteen stores.

John Smith informed me that he no longer wished to stay at Halley Bay next year because he had received no reply to his offer. He reminded me that he made the offer on August 4 and had set October 1 as a deadline for the receipt of a firm reply. I advised him to be patient and to wait a little longer. The 1959 team would be very much weaker without John's sterling qualities. Furthermore, his detailed knowledge of the present scientific programme would make him a uniquely well-qualified team member. I immediately sent off another signal to London on the subject of this regrettable delay, which was obviously worrying John and disturbing to me.

We were glad to hear that Robin, Ron, Ken and Fred were each awarded a Polar Medal for their service here last year. This medal is normally awarded to all persons who winter over in Polar regions. We, too, were eventually awarded this coveted medal but not until two and a half years after we had returned home.

[The long time it took the authorities to award polar medals to those who had wintered over in 1957 and 1958 was first brought to my attention when I met some of the expedition members at a dinner in 1960. They reminded me of how others had been awarded the medal within a year of their return home. I therefore sent the following letter to Dr David Martin, Executive Secretary of the Royal Society:

Luton
2 June 1960

Dr D C Martin
Executive Secretary
The Royal Society
London.

Dear Dr Martin,

Several members of the Expedition have asked me about their position with regard to Polar Medals, and so I was wondering if you can do anything about this.

I must say that it seems strange that this award has not been made to those members of the Main Party who stayed on for two years. I have no doubts in my mind that the award would be well deserved and greatly prized by all at Halley Bay in 1958.

Yours Sincerely,
Joe MacDowall

The long awaited reply to this reminder filtered through the mills of government and, finally, all the members of the Expedition received a letter another year later, in July 1961, similar to the following one I received:

Admiralty
London
22nd July 1961

Joseph MacDowall, Esq, OBE.

Sir,

I am commanded by my Lords Commissioners of the Admiralty to inform you that they have learnt with great pleasure that, on the advice of the First Lord, the Queen has been graciously pleased to award you the Polar Medal for good services as Leader and Meteorologist with the Royal Society Antarctic Expedition for the International Geophysical Year.

This award was published in the London Gazette on 21st July 1961.

I am, Sir,
Your obedient Servant,
Who signed with an illegible signature.

In a letter of congratulations from the Royal Society which I received from Dr Martin, Alan Moore, his administrative assistant, had added the following rather appropriate footnote: 'P. S. It has taken a long time to move those concerned with the awards.'

Six months later we received this coveted award from Her Majesty the Queen in a very moving and impressive investiture held at Buckingham Palace on Tuesday 27 February 1962. In my case, the long delay was a family bonus because it meant that Simon, now aged six, could join Oonagh and me for the occasion. My memories of the day remain deep and clear. Although I had been to the palace before to receive the OBE, I was still overwhelmed by the surroundings, by the ornate nature of the room and its innumerable splendid paintings or sculptures, by the presence of the tall, be-medalled and distinguished-looking retired generals, some of whom were booted and spurred. The generals acted as ushers of the large audience and also escorted to the toilet any children needing assistance. I exchanged a few words with recipients of other honours and was humbled by the tremendous contributions and the varieties of services they had given to society, in many cases over a lifetime. We formed a long line stretching from Her Majesty's right hand. As we moved closer, her magnetism affected us all. In particular I could see how well she related to persons from so many walks of life or station and was able to communicate so effectively with them all, making most of us feel at ease. It was all so different from, and so very much nicer than, what media reports had led me to expect or what seems to be commonly believed. As I stepped up to her, she picked up the eight-sided silver medal with its distinctive white ribbon. She opened the attachment and, with a practised and skilled hand, pinned it proficiently to my lapel. Lightly patting it into place and, noticing the silver bar across the ribbon which read 'Antarctic 1957–58', Her Majesty asked me what I had been doing with myself since then. I replied that I had been busy catching up with family life and, amongst other things, that my wife and I had had two more sons since I had returned. Though brief, it was a very pleasant and natural conversation during which her interest in the individual predominated.]

OCTOBER 2. At 4 a.m. the air temperature was −28ºC. A cloudy day with a moderate breeze.

I dug out and raised to the snow surface the remainder of the canteen stores, comprising chocolate, cigarettes or tobacco, tooth paste and the like, which were issued once a week. Then I restacked the boxes three feet (91 cm) high in a line across the wind and marked their location with bamboo stakes. I also spent some time digging out the stock of bamboo marker poles, which are now in rather short supply.

An ozone sonde was launched today. Unfortunately the balloon burst at a rather lower height than usual.

David Tribble and Alf dug out the radar, hitched it to a tractor and moved it about 15 ft. (4.57 m) and up on to the new snow level, which was three feet (91 cm) higher up.

John Gane continued to raise to the surface the communications feeder wires.

Most of the scientific teams were busy, as they were at the beginning of every month, recording, checking, summarizing and tabulating the observations of the previous month. In some cases the data was also punched on to Holerith cards and transcribed on to the special data forms designed by the central committee for the IGY. These IGY forms will later be sent off to World Data Centres. As we drew closer to the end of the IGY, in December, the pace of this aspect of the work accelerated. The target was to be on top of the job for our departure and, in particular, to be able to complete processing the December data within days of the end of the year. In preparation, each group had already collected the necessary packing cases for their data or equipment, so that they could be sealed up within days of the IGY ending. There would eventually be several tons of data to take back home.

I prepared a lengthy reply to the question I had received from London regarding the 1959 requirement for lifting gear to raise the Meadows electrical generating set in order to shore up the floor of the generator shed.

I also sent off to the Royal Society the details of my recommended design for a new ozone observing hut, to accommodate the Dobson spectrometer in 1959. The design was based on our good experience with the sledge foundation used for the Decca radar. I suggested they have constructed an insulated, 8 ft. (2.44 m) square, building with a flat roof mounted on a sledge foundation and with a total weight of no more than about two tons. There needed to be a roof hatch for observations. For access, I recommended a ladder fixed to the side of the hut leading to a two-foot (61 cm) square hatch entry in the roof. A door in the side of the hut was not recommended. However, there would need to be a small removable wall panel for use during building and to install the Dobson spectrophotometer. I said the hut should sit two or three feet (61 or 91 cm) above the snow surface on its sledge foundation, allowing the free flow of air under the hut. The sledge needed a robust attachment for tractor winching up on top of drifted snow, several times per year. The power supply for this electrically heated hut would require 200 yd. (183 m) of flexible cable capable of remaining flexible at low temperatures and not therefore made with PVC. With regard to flexible cables, it was our experience that polythene or rubber could be used, although the latter could not be bent in the lowest temperatures we experienced.

OCTOBER 3. At 4 a.m. the air temperature was −30°C. The morning was fine with a moderate breeze, there was a fresh breeze later with snow drift and an ice crystal fog.

As a balloon was being filled with hydrogen this evening, it suddenly burst without any provocation. Another one was filled and John Smith launched it very neatly in the difficult conditions which always accompanied a south-westerly breeze. Philip was also down at the balloon shed taking photographs of John and Derek working.

The September weather data showed that the whole of the atmosphere had warmed up slightly. The amount of warming was greatest in the lowest layers of the atmosphere and in the stratosphere. The performance of the balloons in rising to great heights was the best since last March. The mean height of balloon bursting for September was 19.2 km, at an air pressure of 43 mb.

Geomagnetic activity was low for the month of September

OCTOBER 4. At 4 a.m. the air temperature was −29°C. A fine day with a light or gentle breeze.

David Cansfield was limping round the hut as the result of a strain whilst skiing.

Air letters from home had arrived for us at Port Stanley and were being sent to us on the radio link.

We received a mobile meteorological report indicating that a land party of Americans was on its way to Byrd station from Little America. It was located at 79°S 143°W and 260 miles (418 km) from Little America.

After doing some geomagnetic work and examining the year's balloon performance, I skied off to Emperor Bay to take some still and ciné shots of the Emperor chicks. Many of the chicks were grouped together in an independent manner, forming a nursery. Then I did some skiing. It was tremendous fun skiing down the steep slopes from the top of the ice-shelf.

SUNDAY OCTOBER 5. At 4 a.m. the air temperature was −32°C. It was a fine day with a light breeze blowing. Clouds moved over the sky in the afternoon.

An ozone sonde was flown but the instrument failed during the flight.

In the morning we held our service at 11:15 a.m. and afterwards I did some skiing down some steep drift slopes from the ice-shelf on the north side of Halley Bay. I then went out on to the sea-ice and round the headland to Emperor Bay, via some new ice formed since last Sunday. As I skied round the headland, the ice was making a creaking sound but there were no visual signs of any activity.

We hear that the US land party going to Byrd station were at 79°S 137°W.

I baked 8 lb. (3.6 kg) of bread in the evening.

During the night, Derek and Len went down to Halley Bay to take flashlight photographs to simulate winter conditions. Whilst they were down there, they measured the thickness of the fast sea-ice as 7 ft. 4 in. (2.24 m).

OCTOBER 6. At 4 a.m. the air temperature was −34°C. A fine day with a gentle breeze. There were some heavy deposits of hoar frost. At 10 a.m. I noticed that at the top of the anemometer tower, 30 ft. (9 m) above the surface, these frost deposits were one inch (2.5 cm) thick.

Andrew and I commenced a survey of the variations from place to place of the earth's magnetic field, just to the north of the non-magnetic hut in the direction of Halley Bay. The survey therefore covered the region to which the ice-shelf was moving, as I had established by repeated astronomical observations. We set up nine observing stations spaced about two kilometres apart and covered an area of about ten square kilometres. At each site we erected a tripod for the BMZ magnetometer and took measurements of the strength of the vertical component of the earth's magnetic field. Later on, we looked at the continuous recording of the earth's field and allowed for any changes due to time between observations. We were then able to map out the spatial changes of the magnetic field, either due to the topography of the earth below the ice sheet, or changes in the magnetic properties of the underlying rocks. Notable in this map were the greater changes near the ice front, arguably due to a more rugged geography, which could create the features of Halley and Emperor bays.

At 2:20 p.m. an ozone sonde was launched, which worked successfully throughout the flight up to the 31 mb pressure level.

Gwynne's stint of nightly auroral observations finally came to an end as there was now just too much light for him to see the aurora, even though the sun was still just below the horizon for about seven

hours. By the end of the month there would be 24 hours of sunshine every day.

OCTOBER 7. At 4 a.m. the air temperature was −25°C. A cloudy day with a light breeze.

Andrew and I completed our geomagnetic survey of the vicinity.

I prepared two cables for the Royal Society with a great deal of scientific data, including the synopsis of September's weather. It had been a particularly windy month with six days of gale force winds, which occasionally gusted up to 67 kt (124 kph). The air temperatures during the month ranged between −6°C and −43°C. The cable also contained a few small additions to our stores requisitions.

In my second cable we provided the detailed information needed in order correctly to allocate the charges for TAE's radio communications from Shackleton to London via Halley Bay.

John Gane continued to raise the communications feeders.

Gwynne was now working away on the analysis of his night-time auroral observations through the winter.

I saw an Antarctic Petrel fly over the base during the morning. It was the first I had seen since before the winter, but to judge by the speed with which it vanished against a cloudy background, other visits could easily have been missed.

Now the sun had risen higher, we were once again having to correct

Joe conducting a geomagnetic survey of the area between the non-magnetic hut and Halley Bay. The results of this survey are shown in Appendix 4. I found that characteristics of the land, that lay hundreds of metres below, had an effect on the magnetic field above. This could have been associated with the presence of hill tops below, which created the coastal feature seen in the right background. My astro- nomical observations showed that the floating ice-shelf here was moving at a rate of 320 metres per year towards the west.

the temperatures measured by the radio sonde launched at 10 p.m. for the effects of solar radiation warming.

Signs of Summer Despite Continued Gales

OCTOBER 8. At 4 a.m. the air temperature was −33°C. The wind increased and the weather deteriorated during the day. There was cloud and snow drift at 10 a.m. but by 10 p.m. a moderate gale was blowing, with snow falling and drift reducing the visibility to 30 yards (27 m).

The survey of geomagnetic vertical force was analysed. The vicinity of the base was shown to be one of geomagnetic anomaly, closely following the coastal features. The extreme difference in the observations was 1.2 percent of the magnetic field.

Henry's birthday was celebrated in our customary style with a cake produced at supper and a gathering afterwards with port to toast his health. Philip presented Henry with a radio star scintillation chart with birthday greetings from Centaurus, a memento of the fact that, during the night, Henry goes out to the radio echo hut to switch over the scintillation aerials.

OCTOBER 9. At 4 a.m. the air temperature was −20°C. There was snow or drift most of the day with a fresh or strong breeze which developed into another gale just before 11 p.m.

Bill and I talked about the arrangements for his sledging trip, to be taken at the end of October. In preparation, Bill and Jim went out to the emergency store and brought back to the hut a tent and other camping equipment.

I prepared an ozone sonde for its flight and did some of the meteorological analysis necessary for annual reports.

We took two boxes of small radar reflectors from the northern stores dump to the balloon shed. This dump was still clear of the snow surface.

OCTOBER 10. At 4 a.m. the air temperature was −17°C. There was a fresh gale most of the day with moderate or heavy snowfall, which had reduced visibility to 10 yards at 4 a.m. A small depression went through the base in the evening.

The morning ascent was blown out of range of the radar at 101 km due to strong and consistent winds. Jim, Andrew, and Malcolm dug out the balloon shed door in the evening, which, despite the storm, did not require quite as much digging as might have been expected.

David Cansfield continued to limp about the hut with the aid of a copper tube fashioned into a walking stick.

OCTOBER 11. At 4 a.m. the air temperature was −5°C. The weather improved during the day although there was snow and drift for most of the time. By 8 p.m., it was cloudy with a moderate breeze.

At 12:15 p.m., Ben observed five Antarctic Petrels over the base flying from the north-east to the south-west.

Before the film show at 8:15 p.m., Derek projected his colour slides of Emperor Penguins taken during the spring.

SUNDAY OCTOBER 12. At 4 a.m. the air temperature was −22°C. The day was mainly cloudy and there was fog at times. The wind was a gentle breeze for much of the time but stronger during the evening.

John Smith saw a group of at least 36 Antarctic Petrels fly over the base from east to west.

I dug out the entry to the seismological pit and adjusted the horizontal seismometer. Then I started to dig a tunnel up from the centre of the cave to provide a vertical shaft entry. When complete, this shaft will terminate about twenty feet (6 m) further from the bent and threatening ionospheric mast, in a safer area and one which is subject to less drifted snow accumulation. Whilst out digging, I also dug down to the bunkroom window, which now lay three feet (91 cm) under recent snow drift.

I received a cable with the welcome news that the 1959 party would include Mike Blackwell, David Limbert and George Lush.

Andrew dug out five empty radio sonde crates for use in the declination sighting tunnel, which gets longer every time the snow falls or drifts.

Ivor built up the ventilating shaft from the roof of the generator shed.

Malcolm brought in some food boxes.

OCTOBER 13. At 4 a.m. the air temperature was −14°C. There was a fresh breeze with snow drift for most of the day. At night snowfall started and a gale developed before the end of the day, reducing visibility to 10 yards (9 m).

Today was the last of this month's series of Regular World Days. The ionosphere was very quiet so that extensive measurements were possible, and this kept the ionospheric team very busy.

I started making notes for my meteorological report and collecting the information together.

The morning radio sonde flight was an excellent one, using an un-dipped 1000 g silicone balloon which reached the 11 mb pressure level, one of our highest ascents. Unfortunately, the radio sonde failed at 19 mb but we did measure the winds for the whole flight. The air temperatures through the atmosphere were now above −80°C and about 15°C warmer than their winter minimum.

OCTOBER 14. At 4 a.m. the air temperature was –12°C. The wind was gale force for most of the day; as one gale ended another started. Moderate snowfall at times reduced the visibility to about 15 yards (13.7 m).

Two balloons were launched into a moderate gale for the morning ascent. After the first balloon crashed, a second was launched successfully, ascending to a height of 21.4 km. We no longer have to dip the balloons in oil to achieve a satisfactory performance; the sun's heat does the job for us.

We heard on the radio of the death of Sir Douglas Mawson, the Australian Antarctic explorer, author of the classic book entitled *Home of the Blizzard*, and who some of us here believed picked up the mantle of Sir Ernest Shackleton.

OCTOBER 15. At 4 a.m. the air temperature was –12°C. There was snow in the morning with a strong breeze and drift. The snow ended in the early afternoon and the weather improved.

Jim and Henry went to Halley Bay and measured the thickness of fast sea-ice as 7 ft. 6 in. (2.29 m) with two inches (5 cm) of snow on top. Although the edge of the fast sea-ice was unchanged, there was a shore lead off the coast.

During a two-hour period outside, Ben counted 125 Antarctic Petrels all flying to the west. He was out at the time digging a tunnel to the south-east door.

I was on gash duty and cleared the snow from the south-west entry.

Alf and Ivor were servicing the tractor winch.

Philip and Les proposed a visit to the Gin Bottle area on Thursday, to return at about 4 p.m.

It was our third wedding anniversary. Oonagh and I exchanged greetings cables and I read a special letter from her which I had put on one side when I received it last January.

OCTOBER 16. At 4 a.m. the air temperature was –25°C. A fine day with a light or gentle breeze.

Les and Philip skied to the Gin Bottle area. They tried to find a way down to the sea-ice but were not successful either there or at the Chippantodd Creeks.

Alf had a tractor running and cleared up solid gash.

An ozone sonde was launched and reached 20 mb. This ascent marked the start of the spring ozone observing programme.

I worked on the new shaft exit from the seismological cavern and reached the surface eight feet (2.4 m) above.

Andrew was using radio sonde crates to extend the geomagnetic declination sighting tunnel.

Stocks of granulated aluminium and caustic soda were taken by tractor to the balloon shed.

We heard with regret that a US Globemaster aircraft had crashed on the other side of the continent, about thirty miles (48 km) from Cape Hallet. Six persons had been killed and an overland rescue party was experiencing difficulty with crevasses and bad weather.

OCTOBER 17. At 4 a.m. the air temperature was −33°C. Another fine day with a light or gentle breeze.

I saw two flights of Antarctic Petrels flying westwards over the base. I counted 35 on the first flight and six in the second.

Bill was collecting equipment together and preparing for his forthcoming sledging trip.

John Gane continued to dig out and raise the feeders from below the surface.

Gwynne removed from its mounting on the roof the airglow photometer, after hearing that it was to be returned this year.

I finished the hatch entry at the top of the new shaft into the seismological cavern.

OCTOBER 18. At 4 a.m. the air temperature was −20°C. There was snow, drift and a strong breeze for most of the day.

I checked the results of the last ozone sonde flight and then analysed some of the seismograms.

I was asked if I would like to fly directly from Capetown to an Antarctic conference in Australia before returning home. Today I received a reply from Oonagh on her views of the idea. She would be disappointed in any delay of my return but appreciated that, since the others will go by sea and I will be flying, there may not be such a big difference in the date of my return. I would hate to go home and then have to leave again a few days later.

SUNDAY OCTOBER 19. At 4 a.m. the air temperature was −7°C. The weather remained poor with a strong breeze, snow and snow drift. It was not a very good day outside so I spent some of the time indoors mending my trousers.

After the morning religious service, I put out the daily newspapers for 4 November 1957. *The Times* for that day contained the report of my appointment as Leader.

Several people were out helping to dig the tunnel to the southeast door. Whilst digging there, we came across part of the packing case of the Redifon radio. It lay where it had been dropped by the advance party, at the level of the surface in the summer of 1956 and now over ten feet (3 m) below the surface as a result of snowfall and drift.

OCTOBER 20. At 4 a.m. the air temperature was −12°C. There was a strong breeze for most of the day and heavy snow fell during the morning, which was a rare occurrence. There was a slight improvement in the weather late at night.

As has been the practice since the problems we experienced with the Gill hydrogen generator, the new can of granulated aluminium was carefully scrutinized before use. The radio sonde ascent told us that the air temperature at the 50 mb level had risen to −68°C, at the same time last year it was −61°C. These temperatures were being watched with interest for they rise rapidly at this time of the year and bear a close relation to the rapid rise in the quantity of ozone in the atmosphere. From these temperatures alone, the season could be considered ten to fifteen days later than last year.

The valley in drifted snow which lay at the back, or to the west of the main hut has been filled deeply by the recent drifting snow. The drifted accumulation was three feet (91 cm) deep on top of the old entrance to the seismological cavern, whereas the new entrance was perfectly free of snow drift.

I fixed a fault in the time-marking circuit for the seismographs.

John Smith did a wedge test of the Dobson ozone spectrometer.

OCTOBER 21. At 4 a.m. the air temperature was −27°C. It was a sunny day with a moderate breeze and drift,

In the morning Andrew took 16mm ciné shots of the penguins at Emperor Bay.

The declination sighting tunnel was now 100 ft. (30 m) long, running north from the hut towards the declination fixed mark. The recent snowfall had raised the surface to a few inches above the hatch entry we had constructed over the door to the hut.

I prepared a signal for the Royal Society accepting the invitation to present a paper at a scientific conference on Antarctic Meteorology in Melbourne Australia. I would therefore fly from Capetown to Australia and then back home again at the end of the conference. In the meantime I would have a lot of work to do to prepare the paper for presentation in Melbourne. [The 14-page paper was eventually published by Pergamon Press in the book *Antarctic Meteorology* (Ref. MacDowall 1960). When I presented this in February 1959, there was so much interest in the results that I was called on to provide additional information on at least half a dozen occasions replying to questions. Representatives from ten nations were present at the conference. I remember that the Americans, Australians, New Zealanders and South Africans present were particularly interested in our observations at Halley Bay.]

We used 3654 lb. (1657 kg) of anthracite in September, a marked seasonal reduction from the consumption in the previous few months.

The first of a new series of the BBC 'Calling Antarctica' programme was heard tonight at 8 p.m. Our old friend Charlie Le Feuvre, wireless operator of the advance party, spoke to us on the eve of his departure for the Falkland Island Dependencies on the ship *John Biscoe*. Charlie still had no idea where in the Dependencies he would be serving.

I spent some time today analysing seismograms.

A Review of Summer Activity

OCTOBER 22. At 4 a.m. the air temperature was −21°C. A fine day with a light or gentle breeze and occasionally some fog. The temperatures were above −29°C.

I spent much of the time indoors keeping up to date with the analysis of the seismic records. However, I did go for a short walk round the base at about 3 p.m. and did not need to wear gloves or overshoes, just bedroom slippers. Whilst wandering around, I made a note of who was doing what, as follows.

Alf and Ivor were decarbonizing the diesel engine of a Meadows generator, a task they perform once a month. Jim and Gwynne were in the radio sonde room. Gwynne was working up the auroral observations he made during winter nights, whilst Jim was checking the results of a recent radio sonde flight. Across the corridor in the ionospheric laboratory, David Cansfield was measuring the photographic records of ionospheric conditions, and Bill was making a long series of continuous observations of the ionosphere, which was due to become much more disturbed, according to a long series of alerts we had been receiving in the Geocasts sent out from Little America. In the meteorological office, Derek measured radiation records and tabulated the results on to the forms required by both the World Data Centre and the British Meteorological Office. David Harrison and Philip were working in the nearby radio echo hut. Andrew was on gash duty and busy with his domestic chores. Henry was returning from a trip to Halley Bay, where he had made observations of the sea-ice conditions for John Heap. John Gane was digging away outside, where he was raising the feeders to the rhombic aerial used for radio communications with Port Stanley. Up above the kitchen in the ozone loft, John Smith was observing the sun through the Dobson spectrophotometer, to measure the total quantity of ozone in the atmosphere.

OCTOBER 23. At 4 a.m. the air temperature was −27°C. The wind was light for much of the day. Thick fog in the morning cleared up to give a fine afternoon. Some cloud moved in later in the day and then there was some snowfall.

In the early hours of the morning, I went to Halley Bay and then on to Emperor Bay. When I was at Halley Bay, I could already hear the sound of the birds in the distant rookery. At Halley Bay there were 16 penguins who returned with me to their rookery. I reached Emperor Bay at 2:30 a.m. and, although the rookery was fairly noisy, about 5% of the birds were lying down and sound asleep. The rookery had moved up into the bay with about one third of their number installed right up to the drift slope at the head of the bay. The rookery was broken up into several huddles, each comprizing about 150 birds, with chicks and adults forming separate huddles.

John Gane continued work on the feeder to the Port Stanley rhombic aerial.

Jim and Bill were packing up the sledge for their forthcoming survey trip.

A spare alternator for the radar set was dug out from the south side of the balloon shed, placed on a sledge and hauled by tractor to the generator shed. Alf then moved a pile of solid gash to the dump.

In the afternoon Malcolm and I went to Halley Bay with the ice drill and drove a hole through the fast sea-ice to measure its thickness. It took us one hour to drill through the 7 ft. 5 1/4 in. (2.27 m) of sea-ice with 3 in. (8 cm) of snow on top. When I returned to the base, I continued with the analysis of the seismograms.

Andrew extended the sighting tunnel to the declination fixed mark.

OCTOBER 24. At 4 a.m. the air temperature was –12°C. The day was mainly cloudy with a gentle breeze and a little light snow.

At 6 a.m. Bill, Jim, David Harrison and Malcolm left the base for a week's trip to the south-east. The route for the first 30.5 miles (49 km) was to be on a course of 120° magnetic, then on 205° magnetic for about 8 miles (13 km). They carried with them about 40 small flags for the latter part of the route, which was to be on 180° magnetic. When leaving, Malcolm was at the helm position to the rear of the sledge with the compass mounted on the pulpit in front of him, whilst the other three were harnessed to the front of the sledge. The condition of the surface was good for travelling. They carried with them a 15-day supply of food at the full rate of consumption, which could be reduced by 50% during lay-ups. They had a 20-day supply of kerosene fuel for the Primus cooker.

After seeing the party off and taking some ciné shots of their departure, I returned to the hut and continued seismological work and drew up a table to speed up the determination of epicentral distances.

I prepared notes for the guidance of the 1959 party.

Several members remarked on the recent absence of Antarctic Petrels compared with about one week ago. It was now clear that we observed a migration of the birds at that time. Amongst us, Ben was the one most familiar with Antarctic birds and he was keeping a log of their movements.

Philip was using the electrically-driven chain saw to speed up the task of digging a tunnel from the south-east door.

OCTOBER 25. At 4 a.m. the air temperature was −12°C. There was snow in the morning with a light or gentle breeze, then the weather deteriorated to become a gale at 11:45 p.m.

I continued to work on notes for the guidance of the 1959 party.

After supper, some of us showed coloured photographs we had taken recently, then we had our regular Saturday show of the two films entitled *Meet the Huggets* and *Turn the Key Softly*.

SUNDAY OCTOBER 26. At 4 a.m. the air temperature was −16°C. The weather became worse with a strong gale of Force 9 winds in the morning which then rose to Force 10 for the rest of the day. At 10 p.m., you could only see for 3 yards (2.7 m). These conditions were amongst the worst we had experienced.

Les led the Sunday morning service at 11:15 a.m.

The gale finally broke the ionospheric mast which was bent in August and had managed to survive several gales since then. It finally collapsed at some time between 5 and 7 p.m., breaking at the bottom to leave the two upper sections intact but, fortunately, leaning away from the hut supported by one set of guy wires. The delta aerials still provide limited facilities. When the gale subsides, we will dig out the transformer at the foot of the mast in order to resume ionospheric absorption measurements with a replacement aerial.

At 6:30 a.m. John Gane went out to help us clear the balloon shed door but failed to find the hut in the poor conditions. Finally he managed to find the main hut via the chemical dump and his very familiar rhombic aerials.

Hurricane Force Winds Sweep the Base

OCTOBER 27. At 4 a.m. the air temperature was −7°C. The wind blew at hurricane Force 12 or storm Force 11 between 4:30 and 6:30 a.m. There was a gust of 82 knots (152 kph) and the hourly average easterly wind was 67 kt (124 kph). A moderate amount of snow fell in the morning and at 7 a.m. the visibility was down to two yards (1.83 m), when we recorded our lowest air pressure of 947.1 mb. Later in the day the wind moderated to gale force. Air temperatures during the day were generally over −11°C. Ben Ellis was on night duty so he made the weather observations through the worst conditions of the hurricane.

Notwithstanding conditions, a balloon was launched successfully at 10 a.m. The wind was so strong it reached Emperor Bay in under two minutes.

Henry experienced some difficulty getting to and from the radio echo hut in the hurricane. Since his plight was due to an unfamiliarity with the pattern of guide ropes round the base, his misfortune became the butt of some good-humoured ribbing, which Henry took in good part. When we welcomed him back to the main hut, he told us how at one stage, as he groped round in the swirling whiteout conditions, he had followed a cable, which when observed yesterday, had led to the radio echo hut. Unfortunately for Henry, the force of the wind had dragged that cable out of the hut so that it now led nowhere in particular. Now that he was safely back inside, he was just able to see why we were all so mightily entertained.

Les went out to inspect the ionospheric aerials and found one of the drift aerials would need some attention when conditions improved.

I was on gash duty during this rather eventful day and missed much of the action which went on outside the hut.

OCTOBER 28. At 4 a.m. the air temperature was −11°C. A fresh or moderate gale blew during the day, together with some snow or drift through which the sun shone strongly.

Les and I took another look at the ionospheric mast. Then we carried a ladder to the northern drift aerial. I held the ladder whilst Les climbed up and repaired the fault which had occurred during the hurricane.

Andrew cleaned out the drift snow which the wind had packed in behind the roller blind door of the balloon shed.

I sent off the regular Tuesday signal to the Royal Society. It contained several scientific reports. I also told them of the hurricane we had just experienced and the damage it caused to the ionospheric aerials and how we were coping with those problems.

Those who wished to make their own way home from Capetown or elsewhere were disappointed today because they had no further news on the subject.

OCTOBER 29. At 4 a.m. the air temperature was −20°C. A fine day with good visibility and miraging of distant views. There was a gentle breeze blowing; some cloud moved in during the night. It was a good day to clear up the mess caused by the recent hurricane and the gales which drove snow in through every tiny crevice, buried entries and threw up new piles of drifted snow.

Les dug nine feet (3 m) down to the matching transformer fitted at the base of the broken ionospheric aerial and removed it, once it had done its last day's work at that site.

Snow driven by the gales needed to be cleared up and entrances raised to allow for added snow accumulation. David Tribble cleared up the snow drift which had been driven into the balloon shed, Andrew cleared out the declination sighting tunnel, I raised the level of the seismological hatch entry to be well clear of the surface, and Ben built up the hatch entry over the south-east hut door of the main hut.

I skied down to Emperor Bay at 9:30 p.m. and found the storm had had a major impact on the rookery. At the previous site of the rookery, and across the middle of the bay, lay a very large drift, depressing the sea-ice below sea level and causing sea water pools to develop. The penguins had therefore moved away from the puddles of water so that half the rookery was collected together at the head of the bay. The wind had also broken back the sea-ice front so that it was no longer possible to negotiate the headland to Halley Bay, for the sea-ice had cleared away in a line from Penguin Leap to the headland south of Emperor Bay. The open water was producing a thick frost smoke. Many penguins were swimming and leaping in and out of the patch of open water. Near Penguin Leap, I was startled by the sudden collapse into the sea of a large drift slope quite close to me.

Alf had been to Halley Bay and he told me there was little change to the sea-ice edge there, which was still at least a mile (1.6 km) further out than at the same time last year.

To mark the anniversary of the birth of Edmund Halley, we showed a short film at 4:15 p.m. and followed this with an excellent four-course dinner. Then we smoked cigars presented to us by David Dalgleish. The menu for dinner was:

Salmon and crayfish soup,
Fresh roast beef,
Potatoes, beans and peas,
Pineapple flan with strawberries in syrup,
Argentine champagne,
Cigars.

It was all excellently produced by Len and much appreciated. Len worked alone in the kitchen today, aided of course by the gash man, because Malcolm was taking a well-earned break from the usual daily routine by joining in a man-hauling survey trip.

The signal I sent back to the Royal Society included Gwynne's preliminary analysis of last winter's auroral observations. Amongst other things, he reported that an auroral display was seen on every dark clear night of the winter, as was the case last year. However, auroral activity through the 1958 winter was somewhat less than in the previous year.

Ivor hoisted our last new Union flag.

The First Summer Visitor – A Skua

OCTOBER 30. At 4 a.m. the air temperature was −27°C. A fine day with great visibility and much miraging.

Bill and his party returned at 2 p.m. all looking fit and sunburnt. They were a little disappointed in having had to lie up for three days while the hurricane raged round them. As a consequence of the storm and the poor surfaces it left behind, they were not able to get any further than they did on their last trip, to a point about 30 miles (48 km) away. They observed a Skua, the first we have seen since last summer. It was observed at a point about 14 miles (23 km) inland.

John Gane started a shaft, digging down from the surface into the south-west tunnel. Then he made a framework to carry the communications feeders through to the tunnel.

An ozone sonde was launched at 2:32 p.m.

During the past two days we have confirmed that, due to the warmer weather, it is no longer necessary to dip balloons in oil in order to achieve good heights.

A new gash pit was being used in the north-eastern tunnel.

Alf had a tractor running to clear up solid waste.

I took the opportunity of the excellent conditions to make observations of the sun to determine the azimuth of the fixed mark. Len and the dog came out to see what I was doing. Then I returned to the hut to continue with the typing up of end-of-year reports and the paper I was to give in Australia.

OCTOBER 31. At 4 a.m. the air temperature was −29ºC. Much of the morning was fine with hardly any wind. The wind rose a little for the rest of the day and there was some fog. Ice needles were being formed in the atmosphere and this created the splendid optical effects of a sun pillar and two parhelion or mock suns, one on each side of the sun. In addition to the brilliant display in the atmosphere, the newly deposited snow surface was sparkling in the bright sunshine like a field of diamond dust.

Alf and Ivor dug out drums of paraffin, lubricating oil and Avtur, a total of 15 drums. They also dug out and raised to the surface a Maudheim sledge and the stock of eight 44-gallon drums of anti-freeze.

I was outside again using the Tavistock theodolite in the morning, at noon and in the evening, taking a series of observations to fix our position and measure the azimuth of the fixed mark. Whilst outside, I joined Philip to dig out the stock of Dexion angle iron and stacked it on top of some empty fuel drums to prevent it getting buried in snow drift.

John Gane worked on the new termination and the entry for new communications feeders.

Derek and Len measured the fast sea-ice at Halley Bay. It was 7 ft. 10 in. (2.39 m) thick.

Once, for a change, there was a very good radio telephone connection with London.

As usual on Fridays, Bert measured the fat thickness and weight of everybody.

Reference

MacDowall, J 1960, *Notes on the Climatology of Halley Bay in Antarctic Meteorology*, Pergamon Press pp 423–437.

Chapter 7

Summer 1958/9 and the Voyage Home

The Summer Work Programme Intensifies

NOVEMBER 1, 1958. At 4 a.m. the air temperature was −19°C. The day was cloudy with drift or fog at times. The wind was mainly a moderate breeze. The ice crystal fog at 12:30 p.m. produced a 22° halo, two mock suns and a circum-zenithal arc, in a brilliant display of optical fireworks.

Alf and Ivor continued their programme of outdoor work, digging out an Enfield generator and drums of lubricating oil from the dump. Both were placed in the oil store inside the generator shed. The generator will be handy there for the use of the 1959 party and the oil will warm up before it is used.

At 3:55 p.m. John Smith drew my attention to the larger of two bergs by Burlington Bluff, which had moved a little to the north. To be noticed from camp, the movement must have been about 50 ft. (15 m).

John Gane continued working on the feeders, lowering them to ensure there was no interference with the recording of solar radiation.

At 8:30 p.m. we screened a new film called *Front Page*, followed by the second showing of *Three Little Words*, at Jim's request.

I received a message to call my parents and I was concerned. Telephone conditions were not good so I sent a cable to reassure them that I was safe and well, as they had been alarmed occasionally by some news reports concerning our well-being.

After seeing his thorough plans, I gave Les the permission he sought to go with Philip and Bert on a 12-day survey trip commencing on November 19.

For supper we had some seal liver and onions, which were admirably prepared by Len.

We Learn From Norwegian Polar Expertise

SUNDAY NOVEMBER 2. At 4 a.m. the air temperature was −20°C. A cloudy day with a gentle or moderate breeze causing drift at times.

During his period of night duty last night, Bill pulled down the remnants of the fallen ionospheric mast. He and David Cansfield worked away again for most of this evening to clear up the mess.

Our Sunday morning service was held at its usual time.

Philip and I discussed the management of stores dumps with a view to providing guidance to the 1959 party based on our experience, to the extent that it had differed from, or gone beyond, that of the advance party. We had been particularly pleased with what we had learnt from our Norwegian neighbours regarding stores dumps and only wished we had known of their ideas earlier. They make two lines of stores boxes, one box thick, six feet (1.8 m) high and separated by four feet (1.2 m) to form a passage. The roof of the passage is covered with tongue-and-groove boards and a tarpaulin is thrown over the whole structure to seal it against snow drift. Philip and David built an example of this type of dump from the north end of the radio echo hut and it proved to be an unqualified success. You can gain access to all the boxes without removing them and you are left with a permanent addition to your storage facilities when the boxes are emptied. A report of this idea was sent back to London for the consideration of the 1959 party.

I continued with the writing of reports and checked the results of the last ozone ascent.

NOVEMBER 3. At 4 a.m. the air temperature was −17°C. There was some drift in the morning with a strong breeze that moderated for the rest of the day to give us fine weather.

Alf and Ivor started to dig out the 44-gallon drums of Avtur from the main store. The bases of the drums were now about ten feet (3 m) below the level of the present snow surface. These drums will now be stocked alongside the generator shed, where they can be used *in situ* without further movement.

Les and David Cansfield were finishing off work on three new folded dipoles for ionospheric observations. The ionospheric programme was again running at full strength. These aerials were mounted on Dexion about 8 ft. (2.4 m) high and therefore required little effort to erect. It was apparent that the major part of the changeover was accomplished in August, when the standby aerial was erected on scaffold poles.

John Gane was outside finishing off his work on an entry for the communications feeders.

I took out the theodolite and made some more sun shots to determine the direction of true north.

Philip was using the plane table to survey the base area.

NOVEMBER 4. At 4 a.m. the air temperature was −15°C. Most of the day was fine with a clear blue sky and a gentle breeze, there was a little drift and some cloud cover towards the end of the day.

In the morning, water in the waveguides of the radar rendered it unserviceable. So we took out an optical theodolite and followed the balloon to a height of 29 km in perfect atmospheric conditions.

John Gane hurt his back yesterday working on the communications shafts. Bert and I carried him into bed and Henry looked after John's schedules.

Alf continued to excavate the Avtur and had moved 25 drums by the end of the day.

Malcolm was raising our food store in the southern dump.

Andrew, Gwynne and I took out a theodolite and two levelling staffs to redetermine the height of the base above sea level, as required for glaciological studies and to reduce atmospheric pressure measurements to sea level. The tall levelling staffs each have a ruler engraved along their length, which is viewed from a distance through a theodolite's telescope. At each stage on the way down to Halley Bay, Andrew and Gwynne placed the two staffs hundreds of feet (about 50 m) apart and I positioned the theodolite midway between them. With the theodolite set dead level, I sighted on each pole in turn and noted the heights above the surface which I could read with the aid of the telescope. The difference between my readings of the two staffs gave me the difference in the height of the surface from one staff to the other.

Starting with one staff on the floor of the ozone loft and poking it up through the roof of the hut, we gradually worked our way down to the sea. On the way out, we measured the loft to be 92.74 ft. (28.27 m) above sea level and on the way back, 92.95 ft. (28.33 m).

I received two 100-word air letters from Oonagh, one written in September and the other in October.

NOVEMBER 5. At 4 a.m. the air temperature was –15°C. In the morning there was snow and drift with a strong breeze; the afternoon was fine with a gentle breeze.

I tabulated some of the monthly meteorological measurements and then worked with John Smith, using the theodolite and two staffs to level down from the ozone loft to the barometer in the meteorological office, so as to establish the height of the barometer above sea level. We found that the barometer was 10 feet (3 m) lower than when it was when installed in 1956. During the same time, 10 feet (3 m) of snow has accumulated but the surface level has remained at a constant height above sea level.

Alf continued to extract drums of Avtur and placed another 17 alongside the generator shed.

Radio communications were curtailed because of an ionospheric drift-observing programme, postponing the transmittal of some of our signals to London.

NOVEMBER 6. At 4 a.m. the air temperature was −18ºC. There was some drift and snow in the morning with a fresh breeze. The day later became mainly fine.

Water was dripping from under the eaves of the roof in the ionospheric room but causing no special problems.

Bill was very pleased with the performance of his new aerials, although this type would not have been good enough in the winter. When calibrated, he said, the use of two different types would provide some information on ground reflections.

Les gave me the position of three of the flags used to mark the geomagnetic survey. He said that the 30 ft. (9 m) ice-hill near the Gin Bottle was in the same position as marked by a stake last year. The headland had gone which lay to the north of this hill and between the two peaks of Chippantodd.

The major part of a long signal to the Royal Society was sent and one was received from them. There was no firm news on *Tottan*'s itinerary, something eagerly awaited by several persons who wanted to make their own travel arrangements. I spent time preparing the monthly meteorological and geomagnetic reports. In the evening, I baked 6 lb. (2.7 kg) of bread.

NOVEMBER 7. At 4 a.m. the air temperature was −10ºC. Apart from

Below and opposite: *Malcolm Edwards and Joe MacDowall in October 1958 drilling through the sea-ice at Halley Bay. We found the ice was over 2 metres thick.*

the early hours, there was snow and drift all day, driven by a strong south-westerly breeze.

Another long signal was sent to the Royal Society reporting on scientific observations and the damage done to the ionospheric aerials. We also sent our best wishes to Sir James Wordie on his retirement from the Chairmanship of the British National Committee for the IGY.

We reported on the severe weather experienced after the first fine week of October. The average air pressure for the month was the lowest yet observed. The depth of snow accumulation in October was 24 cm, bringing the total for the year to 110 cm, which was already 15 cm more than experienced in each of the preceding two years.

The launching of the evening balloon was difficult due to the strong south-westerly breeze. I took a ciné shot of John Smith and Derek launching. Their first balloon burst but they succeeded with the second one.

A regular Friday evening telephone link to UK is now in operation but its quality is from time to time uncertain.

NOVEMBER 8. At 4 a.m. the air temperature was −11°C. In the early hours some drift occurred, the rest of the day was fine, with clear skies and a moderate breeze.

Henry, Jim, and I went to Halley Bay to measure the sea-ice, which was 7 ft 7 in (2.31 m) thick. There was no change in the position of the edge of the fast sea-ice, which remained about a mile (1.6 km) further out than at the time of *Tottan*'s last visit one year ago. We saw eight Snow Petrels flying south-west along the crests of the cliffs.

The Fierce Summer Sun

SUNDAY NOVEMBER 9. At 4 a.m. the air temperature was −22°C. Another fine day with clear skies and a light breeze. At times there was no wind and then the sun heated up dark surfaces so they became too hot to touch. Many people were out in the fine, summer weather, skiing and sunbathing. Len and I climbed up on to the top of the balloon shed, where we found a cozy place to sunbathe.

We commemorated Remembrance Sunday in our service this morning.

About 12 more Snow Petrels were seen, flying to the west, usually in pairs.

The heat of the sun melted condensation inside the insulation in the roof of the non-magnetic hut, causing water to drip near the instruments. To prevent any damage, we erected Ventile umbrellas over the instruments, as we had done at the same time last year.

David Harrison was on gash duty and he flushed out the latrine gash hole by pouring down about 40 gallons of hot water.

NOVEMBER 10. At 4 a.m. the air temperature was −11°C. There was some fog in the morning but this cleared up to leave a cloudy day with a light air or breeze.

In the morning I arranged a group effort digging out the stock of third-year food for the benefit of the 1959 party. From about 11 a.m. to 6 p.m. we dug out and restacked all but the last few dozen boxes, moving about 25 tons of food boxes and possibly an even greater weight of snow. The boxes were piled up four feet (1.22 m) high, up wind of our excavations and organized systematically according to the numbers marked on each box. Back at the hut, we had lists of the box numbers giving the details of the contents of each box.

Alf and Ivor continued excavating Avtur drums. Alongside the generator shed at the end of the day, the stock was 75 drums.

Len and Philip took a tractor down on to the sea-ice and brought back two seals.

NOVEMBER 11. At 4 a.m. the air temperature was −14°C. There was a little light snow at midday but the day was mainly cloudy with a light or gentle breeze.

We finally learnt the firm details of *Tottan*'s itinerary, confirming that we would leave her in Capetown. However, those who wanted to make their own way from there still did not know their position.

This was the end of the second full year through which I kept a diary, having started it four days prior to the sailing of *Magga Dan* from London on November 15, 1956.

It was satisfactory to note that the last de-coke of the Meadows generator on October 22 revealed no change in the rate of commutator wear. Slip ring wear was maintained at two thousandths of an inch (0.05 mm) per 1000 hours. This rate of wear was less than half that observed before the humidifier was disconnected, thereby reducing the frequency of generator overloading.

The last part of the third-year food dump was completely dug out and restacked.

By the end of the day, 107 drums of Avtur were stacked alongside the generator shed.

The rapid spring rise has started of the total amount of ozone in the atmosphere.

Due to the slow tilting of the hut towards the north-east, the synchronome clock stopped, so I repaired and re-adjusted it. Otherwise, I was occupied with monthly glaciological paper work and preparing a signal for the Royal Society on the subject of our journey home and the reimbursement of those who want to make their own way home from Capetown.

NOVEMBER 12. At 4 a.m. the air temperature was −11°C. It was not a good day for working outside. There was freezing drizzle very early in the morning, followed by a strong breeze with snow drift and then snowfall at night.

Most people were occupied indoors. I worked on the analysis and tabulation of geomagnetic records. The ionospheric group was busy with the drift observations they make on Wednesdays.

The following details were provided of the *Tottan*'s route. She was expected to leave Southampton on November 22, be in Montevideo on December 14 and arrive here on January 6 via South Georgia. During the return voyage, the estimated time of arrival in Capetown was January 28. The revised arrival date at Halley Bay was an improvement over the date originally proposed, because this would give us the few days we needed to pack up our records and equipment after finishing the IGY observations on December 31.

The small group who wished to make their own arrangements from Capetown had still not been advised by the authorities in London of the financial implications. I reassured them that it was my belief they would be happy with these when they were finally decided and I urged patience in the meantime. I well understood their impatience.

For over two years now we have been living as a tiny autonomous self-governing society, making most of the important decisions ourselves, swiftly and efficiently. Now, once again, we have to wait patiently whilst the cumbersome decision-making process of a modern state grinds away. Soon, we would all have to get used to that aspect of life but it would take time and a lot more patience.

Les was making active preparations for a short trip to the north-east, starting on the 19th and returning on the 30th.

NOVEMBER 13. At 4 a.m. the air temperature was −10°C. Snow drift driven by a strong breeze continued all day with snow falling at times.

I worked in the office preparing climatological summaries and then making an analysis of seismograms.

Due to the rise in the level of the snow surface, snow drift was entering into the hut via the auroral hatch entry in the roof. To prevent this happening, we raised the hatch by 18 inches (46 cm).

Bill told me that he was very pleased with the results of observations of ionospheric drifts. With better ionospheric conditions this year, and also with better aerials, he was able to do as many drift runs in one month of 1958 as in the whole of 1957.

For supper we were served a casserole of seal steak and about half of us chose that option. The texture of the meat was slightly coarse and a little tough. The flavour was excellent and superior to any of the tinned meat which was in our regular diet. Seal steak was not as popular as the liver.

Les continued with his preparations for a survey trip. In the evening he unpacked his new tent in the lounge and we all examined it with interest.

NOVEMBER 14. At 4 a.m. the air temperature was –8°C. The day was cloudy with snow drift driven by a strong breeze which went on until 10 p.m.

I was busy with climatological records or reports and then analysed seismological charts.

Jim cleared four sacks of rubbish out of the radio sonde room.

NOVEMBER 15. At 4 a.m. the air temperature was –10°C. The morning was cloudy but the afternoon was fine and clear with a gentle breeze.

An ozone sonde was launched in the afternoon. The total amount of ozone in the atmosphere should now be at its maximum after the rapid spring increase.

There was some slight trouble with the Gill hydrogen generator due to undrained water in the reaction chamber.

I prepared some diagrams to illustrate a paper on the climatology of Halley Bay, for presentation at the conference on Antarctic meteorology to be held in Australia.

For supper, seal steaks were served which were both tender and fine grained. These steaks were cut from near the backbone.

Just before the Saturday film show, Les showed some of his recent colour photographs.

SUNDAY NOVEMBER 16. At 4 a.m. the air temperature was –16°C. It was a fine day with a light breeze.

Alf was out with a tractor clearing up solid gash. He also transported some of the tins of caustic soda from the northern dump to the balloon shed where it was used to generate hydrogen.

The radar was moved using the tractor winch. It was the fourth time it was moved this year, to make a total of eleven moves since we arrived in January 1957. A 16 mm ciné shot was made of the move, which we hoped would be our last.

The Sunday morning service was held at 11:15 a.m.

In the afternoon I skied to the disturbed headland near Burlington Bluff. After taking some still and ciné shots there, I skied up and down the drift slopes under the cornice. There was a particularly exciting and very steep slope which several of us thoroughly enjoyed speeding down, because it terminated in a small but precipitously steep hill of drifted snow on top of the sea-ice. I enjoyed the way you sped up to this final hill and how the skis bent and then catapulted you over the top as they straightened out. The first time I went down this particular hill, at the end of the run, I fell forward so that my face ended up in the snow alongside the tips of my skis. As I saw one ski tip inches from my face, it was driven home to me why David Harrison's book on skiing said you should avoid falling in that particular way. After an afternoon on the ski slopes, I enjoyed the pleasures of my bath night more than ever.

NOVEMBER 17. At 4 a.m. the air temperature was −21°C. It was a fine day so I took out the theodolite and made observations of the azimuth and elevation of the sun to determine the azimuth of the geomagnetic fixed mark. For part of this task, I always needed to remove my sun goggles. As a result, in summer I usually ended up with a very mild dose of snow blindness.

Les gave me a copy of the plans for his man-hauling trip. Together with Philip and the dog, the three of them harnessed to the sledge, they proposed to leave on November 19 and return on November 30. The object was to map the coast to the north-east of base, either until their time was up or they had reached the high ground. This trip would fill a gap in our knowledge of the extent of the ice-shelf and the position of the high ground in that direction. I warned Les about moving or camping near the ice front. He replied that he was aware of the danger and proposed to travel at least one mile (1.6 km) from the edge. They took with them a light mountain tent with double sleeping bags, 21 days' food and three gallons of paraffin. On November 24 at 5:55 p.m. Les said that he would fire up a flare to see if it could be observed from a long distance in the prevailing conditions.

Alf and Ivor continued to excavate and move drums of Avtur.

NOVEMBER 18. At 4 a.m. the air temperature was −19°C. It was a cloudy day with some snow drift.

Following instructions sent by the Postmaster at Port Stanley, we burnt £114–0s–1/2d of TAE overprinted stamps. The entire operation was witnessed by John Smith and Philip Brenan. First, we lit the bonfire boiler in the workshop and, when it was burning brightly, fed the stamps into the blaze whilst the three of us solemnly and carefully supervised their complete destruction, not moving from the scene until we were quite sure all the stamps were completely converted into ashes. It took a surprisingly long time to accomplish.

Gwynne continued working away in the radio sonde room on the analysis of his winter observations. Today he was occupied with the airglow measurements.

At 8 p.m. we had very poor reception of the 'Calling Antarctica' programme. Alan Moore spoke and provided the names of next year's party who will leave on *Tottan* at 3 p.m. GMT on November 21. Captain Leif Jakobsen was again in command of the ship.

It was apparent from Alan's talk that we were rather behind in our knowledge of the developments from rocket and satellite observations made during the IGY. After Philip and I talked about the subject, I decided to ask the Royal Society to send a selection of the new material on *Tottan*, so we can catch up with the satellite era started by the IGY.

Len created for supper a notable cheese and ham pastry.

During the day, Malcolm sorted out, for the 1959 party, a quarter of the third-year food dump.

Two Men and a Dog go for a Walk on the Ice-shelf

NOVEMBER 19. At 4 a.m. the air temperature was −13°C. It was a cloudy day with a gentle breeze, there was a short spell of drift and snow showers at night.

A hole was bored through the interior walls of the non-magnetic hut and the north-south line through the hut was redetermined, for the regular re-alignment of the variometers. The total rotation of the hut, since we erected it in the summer of 1957, was found to be one-third of a degree.

In the morning Les and Philip left with the dog on their surveying trip.

From an examination of the daily snow accumulation measurements, I made an estimate of the amount of snow which had fallen and its water equivalent. In a year, 150 cm of snow fell, a water equivalent of 50 cm (20 inches) of water. The year's accumulation of snow, however, was 100 cm. The 50-cm difference between snowfall and accumulation was the amount of snow which ablated, or in other words, was blown or evaporated away.

Has Summer Finally Arrived?

NOVEMBER 20. At 4 a.m. the air temperature was −13°C. There was drift all morning in partly cloudy weather, a moderate to fresh breeze. The rest of the day was fine with a mainly gentle breeze.

During my spell of gash duty today I cleared some small amounts of drift snow which had entered into the boxes containing emergency stores.

John Gane was putting the finishing touches to the connecting wires, or feeders, leading from our radio transmitter to the rhombic aerial used to beam our transmissions to Port Stanley. The feeders now run directly from the hut through a new shaft, easily raised from year to year and by-passing the now deeply buried run along the south-west side of the hut. The whole length was well clear of the snow surface.

The kitchen stove pipe was raised by three feet (91 cm).

Although radio communication conditions were not disturbed, it was not possible to send the usual signal to the Royal Society, even though it had already been delayed by the Regular World Day and the Wednesday drift runs, both of which cut short the period we can transmit without affecting the range of required scientific observations.

At 5:55 p.m. I saw 12 Antarctic Petrels over the base and flying to the south-west.

Now the summer was well-established, there was a considerable amount of water dripping near the north-east and south-west doors. The water subsequently froze and made it very difficult to use the doors.

We heard that the 8300 ton ice-breaker, USS *Glacier* was operating in the Ross Sea using closed circuit TV from a helicopter to assist in navigation through sea-ice.

NOVEMBER 21. At 4 a.m. the air temperature was −18°C. The day was fine with a light or gentle breeze.

Our new Port Stanley rhombic feeders, constructed so diligently by John Gane, were now operational.

Alf and Ivor continued their work digging out drums of Avtur. By the end of the day there were 160 drums along the side of the generator shed.

John Smith did not feel too well during the day. Bert said that John had a headache but he was not seriously ill.

Malcolm continued sorting out the food.

The declination sighting tunnel was dug out, a job which now needed to be done after every spell of drifting snow. The tunnel was 260 feet (79 m) long. The snow surface was still not quite high enough for us to be able to roof it in, using material we can salvage from old packing cases.

I was outside for most of the day doing sun shots or making ozone observations.

Derek, Len and Bert measured the sea-ice at Halley Bay as 8 ft 1 in. (2.46 m) thick. They noticed that the ice was much wetter than formerly.

Bert made his usual Friday fat thickness and weight measurements.

NOVEMBER 22. At 4 a.m. the air temperature was −15°C. The weather was cloudy with a light or gentle breeze.

In the very early hours of the morning, during their spell of night duty, Ben and Bill visited Halley Bay, where they observed at least 1000 Antarctic Petrels flying south along the ice front. Some Snow Petrels were also present. The latter were more curious and showed less sign of being completly absorbed in a single-minded migration.

I made a start with the task of typing out tables and figures for annual reports and for the paper to be given in Australia.

Today we showed the last of our stock of new films.

Tottan Starts Out on her Voyage of Relief

SUNDAY NOVEMBER 23. At 4 a.m. the air temperature was –11°C. Most of the day was cloudy with a light breeze but at night there was some drifting snow and snowfall in a fresh breeze.

The first attempt to launch a balloon was a failure this morning, so we delayed the commencement of the morning service to 11:30 a.m., so that all wishing to could attend, when they had completed work on the late ascent.

In the morning we received a cable from Alan Moore to say that the *Tottan* sailed as planned on November 21.

In the afternoon I dug out and re-stacked about half of our stock of empty radio sonde and balloon boxes, from the dump to the north of the third-year food. I estimated that I also dug out about six tons of snow in the process.

Malcolm and Alf were also busy outside. Malcolm was sorting the food and Alf used a tractor to haul up the third Maudheim sledge and then moved solid gash to the dump.

Andrew and Jim cleaned out the Gill hydrogen generator chamber.

A cable was sent to the Royal Society with a message from Derek Ward, who did not wish to travel the Atlantic by sea again. His present idea was to travel alone over a three- to six-week period, by rail and air from Capetown through Lusaka in Northern Rhodesia and thence by air to London.

NOVEMBER 24. At 4 a.m. the air temperature was –12°C. In the morning there was some slight drift and snow in a moderate breeze. The rest of the day was cloudy.

I resumed typing tables of scientific data for various reports. In the afternoon I saw four more Antarctic Petrels. Clearly, in our location 4 km from the ice cliffs, we only see a small proportion of the birds that fly in the vicinity.

At night I saw a mirage of the *Tottan* range of mountains over 200 miles (322 km) away on a bearing of 075° to 099°E. For the period from 10:15 to 11 p.m., I could also see high ground between a bearing of 063° and 075°E and to the north of the *Tottan* range.

From 5:55 to 6:02 p.m. I looked out for, but saw nothing of, the rocket Les said he would fire off from his camp site.

At night I baked 6 lb. (2.7 kg) of bread.

NOVEMBER 25. At 4 a.m. the air temperature was −15°C. It was a cloudy day with a gentle breeze.

In the morning our camp was visited and inspected by about 300 Emperor Penguins and at least one chick, who stayed with us all day. Most of them walked along the daily accumulation stake route whilst another group circled the camp at the distance of about a mile (1.6 km).

After sending off a short signal of scientific data to the Royal Society, I spent the remainder of the day excavating boxes from the store of empty crates, to use for building materials and to pack up our records and equipment. This pile of boxes was four feet (1.22 m) high but was now completely buried, with two feet (61 cm) of snow on top of the stack.

Malcolm continued to organize food stocks to make it easier for a new team to take over.

The 'Calling Antarctica' programme was heard fairly well. It included a first-rate talk by Anne Todd of the FIDS office in London. They broadcast a great deal of information on some of the very interesting discoveries of the IGY. In the programme for next week, we were promised some recordings made of *Tottan*'s departure.

An ozone sonde was launched in the afternoon that reached an altitude of 27 km.

NOVEMBER 26. At 4 a.m. the air temperature was −9°C. Light snow fell intermittently for most of the day.

The penguins remained with us. There were several chicks with them who were fed from time to time. There was now a second group of the birds, who remained about a mile (1.6 km) east of our camp.

Alf and Ivor moved more drums of Avtur from the dump to the generator shed.

I went out to the southerly remote aerial site with the theodolite and made observations of the bamboo stakes there. They were set up to see if they moved relative to each other due to any distortion of the ice-shelf. No such distortions were detected.

NOVEMBER 27. At 4 a.m. the air temperature was −9°C. It was either cloudy or snowing all day.

The penguins stayed with us for another day. They came and went on the route from Emperor Bay to us and then back via Halley Bay, usually following the shallow valleys which led to these two bays. They moved to and from the bays in groups of 20 to 50 birds.

Alf and Ivor moved another 30 drums of Avtur from the northern dump to the generator shed.

Malcolm was at work again sorting the food boxes in the third year dump.

For part of the day I typed the base diary up to date, worked on the preparation of meteorological records, and started on some more of the annual reports.

Henry looked after all the tasks normally done by Philip in the radio echo hut. At regular intervals, throughout the 24 hours, he changed the recording charts and switched over from one set of aerials to another.

NOVEMBER 28. At 4 a.m. the air temperature was −9°C. There was some snow in the morning and then drift near midday, after which it was cloudy. There was a gentle or moderate breeze blowing.

I finished excavating the stock of empty crates, a total of 68 sonde boxes, 12 balloon crates plus a few other boxes. A South Polar Skua flew over us to investigate and then flew on to visit Alf and Ivor digging out drums of Avtur.

Jim and Henry measured the fast sea-ice thickness at Halley Bay, that was 8 ft 1 in. (2.46 m) thick.

At 9 a.m. an iceberg paused just off the entrance to Halley Bay. Later it moved to the north for a while and then, at 5 p.m., sailed off to the south.

David Tribble fabricated from angle iron yet another new radar sledge tow bar and fitted it to the front of the sledge.

John Gane raised the level of the hatch entry built over the south-west door to the main hut.

Bert made his usual Friday measurements of our weights and fat thicknesses; I weighed 11 stone and 1/2 pound (154.5 lb or 70 kg).

More Preparations for our Return

NOVEMBER 29. At 4 a.m. the air temperature was −7°C. A cloudy day with a light breeze or calm until after lunch, when the wind rose to a moderate breeze.

Some of the Emperor Penguins were with us at the base but in depleted numbers.

Just after midnight this morning, Les and Philip returned with the dog after walking for a total of 130 miles (209 km) to a point 50 miles (80 km) from base to the ENE. They surveyed much of the coast and found it to be an area of glaciological interest. At one part the ice-shelf was only 10 feet (3 m) above sea level.

As a result of his surveying experiences on the trip, Les reported on the practical value of a small telescope built on to a survey compass for such rapid survey work. The problem arose in our geographic situation because points located with the binoculars could often not be seen through the compass sights. One was therefore compelled to search for a second object to sight on, which, in our particular situation, was not always available. They did fire a rocket when they reached their furthest point, at the agreed time. Both men were fit and sun-bronzed. The dog was very tired.

A few of our members were not at all pleased to learn today that their families had been advised by the Royal Society to send a dark suit to them via *Tottan*. I thought it was prudent and thoughtful of them to do so. However, a year ago several people had lost items sent down to them in the relief ship and the presence of our London-based Stores Officer on this relief voyage did absolutely nothing to assuage their fears for the safety of their goods. Partly as a result, this subject had become a sensitive one. And in any case the men felt they should have been consulted first. But we certainly did need our dark suits. It was not the first or the last time I learnt of insensitive handling of relations with our next of kin.

Excellent pork chops were served for supper, after which we watched the regular Saturday film show.

Each member of the expedition today received from the Secretary of FIDS their bills for cables or purchases made through them. These all had to be paid before we left Halley Bay.

I received a cable from Dr Sutcliff, the Director of Research of the British Meteorological Office, approving of my attendance at the symposium in Melbourne. If we do not reach Capetown before January 23, I will have to fly directly to Australia. (It turned out that we did not get to Capetown before the first week in February, because of the difficulties we experienced during our return voyage in escaping from the formidable clutches of the sea-ice of the Weddell Sea, but that's another story).

I dug out the remaining items from the western dump to complete the excavation of stores supplied last year.

Alf cleared solid waste to the gash dump.

SUNDAY NOVEMBER 30. At 4 a.m. the air temperature was −10°C. It was a dull day with snow falling nearly all day in a gentle breeze.

Most of the Emperor adults had returned to their rookery in the bay. Several chicks remained for a part of the day and were pursued several times by Stumpy, who had fully recovered from her trip. By the end of the day the chicks too had gone.

The Sunday morning service was held at 11:15 a.m.

The Royal Society Standard was flown to commemorate its Anniversary Day.

After taking a short walk, I spent most of the day quietly reading.

Another Survey Trip Commences

DECEMBER 1. At 4 a.m. the air temperature was −19°C. Most of the day was cloudy with some blue sky at times. There was a light breeze for most of the time and the temperature was above −21°C.

Jim, John Gane and David Harrison left at 1:30 p.m. on a three-day trip to an ice hill about 15 miles (24 km) away on a bearing of 080° magnetic. They took with them sufficient supplies for a week. The dog was extremely suspicious of the preparations for this trip, and clearly did not wish to go on another one just yet. She had nothing to fear this time because she was not invited.

Bert made a start on the hatch entry to the emergency box installed by the advance party in 1956. The top of this box was now just above the snow surface and so entry from the side was not convenient.

I went to the movement stakes and later worked up my observations on the sun.

A Snow Petrel flew round the base at 10 p.m. and then went off to the south-west.

DECEMBER 2. At 4 a.m. the air temperature was −11°C. It was cloudy day with a light breeze.

Les showed me the rough map he produced as a result of their survey of the ice-shelf to the north-east. The results clearly showed that they had made the most of the time available. The area was certainly an interesting one.

John Smith received a message from the Meteorological Office to say that the delay in replying to his offer to remain at Halley Bay for 1959 was due to administrative difficulties. John formally accepted the appointment. He was now quite contented and pleased to be able to join the 1959 party.

We received a message from the President, Officers and Council of the Royal Society with their warmest good wishes on the occasion of Anniversary Day (November 30). They look forward to the successful conclusion of our programme and our safe return home.

We received a signal from David Stratton, the Deputy Leader of TAE, reminding us to bring back to them books lent to us by TAE.

I was busy with the compilation of some observations made through November and worked up recent astronomical shots for the position of the base and the azimuth of the fixed mark.

Ines Brown of the BBC spoke very well on the 'Calling Antarctica' programme, which included the promised recordings of the departure of *Tottan*.

DECEMBER 3. A partly cloudy day with a gentle breeze and a minimum air temperature of −13°C.

Jim, John Gane, and David Harrison returned in the afternoon after a successful trip to the ice hill, found at the corrected distance of 14 miles (22 km) from base. The hill was found to be in the same place as on the last trip there. Snow accumulation over it varied from six inches (15 cm) to eight feet (2.44 m).

I cleared up the canteen store and took an inventory of the stock.

Malcolm and Philip have cleared crates of sugar from the north-east tunnel and salvaged the empty crates for packing the scintillation equipment.

DECEMBER 4. At 4 a.m. the air temperature was −8°C. There was some snow in the middle of a cloudy day. A moderate breeze was blowing.

Alf and Ivor were getting in the last of the drums of fuel and oil. Lubricating oil was then moved into the oil store in the generator shed.

I recently re-established the magnetic north-south line through the non-magnetic hut and marked the magnetic meridian with a taut thread. Today, I re-aligned the geomagnetic variometers along this meridian, which takes account of any rotation of the ice-shelf. Although the hut rotated by one third of a degree in the year, the variometers themselves had moved very much less away from the magnetic meridian, so that I could detect, by an unaided eye, no significant change in their orientation with respect to the magnetic meridian. This was possibly due to the fact that the instruments were mounted on piles driven deep into the snow and were physically separated from the hut.

DECEMBER 5. There was some slight snow in the morning and cloud for the rest of the day. There was a gentle or moderate breeze and a minimum temperature of −11°C.

Alf completed the excavation and transport to the generator shed of all fuel and oil drums. All of them were placed in the northern dump in January 1957; now their bases lay ten feet (3 m) below the surface.

All those who wished to arrange to travel independently from Capetown were pleased with the generous terms offered by the Royal Society.

I cleaned up the coal shed whilst on gash duty today.

We made our first attempt to make radio contact with *Tottan*.

DECEMBER 6. Snow fell intermittently for most of the day in a gentle or moderate breeze with air temperatures above −11°C.

Ivor flagged a route to Halley Bay and ran a tractor up and down it to compact the snow in preparation for unloading.

Alf cleared up the solid waste.

Bert helped me to dig the last few feet down to the window of our bunkroom. The window was eleven feet (3.35 m) below the snow surface.

At 8:30 p.m. we held our Saturday film show of *Angels One-Five* and *My Six Convicts*. It was John Smith's and my turn to select the movies shown.

SUNDAY DECEMBER 7. At 4 a.m. the air temperature was −9°C. Snow fell all day in moderate amounts. The wind was a gentle breeze.

We held the usual short service at 11:15 a.m.

I covered, with a radio sonde crate, the top of the lighting shaft down to our bunkroom window and then fitted the top with a pane of glass, sealed in place with some putty.

Our Last Coal Haul

DECEMBER 8. There was snow in the morning and the rest of the day was cloudy. A light or gentle breeze was blowing and the air temperature was no lower than −9°C.

After the morning tea break, we started our last coal haul. The store in the main hut was replenished with 7 tons and then we continued to dig out the remaining 18 tons in the dump for the benefit of the 1959 party. There were only 40 sacks left of the stock we brought with us on *Magga Dan* in January 1957. Untouched was the section of 25 tons which had been brought on *Tottan* in January 1958. We had left this particular section of the stock untouched so as to be absolutely sure of the amount of anthracite left for next year.

At 3:30 p.m. there was a small iceberg just off the northern cape of Halley Bay. At 3:55 p.m. it had moved west a little to the middle of the bay. Then at 4:30 p.m., it had moved east again to lie again off the north cape. This gentle east-west movement fits in with the observations we made last summer of the tidal movement of the sea in Halley Bay.

DECEMBER 9. The day was mainly cloudy with a light or gentle breeze and air temperatures no lower than −15°C.

We continued digging out coal, dragging it up to the snow surface and restacking it in a pile 4 ft 6 in. (1.37 m) high, just upwind of the old dump site.

Alf and Ivor de-carbonized one of the Meadows diesel engines and then ran a tractor up and down the flagged route to Halley Bay.

A signal was sent off to the Royal Society with geomagnetic, ozone, meteorological and radio astronomical data.

The sun came out in the afternoon and so I took out the Tavistock theodolite and made observations of the sun to measure the azimuth of the fixed mark.

John Gane was outside working on his feeders.

At 7:30 p.m. we received radio transmissions from the *Tottan* but they were not able to hear us.

DECEMBER 10. The day was cloudy with a light or gentle breeze in the morning and a light air or calm conditions in the afternoon. The minimum air temperature during the day was −13°C.

In the evening the tractors were out compacting the route to Halley Bay.

I opened the Post Office and sold £30 worth of postage stamps.

We tried again to contact *Tottan,* but with no success.

DECEMBER 11. At 4 a.m. the air temperature was −10°C. A cloudy day with a light or gentle breeze.

In the afternoon an ozone sonde was launched. It was one of our best ascents, reaching the 15 mb level at a height of 29 km.

In the afternoon I went out and did an azimuth shot on the sun and whilst out there saw three skuas.

Philip and Len went out and shot a seal.

We Make Radio Contact With *Tottan*

DECEMBER 12. A cloudy day with occasional slight snow. A light breeze was blowing or it was calm, and the minimum air temperature was −18°C.

A World Meteorological Interval started so we brought out some of the superior performance 1000 g silicone balloons to get the highest possible levels in the atmosphere.

David Cansfield continued to repair the ionospheric equipment boxes.

I spent much of the day typing reports.

We made contact with *Tottan* at 7:30 p.m. and exchanged greetings. They have on board a total of 80 tons of stores occupying 5000 cubic feet (142 cubic meters). We discussed the storage of coal here and told them how we covered the coal dumps with tarpaulins, although we were never sure it was actually worth the extra effort. We spoke to them again at 10:15 p.m.

It gave us all a tremendously good and exciting feeling to speak to our friends on *Tottan* once again.

DECEMBER 13. A cloudy day with occasional slight snow, a light or gentle breeze and a minimum temperature of −16°C.

We received from the Secretary of FIDS the details of insurance for our personal effects during the forthcoming trip home.

The day was declared a World Meteorological Interval, a Special World Interval, and a Regular World Day with unusual meteoric activity. All this means that, despite it being a Saturday, we would make all possible scientific observations, including two radio sonde ascents. Consequently, we had to start our regular film show in the afternoon when there was a brief break in the particularly heavy meteorological schedule. As the films selected were long ones, we held part of the show from 4:15 to 6 p.m. and then we started again at 10:15 p.m.

Good radio contact for over half an hour was established with *Tottan* at 10:15 p.m. Amongst other things, we were told to pack up and return the Leica and the 16 mm ciné cameras. We were delighted to hear that FIDS had followed some of our recommendations by providing the 1959 party with an ozone hut and a new tractor engine.

Jim and I measured the kilometre-long base of the movement stakes and then we dug two glaciological pits, side by side. They were eleven feet (3.35 m) deep and designed to study the accumulation record during the last three years whilst the base was occupied.

SUNDAY DECEMBER 14. It was a fine day with a gentle breeze most of the time. The minimum temperature was −18°C.

Les did the morning service whilst I made observations of the sun through noon for latitude and azimuth measurements. Then I checked the results of the last ozone ascent.

I discussed with Philip my annual report on the status of the main hut.

We made contact with *Tottan* at 10:15 p.m.

I put a roof on the two glaciological pits Jim and I had recently dug.

DECEMBER 15. A fine morning but it was cloudy for the rest of the day. There was a gentle breeze and the minimum air temperature was −15°C.

The sledge-mounted Enfield generator, the digger, and spare parts for the tractors have now all been dug out from the dump so they will be available immediately if required during the unloading period.

I was busy with geomagnetic work and the preparation of reports.

We spoke to *Tottan* again at 10:15 p.m. The ship is now one day's sailing north of Montevideo. I discussed with George Lush the remaining stock of food we will be leaving for them, or what we refer to as the '1959-food'.

The efficiency of the compacted snow route to Halley Bay was most clearly demonstrated by the relative ease with which the Enfield generator was pulled along a section on the way to the base from the dump.

DECEMBER 16. A cloudy day with a light breeze and a minimum temperature of −10°C.

As a very pleasant surprise, we heard Dr Martin of the Royal Society on the 'Calling Antarctica' programme this evening. The reception was rather poor but we could understand what he said. Some of us also heard his talk on 'The End of the IGY', broadcast at 5 p.m. in the General Overseas Service of the BBC.

I spent the day analysing seismograms and reporting on the earthquakes we observed.

The *Tottan* range of mountains was visible at 11 p.m. for three hours on the bearings from 84° to 90°M and also from 92° to 97°M. Three hours later other mountains could be seen between the bearings 69° to 74°M. For several in the party it was their first sighting of these mountains.

We spoke to those sailing south on *Tottan* at 10:15 p.m.; they could now see the lights of Montevideo.

DECEMBER 17. The day was fine with a gentle breeze in the morning which became calm at midday. The minimum temperature was −13°C.

The signal sending scientific data back to the Royal Society was delayed and sent off this morning.

Les helped me to standardize our 100-ft. (30 m) steel tape against one made of invar, which has a very small coefficient of thermal expansion.

I removed the guide ropes, which had been invaluable during the winter, and put them away safely for use next year. Now they just impeded movement and in any case were in places buried under the accumulated snow. When they were installed, they were four feet (1.22 m) above the surface. Whilst I was out in the afternoon, I saw 12 Antarctic Petrels flying to the south-west.

David Tribble was working in the glaciological pits Jim and I had just dug. He was taking photographs of the layering of the accumulated snow.

The Sea-ice Softens up in Halley Bay

DECEMBER 18. A fine day with a gentle or moderate breeze. The minimum temperature was −13°C.

In the morning Les and Philip went to the coast just east of Halley Bay to survey the area. They had hoped to get on to the sea-ice but found this was not possible.

Alf and Ivor were raising up, from below many feet of snow, the last of the the Army-type T34 sledges in further preparations for unloading.

We could not hear any transmission from *Tottan* at the agreed time of 10:15 p.m.

As a result of the recent fine weather, the foundations had been melted under the pile of 1959 food and it had fallen over. Malcolm was out there restacking the boxes.

I remeasured the movement stakes.

It was Gwynne's birthday, his third since leaving home. We celebrated in the usual style with a specially prepared chocolate cake followed by a cheerful gathering in the lounge at 8 p.m.

A bird Alf saw yesterday was identified as a Wilson's Petrel.

Henry measured the thickness of the sea-ice. Although it was eight feet (2.44 m) thick, only the first few inches were hard; the remainder was quite soft and took half the normal time to drill through.

DECEMBER 19. It was a splendidly fine day with a blue sky, gentle breeze and a minimum temperature of −12°C.

The Tottan range of mountains could be seen at 10 p.m.

John Gane was preparing the new run for the feeders to the rhombic aerials we use to communicate with London. This task cannot be finished until our ionospheric observations end on December 31, because the feed runs directly underneath Bill's ionospheric aerials.

Alf went fishing in Halley Bay.

I examined, analysed and made notes on the layers of snow in the 11 foot (3.35 m) deep glaciological pit. Then I went inside and typed up more reports.

We made contact with *Tottan* at 10:15 p.m., when she had steamed for four hours from Montevideo.

DECEMBER 20. The morning was cloudy but this cleared up to leave us with a fine day and a gentle breeze. The minimum temperature was −11°C

I was typing reports for much of the day.

The film show was held at 4:15 p.m. because of the second radio sonde ascent occasioned by a World Meteorological Interval. There were very few persons inside watching the movies because, with the sun shining from a blue sky, it was much nicer outside.

At Halley Bay I saw three Weddell Seals and two Crabeaters. There were about 500 Emperor Penguins on the ice-shelf about two miles (3.2 km) from the base in the shallow valley which led up from Emperor Bay.

We made contact with *Tottan* at night.

We Make Preparation for Christmas and our Departure

SUNDAY DECEMBER 21. A fine day with a light or gentle breeze. The minimum temperature was −13°C.

At Halley Bay there were four Weddell Seals and one Crabeater.

The morning service was held at 11:15 a.m.

Emperor Penguins remained in force up on the ice-shelf. I understand that, due to the extent of recent melting, conditions were very unpleasant at the site of the rookery in Emperor Bay.

I baked 6 lb. (2.7 kg) of bread.

The Christmas messages were prepared.

Many people were packing up their personal effects.

A camera and an alarm clock were launched from a balloon today. The gadget was arranged by Len to take a photograph from a height over the ice-shelf and then release the camera.

DECEMBER 22. A cloudy day with a gentle breeze and the minimum temperature of −14°C.

Len's balloon-borne camera took a photograph from a height of 15,000 ft. (4572 m). Unfortunately, the photograph was taken after the release of the camera, when it was pointing upwards and only showed the balloon and sky.

I spent the day typing.

A set of shear-legs was erected over the south-west hatch to lift out the ionospheric equipment.

A Dexion platform was built to raise up the emergency stores.

Tottan was due in Port Stanley on the 23rd and was expected to set sail again on the 26th.

Malcolm decorated the kitchen and lounge for Christmas.

DECEMBER 23. A cloudy day with a light breeze and minimum temperature of −6°C.

Whilst on gash duty, I packed up some boxes ready for departure and prepared some others for later use.

The Maudheim sledges were completely re-rigged with new ropes and lashings. The daily run was made with the tractor to compact the route to Halley Bay.

A fine edition of the BBC programme 'Calling Antarctica' was received at 8 p.m. Sir David Brunt, Robin Smart, and Sir Vivian Fuchs all spoke. The BBC said goodbye to us in great style, including messages from Jimmy Edwards, Ted Ray and The Goons. The producer of the show, Ines Brown, spoke at the end. After the conclusion of this broadcast, John Smith gave a graphic description of a bitterly cold

Ines making recordings on *Tottan* at Southampton in November 1957.

DECEMBER 24. The morning was cloudy and the rest of the day was fine. The minimum temperature was −7°C. In the afternoon the wind rose to a fresh breeze for a short time.

Several more Christmas greeting messages were received. Many of us prepared for tomorrow's Christmas festivities. Malcolm was making a cake and Jim was typing messages into the Christmas Edition of the *Halley Comet*.

Radio sondes were re-stacked in the loft.

I brought up to date the geomagnetic, seismic and glaciological observations. Then I adjusted one of the seismographs, brought another into the hut for repair, and then re-installed it at the bottom of the 10-metre deep glaciological pit.

In his daily route-compaction run to Halley Bay, Alf saw four seals.

CHRISTMAS DAY DECEMBER 25. The weather was just perfect, with sunshine, blue skies, a minimum temperature of −12°C and practically no wind. In these latitudes, Antarctic summer days do not get much better than this.

After taking breakfast one hour later than usual, at 8:30 a.m., we sent up the morning radio sonde and wind ascent.

At 11:15 a.m. we held a short religious service that was well-attended and included some well-known Christmas carols, rendered in a lusty fashion.

We started to gather together in our best suits near noon to listen to the Queen's Christmas Message, broadcast at 1 p.m. The lunch which followed at 1:15 p.m. was excellent. Len prepared it together with an attractive menu as follows:

> Crawfish salad;
> Roast Turkey;
> Roast potatoes, asparagus,
> Brussels sprouts and tomatoes;
> Christmas Pudding;
> Minced Tarts;
> Fruit salad;
> Crystallized fruits;
> Nuts and figs;
> Argentine champagne;
> David Dalgleish's Cigars.

In good form we retired to the lounge to play the game of pinning a tail on the donkey whilst blindfold.

In the perfect weather of the afternoon, two tractors and sledges

loaded with most of the expedition, went down to Halley Bay, where
we skied or looked at seals and penguins. The day was so warm that
several of us took off our shirts.

In the evening there was an excellent cold buffet, a film show and
the special Christmas edition was issued of the *Halley Comet*.

At Halley Bay, the sea-ice one mile (1.6 km) to the east of Penguin
Leap was half a mile (0.8 km) further out than when *Tottan* unloaded
last year. There was a depth of three feet (91 cm) of snow on top of
the sea-ice. A group of 12 Emperors went into the water as I approached.
On their second dive they remained below water for two and a half
to three and a half minutes. After a 45 second rest, they all remained
below for five minutes on their third dive.

Snow Petrels and Antarctic Petrels were moving south along the
ice front in groups of about a dozen and at frequent intervals. Weddell
Seals were sunning themselves near a crack in the sea-ice. I saw one
Petrel fly north along the sea-ice edge whilst others skimmed over the
glassy smooth water of the shore lead.

The cover for the Christmas Edition of the *Halley Comet* featured
a line drawing by David Tribble showing the *Tottan* moored at Halley
Bay in a frame of small cartoons of features drawn from our life and
personalities. It was all done with great taste and artistry. The Leader's
message in the *Comet* read as follows:

> 'I am glad of this opportunity, offered by the Editors, to wish
> you all the greatest happiness and success on your return home.
> Our work here is almost done and I would like to congratulate
> you on the splendid style in which it was accomplished, your
> efforts will undoubtedly culminate in a significant contribution
> to geophysics.
>
> 'It was encouraging to hear Dr Martin say that the secrets of
> Antarctica were already unfolding. When the full weight of the
> observations is appreciated in the years which lie ahead, we may
> count ourselves fortunate to have played our part in the IGY,
> one of mankind's great adventures.
>
> 			'Joe MacDowall
> 			Base Leader'

The editorial in the paper ponders on the attractive forces of
Antarctica which are bringing back to Halley Bay two persons who
left here two years ago and probably felt then as we do today, David
Limbert and George Lush. It ends with the following quotation from
S. Taylor's book, *Man and Matter – Essays Scientific and Christian*:
'Philosophy and science do not answer our deepest questions nor do
they solve effectively our most pressing problem, that of human
conduct.'

Jim Burton wrote thus about his forthcoming departure: 'I leave

We had been floating on our ice shelf for almost two years when this happy photo was taken on Christmas Day 1958, our third Christmas with the expedition. From left to right are David Cansfield, Les Barclay, Henry Dyer, Andrew Blackie, Bill Bellchambers, Jim Burton, and Gwynne Thomas.

you eager now to see my loved ones, my friends and my homeland, but your presence will linger in my memory and I will live always in the hope of meeting you once again on one of life's highways and byways. And so I come to the last sad sweet word of parting. Goodbye dear friend. Farewell Antarctica. Be seeing you.'

DECEMBER 26. Much of the day was fine with a gentle breeze. The minimum temperature was –15°C.

Our table was still well-laden with Christmas food; there was turkey for lunch.

The day was spent quietly, with most of us back at our scientific duties.

Philip and Les went out to survey Emperor Bay.

Tottan was still at Port Stanley, after which she will pay a short visit to South Georgia on December 31.

There was a good telephone link with London so that many people were able to send Christmas greetings to their loved ones.

I completed the glaciological report.

At Halley Bay at 9 p.m. several of us noticed a slight ocean swell moving the sea-ice up and down.

I received a long and eloquent telegram from Oonagh.

DECEMBER 27. A fine day with a light breeze for most of the day. The minimum temperature was –15°C.

I was tabulating the monthly glaciological and geomagnetic records

Top: *David Harrison skiing at Halley Bay after Christmas lunch in 1957.*

Above: *Bill and Jim on the sea-ice at Halley Bay.*

for most of the day. Then I prepared some more packing cases to transport scientific records home.

The films shown tonight were selected by Malcolm and David Harrison. They chose some Pathé Newsreels and *Meet the Huggets*. John Smith took over from John Gane the job of ciné projectionist, in preparation for next year. John was clearly looking forward to another year here. He will make a strong addition to next year's team.

During our radio contact with *Tottan* at 10:15 p.m. we learnt her ETA at Halley Bay was January 8 to 10.

SUNDAY DECEMBER 28. There was a light or gentle breeze all day with a clear sky in the morning and cloud in the afternoon. The minimum temperature was −16°C.

After the morning service I put out the daily newspapers for 14 November 1957.

I spent a fairly quiet Sunday, walking in the hot sun for part of the time and then reading. Then I sent off a cable to South Georgia ordering some of the excellent and inexpensive Norwegian sweaters sold at the whaling station.

DECEMBER 29. The morning was cloudy with a gentle or moderate breeze. Snow fell for the rest of the day with a moderate breeze. The minimum temperature was −9°C.

Just as noted at Emperor Bay, the recent spell of fine weather made our campsite look very dirty as the snow melted, leaving behind all the dirt. Consequently, snowfall was welcomed for it made our environment look more wholesome.

David Cansfield and I prepared more packing cases.

Probably the last epicentral data signal that I would receive here came in from the US Coast and Geodetic Survey. Throughout the IGY, I received these at regular intervals, giving me their estimate of the location and depth of earthquakes round the world. I could then calculate the approximate times of arrival at Halley Bay of the earth tremors generated. Then I scrutinized the seismograms to identify the exact times of arrival and reported these back to the IGY World Data Centres for seismology. Once I got back home, I would have to finish off reading the seismograms up to the end of the year.

DECEMBER 30. The snow ended in the early hours of the morning. The afternoon was fine. There was a gentle or moderate breeze blowing and the minimum temperature was −13°C.

I prepared a signal for the Royal Society and then wrote reports. In this cable I replied positively to an offer to take charge of the reduction, analysis and publication of the meteorological, geomagnetic, glaciological and seismological reports of the expedition. I replied as follows: 'Would be honoured to undertake work you propose and agreeable you ask the Director General of the Meteorological Office (to extend my secondment to the Royal Society for this purpose). Blackie (is) grateful (for the) opportunity offered and very willing to reduce geomagnetic observations. (I) Consider (it) desirable (for) Burton and Tribble (to) assist (in the) work of reduction. Both are keen and willing (to do so), they also have some of (their) own work (I recommend it) desirable (to) complete.'

The restacking of the 1959 food-dump was complete.

Many people were now preparing packing cases to send back their scientific records and personal effects.

We were surprised to learn from *Tottan* that she had left South Georgia in the afternoon. We made good voice contact with her. In our discussions, the Royal Society had some very interesting proposals for our travel arrangements.

At Halley Bay some sea-ice had gone from the edge, which was now broken back to a position near last year's. There were three cracks in the sea-ice about 18 inches (46 cm) wide that will need filling in, but were not wide enough to require bridging.

With a feeling of deep satisfaction and contentment, we launched our last night-time radio sonde and radio wind ascent. We also launched our last ozone sonde. We were too busy to mark this closure and very conscious of the many tasks we had yet to complete.

DECEMBER 31. It was a fine day with a gentle breeze. The minimum temperature was −16°C.

All of us in the meteorological group were very busy breaking the back of the work required to check and tabulate all the December data.

It was Len's birthday and we celebrated it with a chocolate cake and some whisky after supper. Malcolm had also made a cake to recognise the commencement of the year 1959 as a year of International Geophysical Cooperation (IGC).

At 8:30 p.m. we gathered in the lounge for a New Year's Eve party. We listened to the General Overseas Service of the BBC and then saw the film *For Better or For Worse*. Celebrated with great gusto were the hours of local midnight and then two hours later, midnight in the UK. At both times, we joined hands and sang 'Auld Lang Syne', and then toasted next year's party and the IGC. Just as the party started, a timely message was received from Dr Martin and Alan Moore. The end of the IGY was suitably impressed on our minds. Our two years here will need no such underlining and will live long in our memories.

I opened the Post Office until local midnight and many people took the opportunity to get their letters postmarked with the date, 31 December 1958.

Andrew and I spoke to *Tottan* during the evening; they too were enjoying a good party. Her noon position was 55.9°S 30.7°W.

Chapter 8

Its 1959 and the International Geophysical Year has Ended

O sweet spontaneous earth
how often has the naughty thumb
of science prodded thy beauty
thou answereth them only with spring.

Edward Estlin Cummings 1894–1962.

Packing Up To Go Home

JANUARY 1, 1959. I am now making a note in the base diary of the air temperature at 1 p.m.; in summer this gives a better idea of the outside working conditions of the day. It was a fine day with a gentle breeze and an air temperature of −4°C at 1 p.m.

Packing arrangements moved into top gear. By the end of the day, most of the ionospheric drift equipment was crated and a start was made with the absorption instruments.

Gwynne packed some of his equipment and so did Philip, who had to dig into his remote huts to extricate the equipment inside. Philip was disconnecting his equipment whilst perched on top of a small aerial mast near the radio echo hut.

Malcolm dug out some of the few remaining buried food boxes.

I cleaned up the canteen store and tabulated some of the monthly meteorological records. Then I worked outside for a while. Amongst other things, I climbed down the glaciological pit and adjusted the seismographs at the bottom and then I calibrated some of the radiation instruments.

The noon position of *Tottan* was 58°S 20°W.

Now that ionospheric observations have ended, John Gane was able to start erecting the new feeders to the rhombic aerials for communications with London.

JANUARY 2. There was a little sunshine today with a gentle breeze and at 1 p.m. the temperature was −3°C.

I opened the Post Office and sent off a signal to the Royal Society with some scientific data. Then I went outside and worked shirt-less in the sunshine to dig out some large packing cases.

Packing continued to go well.

The feeder to the London rhombic aerial was completed.

At 8:30 p.m. we met in the lounge for a scientific discussion. Jim, Philip, Bill, David Harrison, and I led off with some prepared material. This was followed by a very enjoyable and animated discussion. For this lively event, Malcolm produced savouries and Les contributed a bottle of Madeira.

When we contacted *Tottan*, I spoke to Mike Blackwell, Dave Limbert, and George Lush on a variety of technical questions. Apparently they were all recruited in a great rush with little or no time for training, and so they were concerned about some aspects of the work they had to do here. I do not think they have too much need to worry and, in any case, we would not leave until they felt happy and confident. Their two biggest scientific programmes are in meteorology and geomagnetism and for those subjects they have the nucleus of a good team in Mike Blackwell, David Limbert and John Smith. However, they will need considerable assistance from the others.

Tottan's noon position was 57.2°S 22.3°W, where she was in open sea. There was pack ice to her south at 1800 UT. They were heading for longitude 12°W and then shaping a course for Cap Norvegia.

JANUARY 3. A fine day with a light or gentle breeze. The temperature at 1 p.m. was −4°C.

Packing continued throughout the day. A hole was cut into the passage from the ionospheric room and the absorption transmitter was taken outside, through the south-westerly door of the hut, and then lifted up about 15 feet (4.6 m) using the shear-legs erected over the top of the hatch.

Contact with *Tottan* was good when I spoke for about two hours to George Lush.

We held the usual Saturday night film show at 8:30 p.m.

We learnt that the USS *Edisto* would not be able to visit us on her way from relieving the US base at Ellsworth. She was making all possible speed to land a sick man at Rio.

The two Meadows electrical generators have run for 8306 and 8612 hours.

There was a large iceberg and two smaller ones moving southwards just off the coast. This was the biggest movement of bergs we have seen since last autumn.

We Celebrate the Second Anniversary
at Halley Bay

SUNDAY JANUARY 4. A fine day with a light breeze. The 1 p.m. temperature was −2°C.

The singing was excellent at our morning service as we gave voice to our thanks.

Most of us continued packing during the day or finished off reports. The absorption transmitter was completely crated and nailed up. David Cansfield was making a very thorough job of this work. It had been anticipated that much of this sensitive equipment would need repacking in Capetown. It is clear now that much less will in fact need to be repacked.

At Halley Bay the position of the fast bay-ice was unchanged but its condition was a little slushy.

Most of the meteorological records were packed.

The position of *Tottan* at 10 p.m. was 61.2°S 13.2°W, where her navigation was not being impeded by sea-ice.

I spoke to Mike Blackwell about the geomagnetic work.

We have completed two full years at Halley Bay.

JANUARY 5. It was a fine day with a light breeze and a 1 p.m. temperature of −4°C.

Packing and the typing up of reports or stores lists occupied us this day.

At 9 a.m. the Union ionosonde was switched off and taken outside for packing on a T34 sledge. We took 16 mm ciné shots of the process.

Radio contact with *Tottan* was poor at 8 p.m. Two hours later they could not be heard at all. The Captain could not see any sea-ice at 7 p.m., when she was at 65.2°S 12.0°W. With a continued clear run, they could be here in three days.

Alf reported that the compacted road to Halley Bay would take a load of over two tons (12 oil drums) on a Maudheim sledge.

JANUARY 6. Most of the day was cloudy with a moderate breeze. There were snow showers at night. The air temperature at 1 p.m. was −3°C.

It was another very busy day for us all, packing, cleaning up the hut, and typing reports or lists of our packing cases and their contents. By the end of the day all the ionospheric equipment was packed, so too were the majority of the meteorological and ionospheric records.

There was a strong smell of furniture and floor polish inside the hut as we continued to clean up.

Radio communications conditions were not good enough for voice contact with *Tottan*. For the first part of the day she continued her way unobstructed by sea-ice. She met heavier ice at 4 p.m. when her position was 67.4°S 11.3°W. Regular meteorological observations from *Tottan* were sent to us and then we passed them on to Port Stanley so they could incorporate them into their meteorological forecasts and sea-ice reports, which were so important at this time of the year.

According to the US base at Ellsworth, at 2 a.m. the Argentine ice breaker *San Martin* was 180 miles from Cap Norvegia and making 10 knots (19 kph) in good conditions. If this is accurate, San Martin could be a few miles ahead of *Tottan*.

I sent a signal to the Royal Society reporting on our good progress with packing. I also informed them that we were now sending up one radio sonde and wind-finding ascent per day, instead of the two we launched during the IGY.

JANUARY 7. A cloudy day with snow showers and a wind that varied between calm and a moderate breeze. The air temperature at 1 p.m. was −4°C.

After the morning ascent, we dug out and stacked the bridging timbers. Two bridges were assembled and made ready for use should any wide cracks develop at Halley Bay during unloading. We also lifted to the surface the two spare stoves in Dump Five. Each stove weighed 318 lb. (144 kg).

We continued to work on report writing and packing. In addition, we removed the Christmas decorations from the lounge and kitchen.

Philip found that he needed more wood wool to protect his equipment inside their crates. A fresh supply is on its way to us, so he will have to leave these cases open until it arrives.

There were two large icebergs off Halley Bay and moving south. Many bergs have moved down the coast since January 2. In the afternoon, small pieces of sea-ice from the ice edge at Halley Bay were breaking off and drifting out to sea.

Tottan was making slow progress through heavy drift ice, at a speed which was down to two knots (4 kph) at times. At 10 p.m. her position was 68.9°S 4.8°W, in heavy drift ice.

JANUARY 8. There was a fresh south-westerly breeze all day with surface drift at times. The air temperature at 1 p.m. was −4°C.

We all continued our work of packing up, cleaning the hut and typing up stores lists.

David Cansfield finished off the documentation of the ionospheric equipment. It comprised 12 crates of records and 20 of equipment.

Malcolm was restocking the kitchen and loft with supplies of 1959 food.

Contact with *Tottan* remained poor but we did manage to get her meteorological observations for 1500 and 1800 UT. We also received the welcome news that she had finally broken through the tongue of sea-ice into the shore lead. At 4 p.m. local time her position was 70.3°S 7.6°W. At this rate she should be with us in two days' time.

JANUARY 9. It was a cloudy day with a moderate south-westerly breeze and light snow at times. The wind became easterly at the end of the day. The air temperature at 1 p.m. was −5°C.

The smaller ionospheric crates were taken to the dump by the old meteorological tower, ready for loading on to sledges for transport to *Tottan.*

Warm days and intense solar radiation had undermined the foundations of more stores dumps. They were rebuilt and then the emergency dump was stacked on to newly-built Dexion platforms.

A number of us participated in a good clear-out and scrub-out of the hut.

Most of us were very well prepared for *Tottan*'s arrival. Several days ago I had completely packed up all the personal gear required for the trip home and put the rest into a packing case to go in the ship's hold and travel independently. The packing case was very well marked with large letters painted on more than one side. I had also typed up lists with the contents of every case for customs purposes. The idea was to be so well prepared that at a moment's notice one could pick up a kitbag and go.

Contact with *Tottan* was still very poor. Her 1800 UT observation gave her position as 71.9°S 15.8°W in a wide shore lead. She is now expected to arrive near midnight tomorrow.

Some of the bay-ice in Halley Bay showed signs of moving out. If it does not move out, a small amount of bridging may be required.

JANUARY 10. It was a cloudy day with a moderate breeze in the morning and a gentle breeze for the rest of the day, The air temperature at 1 p.m. was −7°C.

In the morning John Gane and I went to the sea-ice edge, which was about 1.75 miles (2.8 km) from the base. There were three tide cracks a few feet across and the sea was frozen at the bottom. Alf and Ivor bridged these in the afternoon and 16 of us were there to meet *Tottan* with two tractors towing sledges. *Tottan* was first sighted at 6:26 p.m. and tied up alongside the sea-ice at 7 p.m.

It was quite a hectic day whilst we pumped as much information as possible into the 1959 party.

The time of the handover of the base to the 1959 party will depend on the scientific change over, which was progressing well.

We learnt from the new team that they felt themselves relatively unprepared because FIDS had left recruiting until the last possible moment.

SUNDAY JANUARY 11. There was drift and some snow much of the day in a fresh south-westerly breeze. The air temperature at 1 p.m. was −5°C.

The five-man meteorological group in the 1959 Party came up to the base for breakfast and then took part in the morning radio sonde and radar wind-finding ascent. One of them filled the balloon and another was working in the radar. Back at the main hut, the others assisted with the measurement of the frequency of the signals transmitted by the radio sonde, plotting out the winds etc.

We spent the morning with the new party on the handover of the scientific programme. Then after lunch, we started unloading *Tottan* and continued until 8:15 p.m., when the last tractor of the day reached base.

We were invited to a great party on board *Tottan* in the evening.

Bad Weather Holds Up Unloading

JANUARY 12. Surfaces were poor and became worse. To cap this misfortune, the weather deteriorated, so the tractors had to leave the bay at 3 p.m. due to very poor visibility. Visibility was so bad that David Cansfield nearly went for a trip over the sea-ice to the Gin Bottle to the north of the exit from Halley Bay. At the time, the tractors took three hours to get up to the base with Bill leading the way on foot. I was up at the base whilst George Lush, several others of the 1959 party, and our stores officer were on board *Tottan*. The weather became so bad that *Tottan* had to sail away for safety from the vicinity of the ice-front.

JANUARY 13. The weather became worse with temperatures above freezing, rain, and a 40-knot (74 kph), gale force wind, our first gale since October.

Tottan sheltered to our north.

We spent the day going over the details of the handover with the 1959 party, finishing work at midnight. It was agreed between us that we should move tomorrow from the main hut to *Tottan*. Because of our greater experience of conditions, we undertook full responsibility for unloading the ship, unaided by the 1959 party. We would establish an interim dump for all the 1959 stores, at an agreed site, safely at the top of the ice-shelf. The 1959 Party agreed to move the stores from there to their final position at a later date. We agreed to let Malcolm stay at the base to continue cooking for the 1959 party.

I sent off a report on progress to the Royal Society. In this I also reported on the nasty accident which had befallen our medical officer, Bert Brooker. Once again it turned out that, for the second year in succession, the most serious accident of the year was experienced by our sole medical officer.

In the poor weather Bert had taken out a tractor. In whiteout conditions he had not spotted a sharp dip in the terrain. The tractor tipped over on top of the unfortunate Bert, who was thrown face down into the snow underneath the still-rotating tractor tracks. We stopped the tractor's engine and gingerly extricated him. The tracks had torn into his back and bruised his shoulder. It looked very nasty to me and was obviously very painful for Bert. After examining his own back in a mirror, he pronounced that he had received 'slight abrasions' to his back. That may have been the correct medical term for his condition, but I considered it the understatement of the year. He was clearly incapable of much physical effort during the unloading period, when every pair of hands was needed. However, he was able to give George Hemmen some help with his paper work.

From 10 p.m. to midnight I went up to both of the headlands of Halley Bay. I could not see *Tottan*. The bay ice was broken well back into the bay. It still lay there in several separate pieces looking like a giant's jigsaw puzzle.

In the early hours of the morning an attempt was made to unload again but it was not possible. The sea-ice was moving and we failed in an attempt to rescue a coil of rope which was left on a piece of broken sea-ice.

Disaster Averted by Crew of *Tottan*

JANUARY 14. The Royal Society Base, Halley Bay was closed down.

The gale continued but visibility was good at 8 a.m. so I went to Halley Bay and asked the three 1959 party members remaining on board to get their kit prepared for disembarkation. The 1959 cook, Jim, was one of the party still on board. He then moved up to the base and finally took over the cooking from Malcolm.

The tractors came down but we found *Tottan* still unable to unload. Then the weather deteriorated again and we had another spell of gale force winds and poor visibility. The visibility was so poor that one tractor nearly got lost.

Later, whilst *Tottan* coped with the break-up of the sea-ice in Halley Bay, the Royal Society party on shore moved their 20 tons of scientific records and equipment from the base to a point on the ice-shelf three-quarters of the way to the bay.

Andrew, Jim, Bill, and I were on *Tottan* whilst the sea-ice of Halley Bay broke up. Moments before this occurred, *Tottan* was tied up to the sea-ice edge. Then the wind rose and a huge piece of ice and compacted snow, about 40 ft (12 m) thick, to which she was moored, suddenly broke away and started to drift off. Within a few seconds, the ever-alert Norwegian crew materialized on deck, hopped nimbly over the side of the ship with sledge hammers and pieces of rope in their hands. At times leaping from one piece of moving ice to another with amazing agility, they used the hammers to free the moorings and then jumped back on board. Most impressive of all was the manner in which the crew accomplished all this. As far as I could tell, no alarm was sounded nor was anyone there shouting out orders. It seemed to me that all the crew members were just very alert, knowledgeable and sensitive to the ways of Antarctica. Moreover, they all knew just what was expected of them.

A few days earlier, whilst I was up at base, a similar event occurred. *Tottan* was being unloaded at the time, so there were tractors, sledges and some stores on the sea-ice by the ship. Suddenly, in the freshening gale, the sea-ice broke up near the ship. Once again the captain and crew sprang into action like a well-articulated machine. The crew retrieved moorings, releasing the ship to give her freedom of action. Then the captain skillfully manoeuvred her, nudging the ice floes back together again. Then the ship held them together, by a judicious adjustment of *Tottan's* helm and engine. Whilst the sea-ice was held in place, the tractors were able to cross from floe to floe and find their way back up the slope to the relative safety of the ice-shelf.

There was no doubt in my mind that if these skilful actions had not been take by the crew of *Tottan*, we could very easily have lost some of those on the sea-ice at the time. At the best some people would have been cast adrift in a gale, sailing away on tiny ice floes.

In the afternoon, the weather improved and we then started to move 12 men from base to *Tottan*. Unfortunately by then the sea had risen and *Tottan* was compelled to hold off after only Jim, Bill, Alf, Ben, and Henry had been able to embark.

I was up at the base again at 11:30 p.m., when I distinctly felt the ice-shelf move. I informed George Lush of the incident before we parted.

JANUARY 15. Unloading started after the ship was winched and hauled by tractor alongside the 10 ft. (3 m) high ice-shelf now at the head of Halley Bay. We worked until 9 p.m. and shifted 230 drums of Avtur and about 17 tons of coal. As agreed with the 1959 party, who played no role in this phase of unloading, all this was taken to the site of the temporary dump safely on the ice-shelf and one-third of the way to base.

At 9 p.m. I went up to the base immediately after unloading. Whilst I was there, the 1959 party requested further assistance from us to help them get established, as they were still groping about uncertainly in rather unfamiliar territory. I agreed to provide all the assistance necessary.

I told Captain Jacobsen about sensing the movement of the ice-shelf and he said that he could believe me. He said that he wanted to leave tomorrow because he expected there would be heavy ice near Cap Norvegia as a result of the recent north-easterly gales.

George Lush, leader of the 1959 party and our stores officer, came to the ship in the evening.

It was my first night aboard *Tottan*.

The IGY Harvest-home

We Sail Away on Tottan With 10 Tons of Scientific Data

JANUARY 16. It was overcast all day with a strong breeze blowing.

We returned to the task of unloading after breakfasting on board *Tottan*. The job was completed quickly in the morning and by noon we had also loaded on to *Tottan* the 20 tons of scientific data and equipment we were taking back home, the harvest of the IGY.

I went up to the base in the afternoon after completing the loading and sorted out some mail. Then I sent off a signal to the Royal Society reporting that most of us had now moved to the *Tottan*. Those aboard told me they were pleased with their accommodation.

In the afternoon Lush, Hemmen and I met on *Tottan* to discuss departure. In view of the Captain's recommendation, we agreed that *Tottan* should depart at about 6 p.m., leaving just sufficient time to provide the 1959 party with all the essential assistance they needed.

At 4:30 p.m. Alf brought a tractor to the ship for Captain Jacobsen and we gave him a tour of the base and the equipment inside the non-magnetic hut. We all went back with him to *Tottan* and finally sailed away at 7:30 p.m.

Looking back at Halley Bay, with the minute black figures waving goodby, dwarfed by the ice-cliffs towering above them, on which we had made our home, it was hard to imagine that in several years' time this familiar scene would break away as a huge tabular iceberg drifting out to sea.

In the evening, we sailed along the shore lead accompanied by Antarctic Petrels. We all seemed to be comfortable in our accommodation. There was a slight swell which was just enough to make several persons sea-sick.

JANUARY 17. The 12:00 UT position was 73.6°S 24.8°W; at 22:00 UT it was at 72.5°S 20.0°W. Our northerly movement from Halley Bay had already shortened the duration of the night by one hour.

Since we left Halley Bay, we continued to sail at a speed of about 10 knots (19 kph) through very open, heavy hummocked pack ice, punctuated by very occasional periods at slow speed.

The day was cloudy and the wind fell from a gentle or moderate easterly breeze to a light breeze.

We expect to reach Cap Norvegia tomorrow evening.

During the day the Stores Officer and I did a little work on the cargo lists and found we had loaded 730 cubic feet (21 cubic metres) of cargo from Halley Bay, weighing about 20 tons.

We considered our food on *Tottan* was excellent. At breakfast we could have as many eggs as we wished, there was stew for lunch, and sausages and mash for dinner. The quantities available of anything served were unlimited and there was always, and at any time, cheese or sardines available for sandwiches.

In the evening I read the remainder of the letters I had received and I started to reply to them.

Jim Burton brought a large crate of assorted drinks down to the ship's day room for all of us to share.

SUNDAY JANUARY 18. Progress was quite fast at first but became slower, with many halts when we were off Cap Norvegia, a gateway to the Weddell Sea. The ice floes round the ship were moving very rapidly. In the evening a small hummocked floe became stuck to the bow of the ship. This was removed with the aid of an explosive charge of dynamite.

After supper several of us were invited by the crew to take a cup of coffee with them. They were a very friendly lot. We received invitations to visit some of them at their homes in Tonsberg.

At 22:45 UT the ship was stopped by the ice. It was very heavy and hummocked in places, and covered about three quarters of the sea. The signs are now clear that we will face a difficult passage out of the icy grip of the Weddell Sea.

I saw many Crabeater Seals and some Adelie Penguins.

JANUARY 19. The position of the ship at noon was 71.1°S 14.0°W.

After lunch today I spoke with the Captain and showed him some of the survey maps we had prepared at Halley Bay. He told me that whilst he was riding out the storm, his echo-sounding machine detected a submarine ridge to the north of Halley Bay near the local disturbance we called the Gin Bottle. He said this ridge rose from a depth of 215 metres to about 170 metres below sea-level.

The afternoon was quite warm with the sun shining at times. I spent the time sitting in the bows of the ship and started to read Fuchs' book on the TAE.

As anticipated by Captain Jacobsen, ice conditions in the Weddell Sea must be quite severe this year because at least two other ships were also having difficulties in the area. We therefore took the precaution of keeping one kitbag specially packed with essentials, should the need arise to abandon ship.

Tottan was stationary in very close pack ice until 7 p.m., when the

Captain climbed up into the crow's nest. After he had spotted a route, we pushed through from one small pool of water to the next, threading in between large, heavy hummocked ice floes. Progress was made this way for a few hours only until all the ice floes moved tightly together again. At midnight we lay trapped between two ice floes and listing with the pressure of the ice on the sides of the ship. Two explosive charges were set off in an attempt to free her.

Henry and the *Tottan*'s radio operator got together and they made radio contact with the US icebreaker *Edisto*, whom we must have passed at about noon yesterday. She was about 40 miles (64 km) nearer to the shore and had been trapped in the ice for four days. Also trapped were the Norwegian ships *Polar Hav* and *Polar Biorn*. I asked the Captain what he thought the ice was like round the *Edisto*. He replied that he knew it would be worse than it was here and that was why he kept out here. Of all those trapped, he believed we were in the most favourable position to escape.

Henry also discovered that the Argentine ice breaker *San Martin* left Ellsworth base yesterday morning.

Beset by the Ice of the Weddell Sea

JANUARY 20. The noon position was 71°08′S 14°54′W.

It was cloudy with a moderate north-east breeze and the sun shone at times.

We were beset by the sea-ice and could not move all day. During the evening there was a slight decrease in the list of the ship to port, indicating a slight relaxation or adjustment of the pressure on the vessel. About 30 icebergs could be seen from the ship and they seemed to be moving through the field of sea-ice.

I asked Captain Jacobsen if there was anything we could do to help. He said there was nothing we could do at present with the ice under pressure. Tomorrow, he said, it might be necessary to transfer water in buckets from one tank to another. Apparently, some of the pipes were frozen up and their portable pump would not work.

I received the following cable addressed from the Secretary of FIDS to MacDowall: 'Greetings to all the returning members of the Royal Society party. We are sorry (to) see you go after so pleasant an association and we trust all will go well on (your) return voyages and thereafter. Proverbs 23 Verses 20 and 33. (Signed) SECFIDS.' I gathered the biblical quotation was intended as a friendly warning against the temptations of wine, women and song which could beset our release from years of the monastic life at Halley Bay. I thanked him and replied to the inquiry about the sea-ice conditions. Apparently, now FIDS have the responsibility for the base at Halley Bay, their interest in Weddell sea-ice conditions has been sharpened.

Just before supper, several of us went into the day room to drink a glass of beer with expedition members and some of the crew. Ben Ellis's entrance created quite a stir and was considered by the crew to be particularly entertaining. Ben usually wore a smart white polo sweater with the words 'Halley Bay' embroidered across his chest. He had removed the original embroidery and replaced it with the words 'Weddell Sea'.

JANUARY 21. The noon position of the ship was 71.1°S, 13.9°W. The ship remained beset in the sea-ice although I thought I detected a slight easing in the pressure of sea-ice on the ship.

We had a good breakfast this morning of bacon and eggs. Then I went out for a walk round the deck looking longingly at the clear water sky to our north-west, indicating the presence of open water in that direction.

After lunch, I did some washing and then watched the activities of three very young members of the crew who went hunting for a large Crabeater Seal lying on the sea-ice about half a mile away. They took with them a wooden pole or club, a rope and a bucket, and intended to kill the seal to augment our food supplies, just in case our stay in the Weddell Sea was longer than intended. I was up on the bridge with the Captain and he was looking at the hunters through his field glasses. After looking at them moving round the seal, he said enigmatically, 'They will be back'. I asked him what he meant and he handed me the glasses without replying. Apparently, when they go after a seal in the north, they stun it with a club, slit its throat, collect the blood in the bucket and then haul the carcase back to the ship using the piece of rope they are carrying. As I knew from personal experience, the Antarctic Crabeater Seal is quite aggressive and one is not easy to dispatch in this way. We always had to shoot them. Sure enough, after a short battle of wits, the youngsters retired and returned to the ship empty-handed. When they returned, the would-be hunters said the seal was too big and old and therefore unsuitable for eating. It was a good excuse.

In the afternoon the sun shone, so several of us went on to the ice to take photographs of the ship helplessly trapped there.

A Killer Whale appeared briefly alongside the ship in a small pool of water.

JANUARY 22. The noon position was 71.2°S 15.3°W. We are still beset and moving about 10 to 15 miles (16 to 24 km) to the west trapped in the sea-ice. There was a south-westerly breeze and my hopes of an early release from our icy prison were raised in the morning. This did move the ship and the ice but there was no relaxation of the pressure of the ice field gripping us.

In the morning, the main engines were started to back off a piece of ice trapped under the bow.

The sun shone for most of the day and to the north-west we could see the cumulus clouds rising over the open sea 40 miles (64 km) away.

The US icebreaker *Edisto* was still trapped in the ice.

About 130 miles (200 km) to our north-west, the Argentine ice breaker *San Martin* was moving at a great speed in an area quite free of sea-ice.

We Struggle to Force Our Way Out of the Weddell Sea

JANUARY 23. The noon position of the ship was 71.3°S 15.6°W.

At 10:25 UT we started to move again and in 12 hours made roughly 15 miles (24 km) of progress through fields of large, heavy hummocked ice floes about 8 ft. (2.44 m) thick. They were mixed up with lighter floes ranging from 6 in. (15 cm) to 3 ft. (91 cm) thick. We were heading for the water sky we could see in the north-west. The slackening off in the pressure of the sea-ice field permitted us to move a little. The degree of slackening was very difficult to measure, but I estimated it as no more than 5% in linear measure.

Breaking through the junctions between two heavy ice floes was a long job, requiring the ship to go backwards and then charge forward several times, so that some junctions took half an hour to breach.

At one particular time this evening, the ship became stuck. The captain studied the situation. He sent two crew members over the side with two sticks of dynamite tied to the end of a long bamboo pole. The captain then directed them to insert the dynamite in a very particular crack in the sea-ice about three metres from the side of the ship. After lighting the fuse, they pushed the dynamite down the crack as far as possible. A sailor tamped with his foot round the bamboo pole to keep it in place and retired to safety. The subsequent explosion shook the whole ship but it also freed her instantly. I found the process very impressive because, to the untrained eye, there seemed to be nothing special about that particular ice floe, but it was deliberately selected by the captain and held the key to the lock which held us so tightly. We rather suspect these Norwegians have been in sea-ice before and escaped.

The *San Martin* continued on her uninterrupted progress from yesterday's position of 70.5°S 20.5°W, and was moving further to the west.

The *Edisto* was still beset but managed to move 7 miles (11 km) yesterday.

The 16,000-ton US icebreaker *Glacier* was expected to arrive on

February 4. She was coming from the Ross Sea to relieve *Polar Hav*, which was endangered by a gale whilst she was beset in the sea-ice near the Belgian base.

There were many seals around, mostly Crabeaters. I counted 20 seals in 90 minutes of progress through the ice field. Several small Fin Whales and Adelie Penguins were also observed.

We Dynamite and Dig Ourselves Free of the Ice Again

JANUARY 24. The noon position was 71.0°S 16.1°W.

We started to move in the afternoon at about 16:15 UT. After moving for two hours, we became stuck again. This time we all got over the side of the ship for 'poling', armed with long poles, ice chisels and sticks of dynamite.

I looked over the side of the ship and down at the ice below. It was not solid sea-ice but a thick stew of small pieces of ice, many the size of your fist. Shortly beforehand, when moving forward, there was more water than ice down there. Now, as we were forced to a stop by the pressure of ice, I hoped it was sufficiently well consolidated to hold me. So I jumped and was quickly followed by my colleagues. And yes, it did hold us up, though sometimes you sank about a foot (30 cm) or so into the slushy mixture of ice and water. Occasionally you got your feet wet but not always.

In these circumstances, the reason a ship gets stopped by the ice is partly the pressure of ice on the sides. But just as big an impediment to progress is the quantity of ice which gets trapped under the ship, and you cannot move until this is allowed to float up to the surface.

During the process of poling, the propeller of the ship is left turning and this drives a current of water into the small pool of open water astern of the ship. Then you use your poles and ice chisels to prise ice away from the side of the ship and push it into the pool behind and into the current driven by the propeller. Starting from the stern of the ship, you dig a channel of open water between the ice and the ship. When you first move the ice away from the side, lumps trapped under the ship float up and assist in releasing her. You work away, gradually moving further forward until, at some point amidships, the ship suddenly becomes free again. She can then back out of the ice and make another charge forward in a further attempt to force a passage.

Whilst we were poling near the stern, the crew worked ahead of us armed with sticks of dynamite tied to the end of bamboo poles. At judicious points they set off explosions under the ice to ensure it was all cracked up into a condition we could handle. By poling this way, we freed the ship twice. As a result of these hours of hard work, we made our way through a mile or so of ice. However, at 11:30 p.m. a fresh easterly wind compressed the ice field again so that pressure on the ship prevented any further progress. The pressure of the ice then suddenly forced ice floes rapidly up the side of the ship in a spectacular and alarming way. Fortunately, after rising up four or five feet (1.2 or 1.5 m) above the surface, they stopped moving just as suddenly as they had started.

After we had clambered up the side of the ship, the Captain thanked us all and said that he would wake us if the pressure of the sea-ice slackened and more poling was required.

To see what lay ahead, I climbed up the ladder to the crow's nest perched on a mast 70 ft. (21 m) above the deck. From here I could see that conditions were better ahead of us and I could appreciate how valuable had been those precious few miles we had won by poling. The ice field ahead of us was less densely packed than the ice we had just escaped from, and more open water could be seen in the distance.

The chicken and white Chilean wine served for supper were both excellent.

We Break Out of the Icy Embrace of the Weddell Sea

SUNDAY JANUARY 25. The position of the ship at noon was 71.2°S 16.6°W. It was our fifth day beset by sea-ice.

In the early hours of the morning, the pressure relaxed in the field of ice trapping *Tottan.* All morning and for much of the afternoon, she fought her way through the ice for a few hard-won miles. However, each yard took us into more and more open conditions. She was able to ram her way through ice for a while until 08:00 UT. Then she was held up again until 11:30 UT, when the ship was able to drive forward for another hour. We were stuck again in the ice at 12:30 UT, when there was nothing for it but to go over the side again with dynamite and long poles. The final battle for *Tottan*'s freedom was won by us toiling away on the sea-ice alongside her with our long poles and explosives.

In the afternoon I received the following cable from Dr Martin, Executive Secretary of the Royal Society in London. 'Sorry to hear you are held fast (in the sea-ice). Hope favourable weather changes (situation) soon. Please keep me informed and let me know Captain's wishes about any action desired from here.' (Signed) Martin. I was please to be able to reply that we had managed unaided to extricate ourselves from the icy grip of the Weddell Sea.

The food on board was still very good and there was plenty of variety. For the last few days, the crew was continually on the lookout for seals to add to emergency supplies. They also had a large stock of

Top: *Sailing in a shore lead up the Caird Coast, on our way home through the sea-ice of the Weddell Sea. Tottan arrived to take us home on Saturday evening 10 January 1959 and we left Halley Bay on 16 January 1959.*

Above: *Unusual summer gales caused difficult sea-ice conditions in the Weddell Sea. On 19 January 1959, we became beset in sea-ice at 71°S 13°W, near Cap Norvegia about 800 km north-east of Halley Bay.*

Top: *Making very slow progress through heavy hummocked sea-ice*

Above: *Using dynamite to break up the sea-ice and allow us to release the ship from an icy grip. The two Norwegian sailors first tied a charge of dynamite to the end of a 3 m long bamboo pole. Then they inserted the charge deep into the sea-ice. After lighting the fuse, they retreated.*

These charges were placed perilously close to the side of Tottan and have just exploded. Now the ice alongside can be moved away. The person on the left holds an iron ice chisel, which will soon be used to prize the ice free. Others working on the ice wield long bamboo poles to push the sea-ice into open water behind the ship.

salted cod, which looked singularly unattractive. In the event of a long besetment, seal meat and dried cod would undoubtedly form the basis for our diet.

JANUARY 26. The noon position of Tottan was 68.4°S 18.6°W. Snow fell at times and the visibility was poor.

We sailed in open water all day in a north-easterly gale. There were a few pieces of sea-ice around and some bergy bits, but she had no trouble maintaining a speed of 8 knots (15 kph). Now we were in the open sea, the ship pitched and rolled continually. Polar vessels cannot fit bilge keels, so they roll much more than the average ship, and didn't we know it! All members of the expedition were miserably sea-sick and some almost wished they were back in the peace and quiet of the sea-ice.

JANUARY 27. The poor weather continued with a strong breeze, snow, rain and a heavy sea. A westerly wind had developed quite a swell in the ocean and *Tottan*'s rolling increased. The weather was improving at night and a full moon could be seen at times. There was no ice to be seen.

Many of us were beginning to recover from the misery of sea-sickness.

We were now reasonably confident in estimating our time of arrival in Capetown as February 6. This allowed us to make some progress with our onward travel arrangements. In my own case, I would not now have the time to fly home first before going on to the Antarctic conferences in Australia.

We were still seeing Snow Petrels flying near the ship.

JANUARY 28. The noon position was 62.8 °S 13.3°W. We saw no ice in the area where *Tottan* first spotted sea-ice during her voyage south.

We have seen no more Snow Petrels. Today I spotted a Giant Petrel, a large dark brown bird.

The motion of the ship moderated a little and the majority of the party recovered and were eating again. I formed the impression that our medical officer, Bert, rather enjoyed ministering to us, visiting everyone and dishing out his Avomine pills and good advice. It was the first time he had been so busy with his vocation. The advice he gave to all those in bed was, 'Wrap up warmly and get out of bed'.

JANUARY 29. The noon position was 61.0°S 11.5°W. During the night we passed through an area containing many dangerous icebergs and bergy bits. The latter were particularly hard to spot in the prevailing poor visibility. The weather was cloudy with occasional snowfall. A

Poling is shown here with the party on the ice breaking loose the ice alongside the ship and pushing it astern. So far we had freed the rear third of the vessel. When we passed the halfway point, the ship usually broke loose of the icy grip. She would then back out unaided and take another charge forward. Typically, it would take about five hours of poling to free the ship this way and gain a kilometre of so towards better conditions.

deck watch was posted and the Decca radar switched on, but we did not need to reduce speed.

All the party were well on their way to recovery from sea-sickness and were up and about watching the birds etc. We saw no Snow or Antarctic Petrels but there were many Cape Pigeons, Brown Petrels (Cape Doves) and Whale Birds. We also saw a Giant Petrel and a Sooty Albatross.

JANUARY 30. There was a north-easterly gale in the morning with Force 7 winds. Later in the day we passed near the centre of a depression and the wind moved right round to become westerly and moderated in strength. The ship pitched violently in the heavy seas.

Whilst chatting with Captain Jacobsen on the bridge, he told me something of the history of the *Tottan*. She was built at Goole in Yorkshire, England in 1941 as a 'T' Class ship for the British Royal Navy. She was a trawler in name only because, although modelled on one, she was meant for duty escorting North Atlantic convoys, bringing food to the British civilian population during the Second World War. Her name then was '*Morris Dance*'. After the war she was rebuilt in Norway for her present job. The 900 HP (671 kW) coal-fired steam engine was removed and it was replaced by a 1400 HP (1044 kW) U-Boat diesel engine. The number of ribs in the hull was doubled, three extra steel longitudinal members were added to each side of the hull, the sharp bow was rounded for use in ice, and the superstructure was re-modelled to place the bridge much further aft. Captain Jacobsen, for his part, was curious about the meaning of the name *Morris Dance*. Fortunately, I was able to show him some pictures of Morris dancers and he was mightily amused.

JANUARY 31. I was wakened at 6 a.m. by an unwelcome return of violent rolling. This dislodged some buckets in the cabin, which made a frightful din as they were hurled from side to side of the room. The ship continued to roll this way all day.

In the afternoon the cloud cleared to reveal a hazy blue sky. We photographed an iceberg – probably the last we will see on this voyage.

The noon position was 53.0°S 2.8°W.

There were many birds round the ship. The Albatrosses were now seen in greater numbers but there were no adult wanderers.

SUNDAY FEBRUARY 1. During the morning the sea temperature rose by 5°F (2.8°C) as we crossed the Antarctic Convergence Zone. By doing so, we left Antarctica. The position of the ship at noon was 50.3°S 3.2°E.

The weather improved during the day, clearing away the clouds to display a star-studded sky at night.

Our estimated time of arrival in Capetown was advanced to the evening of Thursday, February 5.

Radio communications with Capetown remained poor. We were unable to confirm our reservations for hotels and ships with our travel agent, Cooks of Capetown.

In the evening, the Royal Society's gift of a chicken was served and very much appreciated.

FEBRUARY 4. At noon the ship's position was 46.7°S 7.1°E.

The time of arrival in Capetown was set back again to the morning of Friday February 6.

The sea temperature had risen to 43°F (6°C), with the air temperature a few degrees higher. These temperatures felt quite warm to our systems, so long acclimatised to Antarctic levels. Many of us therefore changed into lighter clothing.

I spent much of the day ironing my washing and preparing for disembarkation.

In the afternoon I saw a Fin Whale but there were very few birds to be seen now that we had passed out of the fertile waters of the Antarctic Ocean.

FEBRUARY 3. At noon the *Tottan* was at 43.0°S 10.0°E.

The sea temperature rose further to 53°F (12°C) and we felt even warmer. All of us had now changed into light clothing.

Radio communications with Capetown were good. We were now able to tidy up our travel and accommodation arrangements. I will fly to Johannesburg and on to Australia on February 12.

I was busy for the day writing a report of the handover of the Royal Society Base to the Falkland Island Dependencies Survey (FIDS).

FEBRUARY 4. For the past few days we were very much aware that the temperature was increasing by 10°F (6°C) per day. Today the sea temperature was 67°F (19°C), a level our metabolism considered almost sub-tropical. There was a blue sky during the day with a few scattered clouds. At night there was a splendid star-studded sky.

We saw a few flying fish but very few birds.

Most of us were now seriously packing up.

In the evening I accepted an invitation to take a drink with the crew of *Tottan* and we had an enjoyable evening together.

FEBRUARY 5. At noon the ship was at 36.0°S 16.5°E. The air temperature was 65°F (18°C).

At 10:15 p.m. local time, I saw the lights on the Cape of Good Hope. In about eight hours of sailing, we should be in Capetown.

I sat down and wrote a letter to Oonagh with the following details of my travel arrangements. My flight to Australia would pass through Mauritius, Cocos Islands, Perth and possible Sydney. The departure from Capetown was set for 7:30 a.m. on February 11 and I should be in Melbourne three days later on Saturday the 14th. The tentative date for my flight back home had not been set, but should be about Friday February 27. The tentative route was via Darwin, Jakarta, Singapore, Calcutta, Karachi, Beirut and Zurich.

We made arrangements for Alf Amphlett, Ivor Beney, Bill Bell-chambers, Jim Burton and John Gane to leave Capetown on February 10 on board SS *Kenya Castle*. Les Barclay, Andrew Blackie, Philip Brenan, David Cansfield, Len Constantine, Henry Dyer and Malcolm Edwards were booked to leave Capetown on February 13 on SS *Caernarvon Castle*. The only person who had not decided on the route to take home was David Harrison. He wanted to leave the selection of the ship to take until he was in Capetown.

Derek Ward was making his own arrangements for travel home. He planned to stay in Durban until the end of February, then go to Salisbury in the former Southern Rhodesia and leave by air for England in early April.

Ben Ellis was going to stay in Nairobi until mid-March and then fly to England from there.

Bert Brooker, Gwynne Thomas and David Tribble had plans to drive up to Johannesburg and then fly from there to the UK in early March. (Eventually, Derek Ward and Ben Ellis joined with these three in purchasing a large Chevrolet V8 to tour in southern Africa before flying on to the UK.)

We were now all dressed in shorts and sandals, basking in the warm sun.

We presented Captain Jacobsen with a Union Jack. He requested that each member of our expedition sign it. Apparently his wife planned to embroider over our signatures. The decorated flag was destined to hang on the wall of a bar in the new house he was building in Tonsberg, Norway. We were all invited to see it hanging there.

In the dawn light of 6 February 1959 we saw the lights of Capetown itself and first glimpsed the beauty of Table Mountain standing guard over this scenic city. Since Halley Bay was located on a piece of ice floating on the ocean, we had lived at sea for over two years. Our long voyage was almost over.

Chapter 9

First Experiences Outside Antarctica

Capetown South Africa

We arrived in Capetown in the early hours of the morning of February 6, 1959. It was so early, we had to hang about waiting for the South African pilot to arrive. Eventually a launch came alongside and the pilot climbed aboard looking extremely dapper in immaculate white shorts and shirt, as though he had just emerged from a detergent advertisement. Everything about him expressed the fact that we had arrived back in civilization. We could see that we could now forget about the casual clothing *de rigueur* in Antarctica. We were back to carefully pressed clothing, starched collars, neatly knotted ties, highly polished shoes and shaving every morning. And we were, of course, delighted, having had quite enough of the former state, for the moment at any rate.

As soon as we tied up, diplomats from the British High Commission, and South African customs and immigration officials came aboard. Before we could move off the ship, our out-of-date passports had to be renewed. So we hung round for most of our first day whilst the bureaucracy caught up with itself. All we could do was feast our eyes on the unfamiliar scene and watch the dockers swarm over the ship and unload our precious cargo of personal effects, equipment, and scientific records.

On February 7 we checked into the Hotel Metropole in Capetown, where I shared a room with George Hemmen.

One of the first things I did was to buy myself a very light-weight suit. We had a number of social occasions to attend and my English-weight suit was most uncomfortable in the heat. Our first day in the city was a very hectic one, which, combined with the high temperatures and sunshine, left me feeling like a wet rag at its end.

In the morning, I visited my wife's Aunt Tess, who lived in a Capetown suburb with her daughter Juliana. Their house was in an attractive residential part of Capetown, on the side of a steep hill with a view of Table Mountain.

In the evening the manager of a whaling factory took Andrew,

George and me on a motor trip to Simonstown and to a guest house called 'Rhodesia by the Sea'. The ocean drive was superb. Simonstown sits on a rocky promontory jutting into the sea south of Capetown and forms part of the Cape of Good Hope. The spectacular route clings halfway up the steep, scenic cliff of the Cape and offers stunning views of the rocky terrain and the two Oceans, the Atlantic to the west and the Indian to the east. At the most beautiful parts of the road, there were lay-bys for us to park and admire the unique scenery in comfort. It was a scene of breathtaking and grandiose beauty, which must be counted as one of the wonders of the world.

Then we came back to Sea Point, where a photographer took us out to dinner. The photographer, John, had embarked on *Tottan* for her next voyage to Canada for sealing. He planned to take photographs of the sealing. Sea Point was a very attractive place, with a promenade, swimming pool, and a garden equipped with barbecue sites surrounding a dance floor.

The following day at the Port Meteorological Office, Alan Crawford invited me to his home for lunch with his wife, Joyce. Later Joyce took Andrew and me to visit a very old Cape vineyard. The main house had been built by the Dutch in the 17th century. It was very beautiful and perfectly designed for the climate. As we walked up the neat path between perfectly groomed vines, we admired the architectural lines of the building, with its very high, steep pitched roof, effectively providing insulation from the heat of the sun. The burning heat of the South African summer was banished the moment we entered into the entrance hall, floored with huge cool stones.

In the afternoon, the Crawfords drove me to the *Tottan* to say goodbye to the crew. We presented the Captain with a re-chargeable soda fountain and the crew with a large hamper of food which had been thoughtfully selected by Philip and Len. The Captain and crew were all very charming and pressing with their invitations to visit and stay with them in their homes in Tonsberg next June.

My Mother had a school friend in Capetown and so I spent a day with her and her husband, Mr and Mrs Buchanan. Later on I visited their home, set in a spacious and beautiful garden. The Buchanans also invited me for a drive and I took Malcolm Edwards with me as he happened to be at a loose end that day.

On Monday morning, February 9 I had lunch with the Deputy British High Commissioner. I went to Cooks the next day to pick up my airline tickets, which would take me all the way to London via Australia. I was due to arrive in London at 5:45 p.m. on Quantas flight Number 535 on Friday March 13. Reservations were also made for me to stay the night in Johannesburg at the Grand National Hotel.

Before departure, I had an immense amount of business to do. I made arrangements for the return of the expedition members and had yellow fever inoculations, which were required for my flight home through south-east Asia. To get everything done, and also do some sightseeing, I found it best to get up early, before 7 a.m. It was cooler then and had the advantage of being two hours before my room mate arose, so I had the bathroom to myself and could get started early and join my colleagues from the expedition, who also liked to take their breakfast early.

Before leaving Capetown, I sent some bottles of wine to the Crawfords, who had been so kind to me. I also bought some wine for my wife's Aunt Tess and gave a gramophone record to Juliana.

On February 11, I flew in a Vickers Viscount aircraft the 900 miles (1448 km) to Johannesburg. The three-hour flight was very comfortable, and during it we were served a dinner comprising crayfish salad, steak, with beans and mushrooms, trifle, fruit salad and coffee.

Also on the flight were a number of wealthy Americans who were undertaking a world cruise on board the MV *Caronia*, for which they had each paid £12,000. They too were impressed by the Viscount aircraft, which they declared more comfortable than the one they had taken from Los Angeles.

Johannesburg

My plane to Australia left Johannesburg at 7 a.m., so I checked into the Grand National Hotel for the night. After supper I went for a short walk and when I got back, as a matter of habit, I put my dusty shoes outside the door of my room for cleaning. It was a habit I had become accustomed to in Capetown and I had quite ignored the fact that, when I got up at 5 a.m. the next morning, they might not have been returned. And that is just what happened to my only pair of shoes. For a moment I feared that I might have to arrive in Australia barefoot. Such dreary thoughts raced through my mind whilst I went down to the bowels of the hotel, searching for my precious shoes. Finally, I found the workshop of the boot cleaners and there, carefully and systematically placed, was my irreplaceable pair looking beautifully shiny again.

I was encouraged to walk out last night by the strange noise I could hear outside. Just across the street from the hotel a Zulu was playing an accordion. 'Playing' was hardly the right word, because he had absolutely no musical skills whatsoever. He just pumped the instrument with all his very great strength and poked away at the keys in quite a random fashion. He was hugely pleased with the result of his activity. I appreciated that all this flamboyant activity was not directed at any object in particular excepting his own gratification. There was no one else nearby and he clearly had no desire to entertain others or to solicit dues.

I had seen something similar, but more accomplished, in Capetown when a group of boys beat away with some skill on improvised drums whilst one of their number danced energetically. They beat away on tin cans and drums, some of which were covered with sheets of rubber, and did so quite well whilst the dancer moved in harmony and with skill to their impromptu, unrehearsed beat. The Capetown drummers, like the Johannesburg accordionist, were not playing to any audience, it was all done for their own satisfaction, which was clearly expressed in the mien of the players. They were just having a good time.

Before leaving Johannesburg I was interviewed by two newspaper correspondents. It was an experience I was to get more used to because I was to find in Australia that there was a much broader public interest in science and in Antarctica than was the case in the UK.

On a Sunday morning, one of my friends living in Capetown took me for a brief tour of a blacks-only suburb. At one point the road was filled with a vibrant throng of women and children walking to church. There must have been some men there too, but the over-whelming impression was of the smartly attired children and their mothers. The splendid hats of the women and the gaily decorated ones of the girls were particularly striking. Everything about them expressed their great vitality and *joie de vivre* as they walked joyfully with their family and friends to worship a Lord they so clearly loved and trusted. It was very moving and so different from the appearance of the whites-only suburbs at the same time.

Flight to Australia

Morton Rubin of the US Weather Bureau and Jan Taljaard of the South African Weather Bureau in Pretoria were also travelling on the aeroplane with me. I greatly enjoyed their company, which led to a friendship with Morton lasting many years. However, they travelled First Class whilst I was in the Tourist Class. Even then, my ticket from Capetown to London via Australia still cost £498, a sum which was equal to three-quarters of the annual salary paid by the Royal Society for an expedition scientist with Doctor of Philosophy degree.

On the way over to Perth, eight time zones and 6500 miles (10,460 km) from Johannesburg, we stopped at the British Island of Mauritius and the Australian Cocos Islands. On both occasions Jan, Morton and I stretched our legs and chatted away. The longest section of the trip was the 2700 miles (4350 km) from Mauritius to Cocos which took all the night. At one period there was a distant thunderstorm. From the comfort of the plane we could watch the flashing of lightning down to the dark sea below and from cloud to cloud. During the night, one of the crew members came through the cabin with a sextant and climbed up to the small astro-sighting dome which protruded through the roof of the cabin. I discussed this with him and he told me that for much of the trip the only navigational aids available were those supplied by nature, the stars. I later learnt that, because of this lack of radio navigation aids in the Indian Ocean, few of the world's airlines were prepared to risk this particularly long route.

Perth

At 9 a.m. on February 13, 1959, after almost two days of travelling, I landed in Perth. The Deputy Director of the Australian Weather Service, Mr McKay, came to meet Morton, Jan, and me and took us for an eight-hour duration, whirlwind tour of the beautiful city of Perth. Two rivers pass through the city, the Swan and the Canning. I admired the famous black swans and I was charmed by the beautiful stretch of water in the heart of the city with the swans gliding by majestically.

The instant we stepped on to Australian soil, we were most efficiently looked after in every possible way. As I put it in my letter to Oonagh at the time, 'The blokes in Australia are really on the ball – no messing about and no loose ends here.'

At the airport, also waiting for us to land, were some newspaper correspondents. When I reached Melbourne, Mr McKay brought with him the results of the interviews and the photograph published in the local papers.

Melbourne

On arrival in Melbourne at 9 a.m. on Saturday February 14, I was whisked to Scott's Hotel in Collins Street by representatives of the Australian Bureau of Meteorology. As soon as we got there, I handed over the paper I had written entitled, *Notes on the Climatology at Halley Bay*. In the remarkably short period of three months this was published by Pergamon Press in a book called *Antarctic Meteorology* (Ref: Mac-Dowall 1960). The efficient Australian organizers of the symposium also arranged for the translation of the text into Russian and French for the benefit of the six representatives who attended from those two countries. They also produced a set of slides of the illustrations for my lecture.

Cricket

After bathing and changing, I went off to see the 5th Test Match. I had lunch at the ground and stayed there until the end of the day's play. It was a memorable occasion and quite the most enjoyable day of cricket I have ever spent, even though England did lose. I sat in the stands next to a small group of friendly young men from somewhere in the countryside not too far from Melbourne. They immediately took me under their wing. They had a large case of beer with them and from time to time they passed me a can as they called out in a loud voice, 'Here, pass a beer to the Limey over there'.

Everyone at the match seemed particularly knowledgeable about the game. They watched with keen concentration and did not miss anything that happened on the field, responding quickly, loudly and with great good humour to every aspect. If any of the spectators made a remark showing they did not understand a finer point of cricket, they would be put down immediately, usually with an extremely amusing but not too unkind comment.

The following day I met Gordon Robin, Director of the Scott Polar Research Institute. He was staying at his mother's house in Mornington, one of the suburbs of Melbourne and about an hour's train journey from the city centre. The plan was for Gordon to meet me outside the railway station in a nearby town of Frankston. I was not quite sure how long the trip would take; it depended on whether you caught a fast train or one that stopped everywhere. I was lucky enough to catch a fast one and arrived early and before Gordon arrived.

Outside the station, a large, bronzed Australian taxi driver came up to me and said, 'Where are you going, mate?' I already had sufficient experience with these very helpful people and knew it was best to put them fully into the picture. So I told him the full story of not knowing where I was going and that I needed to wait here for my friend, who would arrive in about 30 minutes. The guy thought for a few seconds and then said, 'Don't you worry about that, mate, just tell me all you know and I guarantee to get you there before he leaves home!' Well, I was tempted, but apart from the confusion this could have caused, particularly if he took longer than his guarantee, I had noticed some sort of cycling event and I wanted to watch this whilst I waited. So again I told my would-be chauffeur how I wanted to stay here and take in the local scene. He smiled and left me with a very cheery wave, the very picture of an enterprising young man whose company I would no doubt have enjoyed.

Then a cycling event unfolded along the road in front of me by the station. Something like 500 to 800 young cyclists were approaching. They had come from all over Melbourne to participate in this tour. Their ages ranged from about five to 16 years. They were being shepherded by policemen, some on bicycles and others in cars equipped with loudspeakers to control the herd. As they passed by, you could see they were organized in clubs of from 20 to 50 each. The riders pedalled two abreast with the very young riding alongside an older person. The youngest were in the vanguard to set an appropriate pace all could manage. I had noticed that cyclists in Australia seemed to be very well-disciplined, as too were the pedestrians. Maybe the roots of this lay in the road discipline being taught today. If this was a typical sample of Australian cycling clubs, they were nothing like the muscle-bound speed maniacs who raced along English country roads at the weekends.

Eventually Gordon arrived to pick me up and we went back to his mother's home. In a few days' time he would have to give a public lecture on some of the results we had obtained during the IGY and I had with me most of the scientific data he needed for some of the substance of his discourse. Of course, it was all new to him and he was not a meteorologist, so we needed the time to go over this in detail whilst I explained to him some of the preliminary implications of our results. He was particularly interested in the ozone soundings we had made, since they were amongst the first such observations taken in Antarctica. I had slides of some of our results together with coloured photographs of us doing scientific work at Halley Bay. I lent him these slides to use in his lecture. Later on, I gathered the new data he was able to present proved of great interest to the audience.

I found the summer climate of Melbourne the most pleasant I had experienced since leaving Antarctica. Everywhere else on my way home I had been far too hot. The very lightweight suit I had purchased in Capetown proved quite perfect for my requirements in this climate, although many of the locals seemed quite comfortable in thick Harris tweed sports coats.

First Impressions of Australia

After being cooped up in Antarctica for so long and deprived of wider human contacts, I revelled in them as soon as I landed in Australia. I had always been very curious but the two years in Antarctica made me very much more gregarious too. In the morning before breakfast, I read the Australian newspapers and then exchanged views with some of the other delegates staying at the hotel, who were also soaking up the Australian ambience. I took every opportunity to meet and talk with my contacts, who were all refreshingly open and responsive. In my letters home and notes kept I recorded my first impressions. The conclusions I came to had all that special confidence of someone who had only spent a few weeks in the country and who left before the full complexity of the society might have clouded those vivid first impressions.

In Australia I was struck by the much greater atmosphere of get-up-and-go which prevailed, by comparison with the ethos in so many other parts of the world. I found the Australians were go-ahead, very much aware of, and confident about their position in the world, now and in the future. They were clearly moving forward with the mainstream of the thought and development of the wider world. They seemed confident, unafraid and outgoing as they navigated themselves self-reliantly through prevailing global conditions, playing a full part on the world's stage and contributing their unique, lusty and refreshing character.

International Antarctic Weather Analysis Centre

On February 16 and 17 I was shown the facilities of the International Antarctic Analysis Centre (IAAC) in Melbourne by H. R. Phillpot, the Superintending Meteorologist. Their accommodation was not complete and they were facing difficulties due to staff changes and the shortage of assistants to plot weather charts.

However, the major problem facing the operation of IAAC was a lack of Antarctic weather data, due to poor radio communications. Accordingly, we spent most of the time considering possible ways of improving communications in discussions with representatives from South Africa, US Navy, US Weather Bureau and New Zealand.

The charts plotted so far contained no information from the Falkland Island Dependencies (FIDS) or from South America. A scheme to improve communications between South Africa and Australia was worked out using commercial links, which would contain weather observations from South Africa and whaling ships. In 1958 there was a regular, daily point-to-point schedule between Halley Bay and Little America. During this link, we heard in April 1958 that weather data broadcasts from Port Stanley were not being received. This was due to an error in Little America's information on the schedules for the Port Stanley weather broadcasts. The error was corrected by the radio operator at Halley Bay, so that weather observations made at Halley Bay were available for analysis at the IGY weather central at Little America base from about May 1958.

Apparently the unsatisfactory distribution of meteorological data from FIDS during the IGY was reported to the IGY meetings held in Moscow and in Paris, and was also commented on in 1958 by Tom Grey when he was working at Little America in Antarctica. Unfortunately, the shortage in Melbourne of data from British bases was even more serious than it was at Little America during the IGY.

To improve communications, the closest possible liaison was needed between FIDS and the controlling mother station located at McMurdo Sound and operated by the US Navy. A point-to-point link was required from Port Stanley to McMurdo Sound.

The minimum British data required from FIDS were for weather observations at midnight and 12:00 UT from the following four of their nine stations: Argentine Islands, Port Stanley, South Georgia and Halley Bay. The total daily requirements would be for the transmission of 300 groups per day.

During the visit, the appointment of Tom Grey to the IAAC was announced. In 1958 Tom was the Supervising Meteorologist at US Weather Central located at US Little America base on the Ross Sea, Antarctica.

When I returned to the UK, the Director of the Scott Polar Research Institute and I tried more than once to get the British Meteorological Office to send a meteorologist to join the international team being assembled at IAAC but to no avail. Amongst other things, this would have assured British data was available in Melbourne. We last tried to do something when Jim Burton married a charming girl from Australia and was going off there in any case. We thought it would be a golden opportunity for the Meteorological Office to second him to IAAC, for a short time at any rate. But once again we had no luck.

Symposium on Antarctic Meteorology

The Symposium on Antarctic Meteorology was held under the auspices of the Australian Academy of Sciences and endorsed by the Special Committee for the IGY (CSAGI) and the Special Committee for Antarctic Research (SCAR). CSAGI and SCAR were the two leading international committees dedicated to the IGY and to Antarctic research respectively.

Delegates from ten of the twelve nations operating bases on the Antarctic continent participated; only Chile and Spain were unrepresented. The British Delegation consisted of Dr Frank Debenham, Commander R. R. Fotheringham, Joseph MacDowall, Sir Raymond Priestly and Dr Gordon Robin. In his introduction to the conference, the Director of Meteorology for Australia, J. L. Dwyer said that, 'We were fortunate to have a number of Antarctic veterans at the symposium ...' Debenham and Priestly were both members of Robert Scott's tragic 1910–1913 Polar Expedition. Other veterans included the well-known Australian polar navigator, Captain J. K. Davies, and a member of the Mawson Australian Antarctic Expedition, Dr B. S. Stilwell.

The local organization charged with implementing the Symposium was the Australian Bureau of Meteorology, and they could not have done a better job. Every detail was looked after efficiently and this included an active social programme. They even provided us with a chauffeur-driven car to cart us about all day and to the social events at night. I shared a car with a Belgian and a French delegate, partly because I had some knowledge of French. The Belgian delegate was Professor van Mieghem, a very well-known scientist, who's company I was particularly fortunate to be able to enjoy. At his suggestion, we had dinner together on the first day of the Conference. Later in the week, Dr Kiyoo Wadati, the distinguished Japanese scientist, and I dined together. Dr Wadati was the Official Representative of the Prime

Minister of Japan's Science Council. I also enjoyed long chats with Captain J. K. Davies, who had some fascinating stories to tell of his trips to Antarctica and of the expeditions he had carried out.

The Conference lasted a week and my paper was given in the last session on the Climatology of Antarctica, comprising eight papers and chaired by my South African flying companion, Jan Taljaard. My paper was the second one, presented directly after one on the climate at the US Base, Wilkes. When all the papers had been presented, the session was thrown open to a lively and interesting discussion. The discussion period kept me very much on my toes since the paper sparked off over half a dozen comments or questions for me to reply to.

Each day the Conference broke up for a long lunch break. This was a great idea because it gave you time for further discussions. We soon discovered one of the best deals for lunch in town was what were called 'counter lunches', which were served in the pubs. The pub we frequented for lunch had a counter or shelf fixed to the walls of the room about four feet (1.2 m) above the floor and about 18 inches (46 cm) wide. You ordered the counter lunch at the bar and received a T-bone steak and a pile of mashed potatoes, all for a very modest cost of two shillings and six pence or a very small fraction of our daily food allowance. Jan Taljaard and I went into a pub together for our counter lunch. It was Jan's first experience. I had been there once before so Jan asked me to order for him, as I now qualified as relatively expert. I asked him what he wanted to drink and he said that he liked a glass of milk because he did not drink beer, which was of course the normal. I said I would do my best and ordered two counter lunches, a beer for myself and milk for Jan. The word 'milk' triggered an uproar in the bar as soon as the burly bartender shouted out to all and sundry, 'Hey, there's a bloody Limey here asking for a glass of milk!' Nevertheless, he went out into the kitchen and got Jan's glass of milk – on the house. He then told me it was the first one he had served and would probably be the last.

The active social programme of the Conference led off with a reception given by the Lord Mayor of Melbourne in the Town Hall. After which we went to a party held at the home of Mr and Mrs W. J. Gibbs. At the party, one chap who had been on Mawson's 1929 Antarctic Expedition stood on his head and, whilst doing so, drank a complete glass of beer. He then challenged all comers to do the same but he got no takers. The following day the Minister of State for the Interior of Australia, the Honourable Gordon Freeth MP, invited us to a reception. After the party, Dr Ure Radok, a professor in the Meteorology Department at the University of Melbourne took Professor van Mieghem and me out for an espresso coffee and a pleasant evening of conversation.

Dr Radok later gave a paper at the Symposium entitled, 'Some Properties of Drifting Snow'. The Australian Mawson Base was located on the coast, backed by steep slopes down from the highlands of the interior. The fierce winds there, blowing down from the high plateau, carried large amounts of snow out to sea or on to ice shelves. In order to assess the significance of this snow transport, Australian scientists designed sophisticated snow drift gauges. I found the discussion arising from his paper of interest and participated, using my experience of drift snow at Halley Bay.

At these social gatherings, there was considerable curiosity over the few of us who had come directly from Antarctica, like Morton Rubin, who wintered over at the Russian base, Mirny, and myself. Morton and I were clean shaven but one of the Americans present had not shaved off the beard he had grown in the south and, as a consequence of looking out of place, was treated quite differently. Obviously the old saying also applies to intellectuals: 'When in Rome ...'

When questioned about being in Antarctica for over two years, it soon became clear that the questioners were often ambivalent in their attitudes. On the one hand many envied the experience we had had but, on the other hand, they probably believed we must be a little bit odd to do it at all. I soon learnt it was best to make as little as possible of one's experiences, and certainly to avoid making it go on too long or sound too interesting. I found it best to change the subject as soon as it was reasonably polite to do so. Unless, of course, you happened to be speaking to someone with a genuine, deep interest in the subject and then you had a different problem, because sometimes you could not easily satisfy their thirst for information.

The newspapers in Australia did seem to have a consistent and real interest in Antarctica, and on several occasions interviewed me on various aspects. I also gave a short talk which was broadcast by the Australian Broadcasting Corporation. When I visited people in their homes and met their children, I really enjoyed responding to their curiosity. They were so perceptive in their questions that I could see they were genuinely interested in our work and experiences.

I very much enjoyed every aspect of the conference. At the end of each of the seven sessions there was a discussion period in which I fully participated and for which I afterward wrote up what I had said for the benefit of the editors of the proceedings.

A Day at the Races

At about 11 a.m. Mr Donovan of the Australian Department of External Affairs picked Jan and me up from our hotel. First we saw the beautiful parks set out near the city and the university, with its indoor swimming pool and attractive gardens. Then we watched two eights racing on the Yarra River, only a few minutes from the centre of the city, and examined the cycle racing track and swimming pool built for the Olympic games. After another counter lunch – it was chicken and salad this time – the three of us went to the horse races to see the Melbourne Cup race.

Clearly Australians were very keen on horse racing and this particular race was one of the highlights of the season. At the track, men and women were kept apart in separate facilities. I was told this was so the men could concentrate on the races and betting. Each race was only about a mile (1.6 km) long and was over very quickly. In between each race all the men moved off to the bookies. They all seemed to be dressed in a very similar style, almost as if there was a dress code of dark grey suits and lighter grey trilby hats with a wide brim.

There were seven races. One of my friends there won £45 betting on these races and those going on in Sydney at the same time. Apparently he studied form. Then we went in for tea at the Members Pavilion. Gregory Peck was also at the races accompanied by some very attractive female actresses, who were not allowed inside the members' facilities. Betting was not in my line; my studies of the mathematics of choice and chance had put me off the game, so I concentrated on photographing the colourful scene and just watching the people.

For part of the time, I sat up in the stands with the Argentine Rear Admiral R. N. Panzarini. He was a very interesting man to listen to and knew a considerable amount about horses. He told me that the build of these horses was not ideal for the short distances they were running. Apparently, some of the Argentine horses could run much faster over these distances but could not beat Australian horses over longer distances. I don't know whether or not he was right, but his comments on the chances of various competitors seemed to be spot on. I only wished that I had used his tips to place a few bets, but both of us were quite content to watch this fascinating scene.

With an Australian Family

On Sunday February 22, at 10:30 a.m., Mr A. K. Hannay picked me up at the hotel. Then he drove back to his home to collect six of his seven children. The Hannays had a girl of 15, a boy of 13 who was at the beach for rugby practice, a 10 year old girl, 7 year old triplets, and another boy of one. We drove into the countryside for a picnic lunch and then toured an animal sanctuary containing kangaroos and several other native animals. I was mightily impressed by the disciplined way this large family worked together. As soon as we got home, Mrs Hannay gave each child a job to do and in no time at all the youngsters were fed, washed and ready for bed. It was impressive the way the children organized themselves. As Mrs Hannay said, 'It has to be that way with so many children'. She added that they had not actually planned for such a large family. They wanted four children but the fourth happened to be triplets and the last was an added bonus. The seven year-old and I had fun flying a model aeroplane and then I carried two of the triplets up to bed, one under each arm, and when they were in bed, they told me stories.

When they were all in bed, except the 15 year-old, we had a glass of wine and supper. Just before I left, I saw Mrs Hannay cut up the sandwiches for the children's lunch on Monday – it was a very large pile.

I was still rising early each morning and taking a short walk. Then, after reading a newspaper, I was quite ready for an Australian breakfast of porridge, two lamb chops or a steak with a fried egg on top, toast and marmalade, washed down with plenty of tea.

On Tuesday February 24 I was interviewed by Australian Broadcasting Commission (ABC). At their request, I composed a short talk for broadcasting of about five minutes' duration. To my surprise and delight, soon afterward I was presented with a neatly typed up copy of my talk together with a cheque for £6. Clearly the ABC don't play to the rules set for the BBC.

Later on Tuesday Dr Radok and I had lunch together, after which he took me on a tour of the Meteorology Department at the University. In the afternoon, I took a major part in the Symposium and showed slides of some of our results. In the evening, Professor Van Mieghem, Dr E. B. Kraus of the Snowy Mountains Hydro-Electric Authority and I had a very enjoyable dinner together. After that we went off to see *Summer of the Seventeenth Doll.*

The following night I went to a dinner party at the home of Gwynne Wilson, the Secretary of the Symposium and his wife Helen. It was the day I gave my presentation of our meteorological results, which seemed to be very well received. This, therefore, greatly stimulated the amount of discussion at the party. Amongst those I spoke to about the Antarctic were an American from Wilkes base and a New Zealander just returned from Scott base. Gwynne and Helen had a very active three year-old son and a baby boy aged eight months.

On returning to the hotel, I found a present had been sent to me from the Hannays. It was a very amusing book about Australians and called, *They're a Weird Mob*. I really did appreciate this memento of a very pleasant day and I wrote and thanked them once again for their memorable hospitality.

After the Symposium closed, we spent a day at the splendid research facilities of the Commonwealth Scientific and Industrial Research Organization (CSIRO). The Director, Dr C. H. B. Priestley, showed us round and then hosted a buffet lunch.

Australian National Antarctic
Research Expedition

On the day of my departure for Cooma, on Friday February 27, I was able to enjoy an all too brief visit to the facilities of the Australian Antarctic Research Expedition (ANARE). I would have liked to have spent more time there. They impressed me as being a very knowledge-able and well-organized group. Their permanent base at Mawson had an enviable record for scientific work. Moreover, in the winter of 1956 they had set a record for the amount of travel they had undertaken in total darkness during the Antarctic winter months. In June and July 1956 they had explored with both dog sledge teams and using the Weasel tractor. In addition, the RAAF Antarctic Flight at Mawson had maintained operations through the winter. Amongst the twelve nations with bases in Antarctica, only Australia planned to expand her work there in the future.

I was asked about the health of our team and I outlined our experiences. There was some knowing laughter when I said that the two most serious medical incidents, in both years, involved our medical officers. I asked them why they laughed and either one of the Austra-lians or a New Zealander present said, 'We also discovered that occurred some time ago, if you only have one doctor on an expedition. What we do now is to give another person some advanced first aid and nursing training.'

Then, just after lunch, I took an Ansett airways flight to Cooma, which in winter was the principal ski resort in the Snowy Mountains.

The Snowy Mountains

The Snowy Mountains Hydro-Electric scheme was a giant civil engi-neering endeavour to turn the waters of the Snowy River westwards through the Great Dividing Range into the dry interior, where it could be used for irrigation and also to generate electrical power. One of the tunnels through the mountains was thirty miles (48 km) long. It was a hugely impressive collection of large-scale civil engineering, digging tunnels deep under the mountains, building several huge dams of concrete or earth, etc. At the same time massive turbines were installed deep underground to drive banks of electrical generators. Before anything could be done, a network of access roads had to be laid down.

When they commenced work, the engineers soon found out that the geological conditions were especially challenging. They discovered Australia provided conditions unlike any previously faced in Europe or North America. One of the principal reasons for this was that

Australia had not been subjected to the scouring of glacial action. As a consequence, the rocky foundations of the mountains were weathered and cracked up to great depths. In order to succeed in the peculiar conditions, entirely new and extensive research laboratories had to be set up to conquer unique engineering and geological challenges.

One of our principal guides was the meteorologist, Dr Kraus, whom we had met in Melbourne. The meteorologists of the authority, like the engineers, faced a number of challenges in the Snowy Mountains. Amongst these were the task of setting up a hydrological network which would measure the snow accumulation in the catchment area. It was also necessary to estimate the ultimate size of a huge lake backing up behind a large earth-filled dam. It was very important to get this right. Should too much water accumulate, the earth-filled dam would be washed away. On the other hand, too little water accumulation would jeopardise the recreational potential of the lake and the ability of the scheme to pay for itself from the sale of electricity. To determine one component of the lake's water budget, whilst we were there, CSIRO conducted a series of micro-meteorological studies to measure its evaporation.

We were very much impressed by the way Australians tackled their problems in their admirable research facilities. We were to hear of several other such initiatives where the power of scientific method was used with great success to solve problems peculiar to Australia.

As we sped through the Australian countryside in our large black limousines, we saw too many things to remember them all. However, amongst the many scenes which did stick in my memory was a long abandoned gold field. It now looked strangely out of place with its lumpy, messed-up appearance, out of character with the normal landscape. One of the local guides satisfied my curiosity by pointing it out as a region of a former alluvial gold field. Then he went on to give us a brief history of what had gone on there so many years ago. It seems the whole area had been dug over by hand by thousands of prospectors, sifted in running water and a fortune in gold had been extracted laboriously, grain by precious grain. He said that not only was the muscle power provided by Chinese migrants, but also that their inherent engineering skills enabled them to build a large dam to provide sufficient water to sluice out the gold. And all this was done without the aid of modern equipment, using only the simplest of hand tools. Then he added: 'And they didn't need any fancy research facilities to tell them how to do it!'

Special Committee for Antarctic Research

On Sunday March 1, 1959 I checked into the Hotel Kurrajong in

Canberra. It was a beautiful city with large open spaces planted with roses and acres of what, when they were filled with water, became small attractive lakes. I had never seen such an artificially created city before and I found it a dead loss to work in. It seemed to have been designed on the assumption that you would always go by car from one sector to the next, using large curving avenues in what seemed to a pedestrian to be a very long way round. If you tried, as I did, to walk from the hotel to the conference location, or to some shops, you found no direct footpath and a road which was too circuitous to be practical for a walker. So I cut across the grassy areas, which I soon found were not in a state to be used in that way. In my letter home I included some attractive pictures of Canberra and noted that, 'It all looks very fine but it is hopelessly impracticable.' But the thing that struck me most forcibly was that there did not seem to be any people out there. As I trekked through the trackless long grass, I seemed to be the only person in a city dominated by large buildings set in photogenic surroundings. At the mid-point of my solo march, I felt as lonely as if I had been back in Antarctica but less at ease. I felt strangely exposed and only hoped that the giant architect who created this scene would not spot me and wipe me off the scene as a component not specified in his plans.

We were gathered in Canberra for a meeting of the Special Com-mittee for Antarctic Research (SCAR) a relatively new committee created by the main committee of the IGY, CSAGI, which itself was a creation of the International Council of Scientific Unions (ICSU). SCAR was established in August 1958 at the 5th Annual Assembly of CSAGI held in Moscow. The committee was divided into 14 working groups, one for each of the scientific disciplines studied during the IGY, such as meteorology, geomagnetism, ionospheric physics, and so on.

On Monday evening, to mark the SCAR Meeting in Canberra, the Australian Minister of State for External Affairs arranged a dinner for the delegates in Parliament House. Then on the Wednesday, the British High Commissioner and Lady Carrington held a reception in Canberra House for us to meet Sir Gilbert Laithwaite.

In the SCAR meeting, each of the 14 groups met individually and then presented their reports, which were discussed and dealt with according to the will of the assembly.

Acting as a secretary for SCAR was Gordon Robin of the Scott Polar Research Institute. As soon as we got inside the building, Gordon asked me to sit beside him and assist in keeping notes of the discussion. So that is just what I did, and at the end of the day I passed over to him my notes, hoping that he would be able to decipher them.

On Tuesday I spent the evening with Norman Rider, his wife and family. When I was an undergraduate at Cambridge, I had worked as a summer student in Norman's small research group at the University Department of Agriculture. We spent the summer measuring the evaporation from grassland and exchanges of heat and momentum to the atmosphere, on a field bordering a college playing ground. In the intervening years we had kept in touch, so it was a great pleasure to be able to see him again.

Later in the week, I went to see the scientific work he was doing in Australia. He was still measuring evaporation but with much more sophisticated equipment than we had used in those days in Cambridge. He gave me a long list of specialized equipment that could not be obtained in Australia and which he needed to complete his two-year assignment. A decade later, when meeting him again in England, he told me that when he left Australia, he brought back with him lumber for his house of a kind which could not be obtained in England. It seemed to me like a very satisfactory quid pro quo worked out between Norman and Australia.

Scar Tour

After completing our work round the committee table, we left Canberra on Saturday March 7 for a four-day tour, first to Sydney and then on to a resort in the Blue Mountains. We were picked up by another fleet of large black limousines at 8:45 a.m. and travelled to Sydney on a magnificent route via Goulburn, Bowral for lunch, Fitzroy Falls, Kangaroo Valley, Kima, Wollongong, and Bulli Pass. We arrived in Sydney at about 6 p.m. and checked into the Hotel Hampton Court.

After taking a quick shower, we piled into the cars again at 7:30 p.m. and were taken to the Hermitage Restaurant in Manley for a special dinner. The restaurant was built in a magnificently scenic location overlooking Sydney Harbour. At dinner I was happy to be sitting next to Dr R. G. Simmers, an engaging New Zealand meteorologist. As a part of their warm hospitality, the restaurant took a picture of Richie and me, which still reminds me of that very pleasant evening. When the excellent wines were served, one of the delegates from Europe, took a speculative sip of one and declared it to be excellent, speculating further on its provenance, from France of course, and he even went into some detail. The manager of the restaurant watched and listened to this virtuoso performance in silence. At its conclusion, he had the greatest of pleasure in showing our self-appointed vinologist the bottle, which was filled in Australia with this superlative *vino locale*.

It was a pleasant night, so we returned to the hotel by ferry to Circular Quay, where the cars were waiting to pick us up for the return to Hotel Hampton Court.

On Sunday the cars picked us up after breakfast for a morning's sightseeing drive, visiting the incomparable Northern Beaches and

Kuringai Chase, stopping for lunch at a restaurant on the North Shore. After lunch, the cars returned to the city for a tour of some city highlights and southern suburbs and back to the Hotel Hampton Court for dinner.

We checked out of the Hampton Court on Monday for a two-day tour of the beautiful Blue Mountains resort area. Whilst going off into the country, we took the opportunity to leave some of our clothing behind for cleaning. So I left my suit there and travelled in what I thought was more suitable attire in the country. On the way we took a break at the Kurrajong Heights Hotel. Then we drove via Mount Wilson and Mount Victoria to the Jenolan Caves, which we inspected after lunch. We returned to the Blue Mountains via Mount Victoria, Blackheath, and Medlow Bath, arriving in Katoomba at about 6 p.m. and checking into the Carrington Hotel for dinner and an overnight stay.

When I got into my room I was alarmed to see, under the glass top of the dressing table, the most rigorous and specific details of their dress code. It was the first dress code I had seen displayed in this way and I was quite dumbfounded that it should be there in an Australian county inn. Clearly in the Carrington Hotel, thou shalt not sit down for dinner without your full suit. Smartly pressed grey flannel slacks, with a shirt and tie were just not good enough for them. To tone down the glaring white of my shirt, I donned a sober maroon sweater and sat down with the party, hoping I would not be noticed by the waiters, or that if one did notice me, I prayed he might be one of the many migrant workers who could barely speak English and might not have read the notice on my dressing table. No such luck! Soon after I sat down, a very formally dressed waiter asked if he could bring me a coat from my room. I told him the truth, that he would have to go back to Sydney for it at the Hotel Hampton Court. To my great relief he smiled, bowed slightly and retreated whilst his body language clearly indicated he was satisfied with my answer.

After breakfast on Tuesday, the fleet of cars took us on a sightseeing tour of the scenic attractions of the Katoomba area. Now that I was well-known there as a slightly eccentric Antarctic explorer with his own dress code, I had no problem getting a lunch at the Carrington Hotel. After a brief pause at the Log Cabin Hotel in Penrith, we arrived in Sydney at about 6 p.m. and checked back into the Hampton Court Hotel. That evening a farewell dinner was laid on for us at the Prince's Restaurant.

On Wednesday March 11, I left Sydney airport on my long flight home.

Flight Home

My flight home from Australia took three days and included stops at

Jakarta, Singapore, Colombo, Bombay, Karachi, Cairo, Istanbul and Rome. Despite the exotic associations of some of these names, I mostly saw a succession of airport lounges. However, if the facilities were depressingly familiar, the people filling them were most certainly not and did exude just a touch of the essence of each country.

In Jakarta we had some time to wander about. The Indonesians were in the process of developing and extending the airport. The lounge included a recently completed large concrete or plaster mural that covered one wall. It was quite an impressive piece of art, intended to display the progress of the Indonesian people from the primitive conditions of jungle life, through their period of colonisation, and into an industrialized future. It was the sort of thing the USSR revelled in. The section illustrating their colonial past included vignettes of several colonial masters at their work, sometimes beating, shooting or otherwise encouraging the indigenous population to do their bidding. They were a revealing illustration of what the Indonesians really thought of each of several nationalities who had done so much to bring them more rapidly to their desired goal than they could ever have done unaided by that phase. But it wasn't exactly flattering. The most benign colonialist illustrated was a moustachioed, pipe-smoking figure sitting reflectively on a rock. I got the message that he was a symbol of colonial indolence contrasted with the activity of his serfs, but at least he did not have a raised whip in his hand like one of his companions. The elements of the future displayed there did not look all that appealing to me and consisted of an highly industrialized one, with oil refineries and such like industrial structures figuring prominently.

On leaving the plane in Bombay, I was at first taken aback by the tremendous number of people there, which included a very high proportion of quite young children. They were clearly having a good time and expressing their happiness in a tremendous din of excited chattering voices. Their pleasure was quite infectious and you could hardly resist its power. It seemed as though whole families visited the airport not only to meet friends coming and going, but also just to see the action there.

When we reached the airport lounge, to my surprise, I heard my name called out over a loudspeaker. So I went over to the information desk where I found waiting for me two representatives of a newspaper who wanted to write a report about my sojourn in Antarctica. Some time later, when back in my home, I received a letter from an Indian politician, which was triggered off by the article based on that interview.

The only airport lounge I really enjoyed was the one in Karachi. There we were led into a tea-room by tall, distinguished looking, bearded Sikhs and sat down in wicker chairs round a table covered with a crisply laundered white cloth. When we were comfortably ensconced, the Sikhs served out cooling draughts of tea. It was all highly civilized and smoothly accomplished.

Thankfully, when we landed in the steamy, oppressive heat of Singapore, we were led to some bedrooms on the airport where at least we could stretch out and sleep for one night.

The plane was full most of the way but, as far as I could see, only myself and two engaging nuns remained with the aircraft for the complete flight from Sydney to London. The nuns made a name for themselves when we circled the Holy City. Chattering away like excited children and radiant, they left their seats, deaf to the orders of the stewards, and moved over to feast their eyes at the best window, moving from side to side of the plane at will and to the despair of the stewards, who finally gave up their attempts to get the two ladies back into their assigned seats and imprisoned by their seat belts.

At each landing I tried to find a small memento for Oonagh. One of the most successful of these was the elegant umbrella I purchased for her in Rome. But the best of all, and the most long-lasting gift, was the stuffed Australian Koala bear I brought back for Simon.

As soon as there was a a gap between the clouds, I caught my first sight of a deliciously green England that lay below me just before twilight. Nothing could have prepared me for the impact of this scene. In a flash it was driven home to me that that was a sight I had been waiting for. Of course, I had been delighted by the many beauties of nature in South Africa and Australia, but none of them affected me quite so much as those green English fields.

We finally landed at Heathrow on 14 March 1959, two years and four months after I had left England. As all the other passengers retrieved their baggage, the two nuns and I waited alone for ours, which, I gathered, had steadily moved to the back of the baggage compartment, as all the other passengers disembarked along the circuitous route and the suitcases of new travellers pushed ours further back.

It was raining in London, which I found to be a very pleasant change from snow and ice, and then steamy heat or blazing sunshine.

When I finally emerged from customs, there was Oonagh waiting for me. She had been waiting for 803 days.

Reference

MacDowall, J, 1960. *Antarctic Meteorology*, Pergamon Press, pp. 423 – 437.

Appendix 1

The Main Party of the Royal Society IGY Expedition

At Halley Bay from 4 January 1957 to 16 January 1959

Alf Amphlett
Les Barclay
Bill Bellchambers
Ivor Beney*
Andrew Blackie
Philip Brenan
Jim Burton
David Cansfield
Len Constantine
Henry Dyer
Malcolm Edwards
David Harrison
Joe MacDowall
Gwynne Thomas
David Tribble
Derek Ward

At Halley Bay from 4 January 1957 to 7 January 1958

Ken Amy
Ron Evans
Peter Jeffries
Fred Morris *
Robin Smart

At Halley Bay from 7 January 1958 to 16 January 1959

Bert Brooker
Ben Ellis
John Gane
John Smith (who remained behind for an additional year)

* Spent October to December 1957 at Shackleton or South Ice bases, helping the Trans-Antarctic Expedition.

Appendix 2

Articles Published in the Maggazette Whilst Sailing To Halley Bay in December 1956

Bird Life

The birds we have seen on passage have followed very much the normal pattern for the South American run, and to date 17 species have been sighted.

The English Channel had the usual attendant Herring Gulls, and at Ushant we saw the first Gannets, characteristically diving for their food from 50 to 100 feet. Kittiwakes were the common gull from this point until Southern Portugal, thus living up to their reputation of being the only oceanic gull. Over this area, winter migrants from the Arctic were in evidence, the Great Skua and Little Auk, and for good measure we had a Starling on board blown offshore from Portugal.

During the last two days before Madeira, we entered the northern winter limit of most of the Petrel and Storm Petrel family. The Madeiran Storm Petrel, Bulwer's Petrel – an entirely dark bird rather larger than the Madeiran – and the Soft Plumaged Petrel. All these birds breed on one or other of the various island groups off the West coast of Africa.

The scavenger of Madeira, the Lesser Black-backed Gull, followed us 80 miles to the southward; and from there to the last of the island groups the Madeiran Storm Petrel was frequently sighted. Like all the family, the Madeiran is a great wanderer, and its range extends from the British Isles in the northern summer to just south of the Equator in the northern winter. Three of them were found stunned on board at this time, as was a Bosun Bird (Red-billed Tropic Bird).

The passage between the Cape Verde Islands and the off-lying rocks and islands of South America – St. Paul Rocks, Fernando da Noronha, et cetera – was, as always, rather barren of bird life. The most frequently sighted birds were the Greater Shearwater, which is only known to breed at Tristan da Cunha, and the Madeiran Storm Petrel. One Bulwer's Petrel and one Brown Booby were also seen.

In the vicinity of Fernando da Noronha, Greater Shearwaters became much more frequent, and on the first of December over 40 were seen flying over a shoal of fish, in company with large numbers of Red-footed and Brown Boobies. Two Common Noddy, a distinctive black and white bird rather like a Tern, but without the forked tail, were also seen on the same day.

Our track down the coast of South America was generally some 250 miles off shore, so only the truly pelagic sea-birds were sighted; again large numbers of Greater Shearwaters, and the occasional Schlegel's Petrel, the latter a dark bird, a little smaller than the Shearwater, with white chest and abdomen. At about 29°S, the first Albatross were seen (Wandering Albatross), and all were immature birds, the adults being on the breeding grounds at this season in the sub-Antarctic islands.

The next part of our voyage, from Montevideo to the Weddell Sea, should prove to be the most interesting with regard to bird life. Once we have crossed the Antarctic Convergence – the transition zone between the cold, Polar waters and the more temperate waters of the South Atlantic, we may well see as many as a dozen different species in one day.

Sailing South with the IGY

When Maggie sailed forth
From old Butler's Wharf
En route for the Island Dependencies,
How little I thought
Of what might be bought
With a bundle of alien currencies.

The Magga Dan docked
Off brown Funchal rock
And the Captain closed all the throttles.
I found all the wine
Too excessively fine
To be left in Blandy's tall bottles.

I collected my lolly
from dear Uncle Bobby
And took it ashore in the Plate;
But I spent far too much
Of the thin limpid stuff
On a blind South American date.

Our next destination
Before complete isolation
Is Georgia, the island that's dry:

And there the sailors
Are nearly all whalers,
And there's not even a woman to buy.

At the long journey's end
To the ice we descend,
To make observations precise
Of the wind and the snow
And the Auroral glow,
And the chances of winning at dice.

Appendix 3

Material Written at Halley Bay and Published in the Halley Comet

Frankly Phew

The wind at Halley Bay it blew
The cold it chilled us threw and threw
And Gwynne, the Welshman bold and trew,
Looked for Aurora green and blew.
Whilst Henry, asked gone all askew,
The ice he dropped a thermo threw
And back to Joe then quickly flew.
Joe said, 'You should have stuck like glew
And then we would have been one few.'

And while this passed the Jinx he flew
A glob, which as it rose in vew
Had nought that was attached theretew,
The Jinx he cried, 'Boo hew boo hew.'
As Pete at him the can then threw
And D. T. said to Andrew,
'There's one from Halley we must shew.'

By the sink the gashman blew
For washing pots he had his dew
And Malcolm cooked a luscious stew,
Whilst Leonard down in his iglew
Was making stuff for us to chew -
Contents I can't reveal to yew
As I write out this brief revew.

And yet I still did have no clew
Regarding what Bill wished to dew
Down in a room with the other tew,
D. C. and Les, a trio hew
Search high above our heads to vew
What happens right up in the blew,
And higher yet, for twinkles new

Looks Philip, we'll complete the few
With Dipole – David H. to yew.

The chippies, Ken and Fred are tew
Who at wood thump the whole day threw,
And Ron, from reels both old and new,
Selects the films for us to vew.

The 'orrors now begin anew
As Derek on the horn he blew
At supper time, to summon tew
That heretoaforementioned stew
The members of this motley crew,
Then from a hole there rose up threw
In harmy style a-one pause tew
For Alf and Ivor did not rew
The smell of that delicious stew.

The Colonel, last I've left him tew,
Now came along and took a pew
(The words to rhyme I now find few)
And smiled benignedly in the clew-
Less clot who then did down ontew
Him spill that very noble stew.

The culprit we then quickly slew
From his remains we had our stew.
And still the wind at Halley blew
The cold still chilled us yet anew,
The time has come to bid adew,
For to write more I cannot dew.
FRANKLY PEW.

A Nightmare

'My God. She's sailed: She must come back:
They're sure to see my empty berth.'
He waved and cried for all his worth,
He called them all the names on earth
But the ship sailed on towards the pack.

Slowly he tramped back to the base,
Mumbling incoherently:
'There were nineteen others it could be
Why should this occur to me?
What a cold deserted cheerless place.
'But what's the point of moaning so?

There's lots of food for me to eat,
Tongue, brisket, veal, and luncheon meat,
Tinned potatoes – soft but sweet:
And plenty more out in the snow.

'A case or so of Dublin stout
- the situation could be worse -
Forty boxes of various beers.
A can a week for twenty years;
If only I can dig them out.

'There's just one thing I've not assessed:
The long days here will quickly pall
. . . Don't they feel the cold at all
Posing there upon the wall;
The glint of frost on every breast?'

His morbid thoughts began to climb
When something tapped him on the head.
He could have sworn a voice had said,
'What are you doing here in bed?
Come on wake up it's breakfast time.'

Ode to a Monster

It says in the book
That thow't fall on thy face
When balance on skis does evade you,
But what it don't say
Is, if you fall t'other way,
A cushion's the best thing to aid you.

Guinness

It doesn't matter where you are,'
The Penguin said to me,
'A Guinness when the blizzard blows
Will keep you warm like me,
At Halley Bay, Cape Crozier, or islands near Horseshoe,
It looks the same,
It tastes the same,
It's just as good for you,
so will you, won't you, join with me
and have a Guinness too.'

Appendix 4

Parameters Recorded at Halley Bay 1957–58

General

Latitude and longitude	75° 31′S 26°37′W
Local Mean Time	GMT minus 01 hr 45 min
Altitude of the base above sea level	28.6 m

Meteorological

Annual mean air temperature	−18.5°C	
Minimum air temperature	−50.6°C	
Maximum air temperature	+1.8°C	
Mean air pressure	989.12 mb	
Mean vapour pressure	1.60 mb	
Annual mean wind speed	12.8 m/s	
Maximum mean wind speed	34.5 m/s	
Maximum gust wind speed (on 27/10/58)	42.2 m/s	(94 mph)
Frequency of calms	5%	
Mean cloud cover	5.1 eighths	
Max. total solar radiation	78988.8 cal per sq cm	
Max. diffuse solar radiation	52623.2 cal per sq cm	
Annual radiation balance	−490 cal per sq cm	

Geomagnetism

Geomagnetic latitude and longitude	65.6°S	24.2°E
Bearing of the geomagnetic axis pole	161°E of N	
Declination	1.2° W of N	
Inclination	65.1°	

Glaciology

Ice-shelf movement	375 m/yr 267°E of N
Ice-shelf thickness	143 m
Net accumulation	38 cm water per yr

Apparent ablation   12 cm water per yr
Surface density   0.38 g per cubic cm
Ice shelf temperature at 12 m   −18.4°C

Aurora

Zone of quite arc centred at 71.1°S geomagnetic latitude

Ionospheric Physics

Minimum virtual height of E layer   80 km
Height of maximum in F2 layer   430 km
Average occurrence of sporadic E   40%

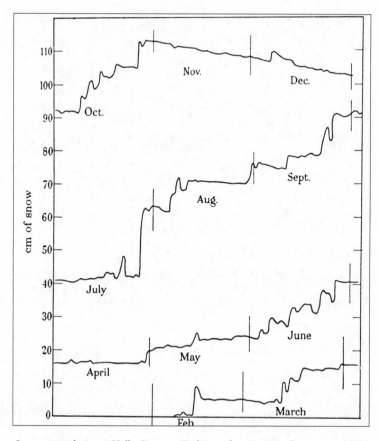

Snow accumulation at Halley Bay 1957. Each year about a metre of snow accumulated.

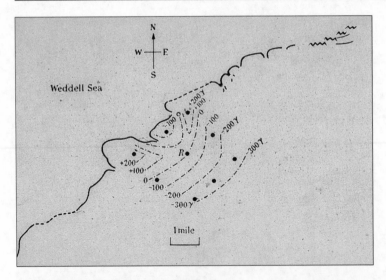

The results of a geomagnetic survey at Halley Bay

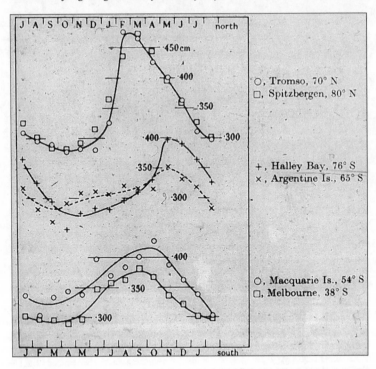

The annual variation of total atmospheric ozone at Halley Bay compared with that observed in high northern latitudes (upper curves) and in moderate southern latitudes (lower curves).

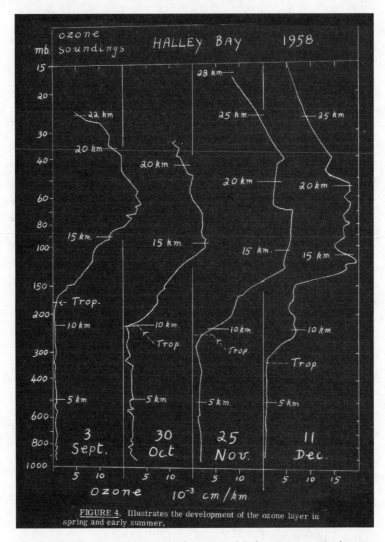

FIGURE 4. Illustrates the development of the ozone layer in spring and early summer.

Some of the first successful ozone soundings accomplished in Antarctica. In the spring of each year the amount of ozone rose sharply but much later than in high northern latitudes. These soundings were made through this interesting spring period.

Appendix 5

Tables

Wind Speeds

Beaufort Force	Speed Range Knots	Speed Range Kph	Description
1	1–3	5	*Light air*
2	4–6	7–11	*Light breeze*
3	7–10	13–19	*Gentle breeze*
4	11–16	20–30	*Moderate breeze*
5	17–21	31–39	*Fresh breeze*
6	22–27	41–50	*Strong breeze*
7	28–33	52–61	*Moderate gale*
8	34–40	63–74	*Fresh gale*
9	41–47	76–87	*Strong gale*
10	48–55	89–102	*Whole gale*
11	56–63	104–117	*Storm*
12	64–71	119–131	*Hurricane*

Conversion Factors

1 kt = 1.8519 kph = 1.1507 mph = 0.514 m/s = 51.4 m/s
1 mph = 1.6093 kph = 0.447 m/s = 0.869 kt
1 ft/s = 1.0973 kph
1 mile = 1.6093 km
1 nm = 1.8533 km = 1.1516 mile
1 cal/min = 69.7 mW
1 lb. = 0.4536 kg
1 cubic foot = 0.02832 cubic metres
1 long ton = 2240 lb. = 1.016 metric ton, or just about 1
1 HP = 0.7457 kW